SIXTY YEARS
OF AMERICAN HUMOR

A PROSE ANTHOLOGY

EDITED BY
JOSEPH LEWIS FRENCH

BOSTON
LITTLE, BROWN, AND COMPANY
1925

FOREWORD

AMERICAN humor was the final progeny of the family of the native muse. Of a native humor, there will be found gleams from the beginning, particularly in the Yankee, who from the very stress of Puritan inhibition developed into a born wit. It therefore seems natural enough that the first American classic should have chronicled the sayings of one "Sam Slick", the Yankee clock-maker, although the chronicler happened to be a Nova Scotian. History, poetry, fiction, and the drama were fairly well established among us before he appeared upon the scene. There is a faltering but fairly continuous line of succession through the forties and fifties, till finally the comic mask is fixed as an undeniable American inheritance by the irrepressible Artemus Ward. The line has never wavered since, as the present volume will prove, and the product has only grown in value and variety until whatever may be its faults, it occupies a recognized position in the sphere of belles-lettres in general.

Humorous literature has been so rapturously received by an overburdened and over-strung people during the past decade or two that it shows signs of overdevelopment as an art — the métier has occasionally become somewhat strained. The humorist, to speak baldly, sure of a wide and eager audience, has sometimes forced his note. But this is unquestionably a phase that will disappear with a serener general outlook, — a calmer and more equable national spirit.

The obvious point to be made is that we have, when all is said, an already well-developed humorous literature, whose value is certain to increase, as the accompanying pages constitute ample assurance.

JOSEPH LEWIS FRENCH.

CONTENTS

SIXTY YEARS
OF AMERICAN HUMOR

ARTEMUS WARD

"Artemus Ward" is the *nom de plume* of Charles Farrar Browne, who was born in Maine, in 1834. He led a roving life from his early years and it was as a printer in the office of the *Cleveland Plain Dealer* that his native Yankee wit burst forth in a series of highly original "letters" on current topics over the signature of "A. Ward, Showman." His "Grate Moral Show" soon became famous, and like all geniuses of the time Browne came to New York City where he attained a great popularity as a writer and lecturer. He was accepted at once, not only as a highly original character but as a real national humorist, and his sayings were in everybody's mouth. He went to California in the early sixties and finally to London where, strangely enough, his vogue became at once as unequivocal as at home. He lectured to crowded houses, became a contributor to *Punch*, and died in England at the height of his fame, in 1864. Artemus Ward is the first American humorist who attained a nation-wide renown.

THE SHAKERS

THE Shakers is the strangest religious sex I ever met. I'd hearn tell of 'em and I'd seen 'em, with their broad brim'd hats and long wastid coats; but I'd never cum into immejit contack with 'em, and I'd sot 'em down as lackin intelleck, as I'd never seen 'em to my Show — leastways, if they cum they was disgised in white peple's close, so I did n't know 'em.

But in the Spring of 18—, I got swampt in the exterior of New York State, one dark and stormy night, when the winds Blue pityusly, and I was forced to tie up with the Shakers.

I was toilin threw the mud, when in the dim vister of the futer I obsarved the gleams of a taller candle. Tiein a hornet's nest to my off hoss's tail to kinder encourage him, I soon reached the place. I knockt at the door, which it was opened unto me by a tall, slick-faced, solum lookin individooal, who turn'd out to be a Elder.

" Mr. Shaker," sed I, " you see before you a Babe in the Woods, so to speak, and he axes shelter of you."

" Yay," sed the Shaker, and he led the way into the house, another Shaker bein sent to put my hosses and waggin under kiver.

A solum female, lookin sumwhat like a last year's bean-pole stuck into a long meal bag, cum in and axed me was I athurst and did I hunger? to which I urbanely anserd " a few." She went orf and I endeverd to open a conversashun with the old man.

" Elder, I spect?" sed I.

" Yay," he sed.

" Helth's good, I reckon?"

" Yay."

" What's the wages of a Elder, when he understans his bizness — or do you devote your sarvices gratooitus?"

" Yay."

" Stormy night, sir."

" Yay."

" If the storm continners there'll be a mess underfoot, hay?"

" Yay."

" It's onpleasant when there's a mess underfoot?"

" Yay."

" If I may be so bold, kind sir, what's the price of that pecooler kind of weskit you wear, incloodin trimmins?"

" Yay."

I pawsd a minit, and then, thinkin I'd be faseshus with him and see how that would go, I slapt him on the shoulder, bust into a harty larf, and told him that as a yayer he had no livin ekal.

He jumpt up as if Bilin water had bin squirted into his ears, groaned, rolled his eyes up tords the sealin and sed: " You're a man of sin!" He then walkt out of the room.

Jest then the female in the meal bag stuck her hed into the room and statid that refreshments awaited the weary travler, and I sed if it was vittles she ment, the weary travler was agreeable, and I follerd her into the next room.

I sot down to the table and the female in the meal bag pored out sum tea. She sed nothin, and for five minutes the only live thing in that room was a old wooden clock, which tickt in a subdood and bashful manner in the corner. This dethly stillness made me oneasy, and I determined to talk to the female or bust. So sez I, "marrige is agin your rules, I bleeve, marm?"

"Yay."

"The sexes liv strickly apart, I spect?"

"Yay."

"It's kinder singler," sez I, puttin on my most sweetest look and speakin in a winnin voice, "that so fair a made as thou never got hitched to some likely feller." [N. B. — She was upards of 40 and homely as a stump fence, but I thawt I'd tickil her.]

"I don't like men!" she sed, very short.

"Wall, I dunno," sez I, "they're a rayther important part of the populashun. I don't scacely see how we could git along without 'em."

"Us poor wimin folks would git along a grate deal better if there was no men!"

"You'll excoos me, marm, but I don't think that air would work. It wouldn't be regler."

"I'm fraid of men!" she sed.

"That's onnecessary, marm. You ain't in no danger. Don't fret yourself on that pint."

"Here we're shot out from the sinful world. Here all is peas. Here we air brothers and sisters. We don't marry and consekently we hav no domestic difficulties. Husbans don't abooze their wives—wives don't worrit their husbans. There's no children here to worrit us. Nothin to worrit us here. No wicked matrimony here. Would thow like to be a Shaker?"

"No," sez I, "it ain't my stile."

I had now histed in as big a load of pervishuns as I could carry comfortable, and, leanin back in my cheer, commenst pickin my teeth with a fork. The female went out, leavin me all alone with the clock. I hadn't sot thar long before the Elder poked his hed in at the door. "You're a man of sin!" he sed and groaned and went away.

Direckly thar cum in two young Shakeresses, as putty and slick lookin gals as I ever met. It is troo they was drest in meal bags like the old one I'd met previsly, and their shiny, silky har was hid from sight by long white caps, sich as I spose female Josts wear; but their eyes sparkled like diminds, their cheeks was like roses, and they was charmin enuff to make a man throw stuns at his granmother, if they axed him to. They commenst clearin away the dishes, castin shy glances at me all the time. I got excited. I forgot Betsy Jane in my rapter, and sez I, "my pretty dears, how air you?"

"We air well," they solumnly sed.

"Whar's the old man?" sed I, in a soft voice.

"Of whom dost thow speak — Brother Uriah?"

"I mean the gay and festiv cuss who calls me a man of sin. Shouldn't wonder if his name was Uriah."

"He has retired."

"Wall, my pretty dears," sez I, "let's have sum fun. Let's play puss in the corner. What say?"

"Air you a Shaker, sir?" they axed.

"Wall, my pretty dears, I haven't arrayed my proud form in a long weskit yit, but if they was all like you perhaps I'd jine 'em. As it is, I'm a Shaker pro-temporary."

They was full of fun. I seed that at fust, only they was a leetle skeery. I tawt 'em Puss in the corner and sich like plase, and we had a nice time, keepin quiet of course so the old man shouldn't hear. When we broke up, sez I, "my pretty dears, ear I go you hav no objections, have you, to a innersent kiss at partin?"

"Yay," they sed, and I yay'd.

I went up stairs to bed. I spose I'd bin snoozin half a hour when I was woke up by a noise at the door. I sot up in bed, leanin on my elbers and rubbin my eyes, and I saw the follerin picter: The Elder stood in the doorway, with a taller candle in his hand. He had n't no wearin appeerel on except his night close, which flutterd in the breeze like a Seseshun flag. He sed, "You're a man of sin!" then groaned and went away.

I went to sleep agin, and drempt of runnin orf with the pretty little Shakeresses, mounted on my Californy Bar. I thawt the Bar insisted on steerin strate for my dooryard in Baldinsville and that Betsy Jane cum out and giv us a warm recepshun with a panfull of Bilin water. I was woke up arly by the Elder. He sed refreshments was reddy for me down stairs. Then sayin I was a man of sin, he went groanin away.

As I was going threw the entry to the room where the vittles was, I cum across the Elder and the old female I'd met the night before, and what d'ye spose they was up to? Huggin and kissin like young lovers in their gushingist state. Sez I, "my Shaker frends, I reckon you'd better suspend the rules, and git marrid!"

"You must excoos Brother Uriah," sed the female: "he's subjeck to fits and hain't got no command over his-self when he's into 'em."

"Sartinly," sez I, "I've bin took that way myself frequent."

"You're a man of sin!" sed the Elder.

Arter breakfust my little Shaker frends cum in agin to clear away the dishes.

"My pretty dears," sez I, "shall we yay agin?"

"Nay," they sed, and I nay'd.

The Shakers axed me to go to their meetin, as they was to hav sarvices that mornin, so I put on a clean biled rag and went. The meetin house was as neat as a pin. The floor was white as chalk and smooth as glass. The Shakers was all on hand, in clean weskits and meal bags, ranged on the floor like milingtery companies, the mails on one side of the room and the females on tother. They commenst clappin their hands and singin and dancin. They danced kinder slow at fust, but as they got warmed up they shaved it down very brisk, I tell you. Elder Uriah, in particler, exhiberted a right smart chance of spryness in his legs, considerin his time of life, and as he cum a dubble shuffle near where I sot, I rewarded him with a approvin smile and sed: "Hunky boy! Go it, my gay and festiv cuss!"

"You're a man of sin!" he sed, continnerin his shuffle.

The Sperret, as they called it, then moved a short fat Shaker to say a few remarks. He sed they was Shakers and all was ekal. They was the purest and seleckest peple on the yearth. Other peple was sinful as they could be, but Shakers was all right. Shakers was all goin kerslap to the Promist Land, and nobody want goin to stand at the gate to bar 'em out, if they did they'd git run over.

The Shakers then danced and sung agin, and arter they was threw, one of 'em axed me what I thawt of it.

Sez I, "What duz it siggerfy?"

"What?" sez he.

"Why this jumpin up and singin? This long weskit bizniss, and this anty-matrimony idee? My friends, you air neat and tidy. Your lands is flowin with milk and honey. Your brooms is fine, and your apple sass is honest. When a man buys a kag of apple sass of you he don't find a grate many shavins under a few layers of sass — a little Game I'm sorry to say sum of my New England ancestors used to practiss. Your garding seeds is fine, and if I should sow 'em on the rock of Gibralter probly I should raise a good mess of garding sass. You air honest in your dealins. You air quiet and don't distarb nobody. For all this I givs you credit. But your religion is small pertaters, I must say. You mope away your lives here in single retchidness, and as you air all by yourselves nothing ever conflicks with your pecooler idees, except when Human Nater busts out among you, as I understan she sumtimes do. [I giv Uriah a sly wink here, which made the old feller squirm like a speared Eel.] You wear long weskits and long faces, and lead a gloomy life indeed. No children's prattle is ever hearn around your harthstuns — you air in a dreary fog all the time, and you treat the jolly sunshine of life as tho' it was a thief, drivin it from your doors by them weskits, and meal bags, and pecooler noshuns of yourn. The gals among you, sum of which air as slick pieces of caliker as I ever sot eyes on, air syin to place their heds agin weskits which kiver honest, manly harts, while you old heds fool yerselves with the idee that they air fulfillin their mishun here, and air contented. Here you are, all pend up by yerselves, talkin about the sins of a world you don't know nothin of. Meanwhile said world continners to resolve round on her own axeltree onct in every 24 hours, subjeck to the Constitooshun of the United States, and is a very pleasant place of residence. It's a unnatural, onreasonable and dismal life you're leadin here. So it strikes me. My Shaker frends, I now bid you a welcome adoo. You hav treated me exceedin well. Thank you kindly, one and all."

"A base exhibiter of depraved monkeys and onprincipled wax works!" sed Uriah.

"Hello, Uriah," sez I, "I'd most forgot you. Wall, look out for them fits of yourn, and don't catch cold and die in the flour of your youth and beauty."

And I resoomed my jerney.

AMONG THE SPIRITS

My naburs is mourn harf crazy on the new fangled idear about Sperrets. Sperretooul Sircles is held nitely & 4 or 5 long hared fellers has settled here and gone into the sperret biznis excloosively. A atemt was made to git Mrs. A. Ward to embark into the Sperret biznis but the atemt faled. 1 of the long hared fellers told her she was a ethereal creeter & wood make a sweet mejium, whareupon she attact him with a mop handle & drove him out of the house. I will hear obsarve that Mrs. Ward is a invalerble womun — the partner of my goys & the shairer of my sorrers. In my absunse she watchis my interests & things with a Eagle Eye & when I return she welcums me in afectionate stile. Trooly it is with us as it was with Mr. & Mrs. Ingomer in the Play, to whit—

> 2 soles with but a single thawt
> 2 harts which beet as 1.

My naburs injooced me to attend a Sperretooul Sircle at Squire Smith's. When I arrove I found the east room chock full includin all the old maids in the village & the long hared fellers a4sed. When I went in I was saluted with "hear cums the benited man"—"hear cums the hory-heded unbeleever"—"hear cums the skoffer at trooth," etsettery, etsettery.

Sez I, "my frens, it's troo I'm hear, & now bring on your Sperrets."

1 of the long hared fellers riz up and sed he would state a few remarks. He sed man was a critter of intelleck & was movin on to a Gole. Sum men had bigger intellecks than other men had and thay wood git to the Gole the soonerest. Sum men was beests & wood never git into the Gole at all. He sed the Erth was materiel but man was im-material, and hens man was different from the Erth. The Erth, continnered the speakers, resolves round on its own axeltree onct in 24 hours, but as man haint gut no axeltree he can't resolve. He sed the ethereal essunce of the koor-dinate branchis of superhuman natur becum mettymor-fussed as man progrest in harmonial coexistunce & even-tooally anty humanized theirselves & turned into reglar sperretuellers. [This was versifferusly applauded by the cumpany, and as I make it a pint to get along as pleasant as possible, I sung out "bully for you, old boy."]

The cumpany then drew round the table and the Sircle kommenst to go it. They axed me if thare was anbody in the Sperrit land which I wood like to convarse with. I sed if Bill Tompkins, who was onct my partner in the show biznis, was sober, I should like to convarse with him a few periods.

" Is the Sperret of William Tompkins present?" sed 1 of the long hared chaps, and there was three knox on the table.

Sez I, " William, how goze it, Old Sweetness?"

" Pretty ruff, old hoss," he replide.

That was a pleasant way we had of addressin each other when he was in the flesh.

" Air you in the show biznis, William?" sed I.

He sed he was. He sed he & John Bunyan was travelin with a side show in connection with Shakspere, Jonson & Co.'s Circus. He sed Old Bun (meaning Mr. Bunyan), stired up the animils & ground the organ while he tended door. Occasshunally Mr. Bunyan sung a comic song. The Circus was doin middlin well. Bill Shakspere had made a grate hit with old Bob Ridley, and Ben Johnson was delitin the peple with his trooly grate ax of hossmanship without saddul or bridal. Thay was rehersin Dixey's Land & expected it would knock the peple.

Sez I, " William, my luvly frend, can you pay me that 13 dollars you owe me?" He sed no with one of the most tremenjis knox I ever experiunsed.

The Sircle sed he had gone. " Air you gone, William?" I axed. " Rayther," he replide, and I know it was no use to pursoo the subjeck furder.

I then called fur my farther.

" How's things, daddy?"

" Middlin, my son, middlin."

" Ain't you proud of your orfurn boy?"

" Scacely."

" Why not, my parient?"

" Becawz you hav gone to writin for the noospapers, my son. Bimeby you'll lose all your character for trooth and verrasserty. When I helpt you into the show biznis I told you to dignerfy that there profeshun. Litteratoor is low."

He also statid that he was doin middlin well in the peanut biznis & liked it putty well, tho' the climit was rather warm.

When the Sircle stopt they axed me what I thawt of it.

Sez I, "my frends I've been into the show biznis now

goin on 23 years. Theres a artikil in the Constitooshun of the United States which sez in effeck that everybody may think just as he darn pleazes, & them is my sentiments to a hare. You dowtlis beleeve this Sperret doctrin while I think it is a little mixt. Just so soon as a man becums a reglar out & out Sperret rapper he leeves orf workin, lets his hare grow all over his face & commensis spungin his livin out of other peple. He eats all the dickshunaries he can find & goze round chock full of big words, scarein the wimmin folks & little children & destroyin the piece of mind of evry famerlee he enters. He don't do nobody no good & is a cuss to society & a pirit on honest peple's corn beef barrils. Admittin all you say abowt the doctrin to be troo, I must say the regular professional Sperret rappers — them as makes a biznis on it — air abowt the most ornery set of cusses I ever enkountered in my life."

So sayin I put on my surtoot and went home.

AMONG THE FREE LOVERS [1]

Some years ago I pitched my tent and onfurled my banner to the breeze, in Berlin Hites, Ohio. I had hearn that Berlin Hites was ockepied by a extensive seck called Free Lovers, who beleeved in affinertys and sich, goin back on their domestic ties without no hesitation whatsomever. They was likewise spirit rappers and high presher reformers on gineral principles. If I can improve these 'ere misgided peple by showin them my onparalleld show at the usual low price of admitants, methunk, I shall not have lived in vane! But bitterly did I cuss the day I ever sot foot in the retchid place. I sot up my tent in a field near the Love Cure, as they called it, and bimeby the free lovers begun for to con-

[1] Some queer people, calling themselves "Free Lovers," and possessing very original ideas about life and morality, established themselves at Berlin Heights, in Ohio. Public opinion was resistlessly against them, however, and the association was soon disbanded.

gregate around the door. A ornreer set I have never sawn. The men's faces was all covered with hare and they lookt half-starved to deth. They did n't wear no weskuts for the purpuss (as they sed) of allowin the free air of hevun to blow onto their boozums. Their pockets was filled with tracks and pamplits and they was bare-footed. They sed the Postles did n't wear boots, & why should they? That was their stile of argyment. The wimin was wuss than the men. They wore trowsis, short gownds, straw hats with green ribbins, and all carried bloo cotton umbrellers.

Presently a perfeckly orful lookin female presented herself at the door. Her gownd was skanderlusly short and her trowsis was shameful to behold.

She eyed me over very sharp, and then startin back she sed, in a wild voice:

"Ah, can it be?"

"Which?" sed I.

"Yes, 't is troo, O 't is troo!"

"15 cents, marm," I anserd.

She bust out a cryin & sed:

"And so I have found you at larst — at larst, O at larst!"

"Yes," I anserd, "you have found me at larst, and you would have found me at fust, if you had cum sooner."

She grabd me vilently by the coat collar, and brandishin her umbreller wildly round, exclaimed:

"Air you a man?"

Sez I, "I think I air, but if you doubt it, you can address Mrs. A. Ward, Baldinsville, Injianny, postage pade, & she will probly giv you the desired informashun."

"Then thou ist what the cold world calls marrid?"

"Madam, I istest!"

The exsentric female then clutched me franticly by the arm and hollerd:

"You air mine, O you air mine!"

"Scacely," I sed, endeverin to git loose from her. But she clung to me and sed:

"You air my Affinerty!"

"What upon arth is that?" I shouted.

"Dost thou not know?"

"No, I dostent!"

"Listin man, & I'll tell ye!" sed the strange female; "for years I hav yearned for thee. I knowd thou wast in the world, sumwhares, tho I didn't know whare. My hart sed he would cum and I took courage. He has cum—he's here—you air him—you air my Affinerty! O 'tis too mutch! too mutch!" and she sobbed agin.

"Yes," I anserd, "I think it is a darn site too mutch!"

"Hast thou not yearned for me?" she yelled, ringin her hands like a female play acter.

"Not a yearn!" I bellerd at the top of my voice, thrown her away from me.

The free lovers who was standin round obsarvin the scene commenst for to holler "shame!" "beast," etsettery, etsettery.

I was very mutch riled, and fortifyin myself with a spare tent stake, I addrest them as follers "You pussylanermus critters, go away from me and take this retchid woman with you. I'm a law-abidin man, and bleeve in good, old-fashioned institutions. I am marrid & my orfsprings resemble me, if I am a showman! I think your Affinity bizniss is cussed noncents, besides bein outrajusly wicked. Why don't you behave desunt like other folks? Go to work and earn a honist livin and not stay round here in this lazy, shiftless way, pizenin the moral atmosphere with your pestifrous idees! You wimin folks go back to your lawful husbands if you've got any, and take orf them skanderlous gownds and trowsis, and dress respectful like other wimin. You men folks, cut them pirattercal whiskers, burn up them infurnel pamplits, put sum weskuts on, go to work choppin wood, splittin fence rales, or tillin the sile."

I pored 4th my indignashun in this way till I got out of breth, when I stopt. I shant go to Berlin Hites agin, not if I live to be as old as Methooseler.

Bad grammar & spelling — affectation of simplicity

JOSH BILLINGS

"Josh Billings" is the pen name of Henry Wheeler Shaw, a typical Yankee, born in 1818, in Massachusetts, of a long Puritan descent. He was a man of middle age, and the town auctioneer of Poughkeepsie, New York, when he began to write in the early sixties. One of his contemporaries calls him a combination of Artemus Ward and Martin Farquhar Tupper but this scarcely does him justice. He is as readable to-day by any one with a genuine sense of humor as he ever was. For some time his writings were published anonymously, but fame and fortune burst upon him with the revelation of their authorship, and he lived and died a celebrated character. The editor of this volume well remembers seeing him in 1882, with his long hair, grave demeanor and dignified black broadcloth, in the lobby of the Windsor Hotel, then the best hostelry in New York City, where he lived for several years. He had a great mind, with a well-developed philosophy of life and a genuine gift of turning it all into sheer laughter such as few men of any age or clime have possessed. The divine gift of sheer nonsense was his also. Perhaps when all is said he shares — albeit uncouthly enough — with James Russell Lowell the laurel of supremacy in the field of American humor. He died in 1884.

THE MULE

THE mule is haf hoss, and haf Jackass, and then kums tu a full stop, natur diskovering her mistake. Tha weigh more, akordin tu their heft, than enny other kreetur, except a crowbar. Tha kant hear enny quicker, nor further than the hoss, yet their ears are big enuff for snow shoes. You kan trust them with enny one whose life aint worth enny more than the mules. The only wa tu keep them into a paster, is tu turn them into a medder jineing, and let them jump out. Tha are reddy for use, just as soon as they will du tu abuse. Tha haint got enny friends, and will live on huckel berry brush, with an ockasional chanse at Kanada thissels. Tha are a modern invenshun, i dont think the Bible deludes tu them at tall. Tha sel for more money than enny other domestik animile. Yu kant tell their age by looking into their mouth, enny more than you kould a Mexican cannons. Tha never hav no dissease that a good club wont heal. If tha ever die tha must kum rite tu life agin, for i never herd nobody sa "ded mule." Tha are like sum men, very korrupt at harte; ive known them tu be good mules for 6 months, just tu git a good chanse to kick sumbody. I never owned one, nor never mean to, unless there is a United Staits law passed, requiring it. The only reason why tha are pashunt, is bekause tha are ashamed ov themselfs. I have seen eddikated mules in a sirkus. Tha kould kick, and bite, tremenjis. I would not sa what I am forced tu sa again the mule, if his birth want an outrage, and man want tu blame for it. Enny man who is willing tu drive a mule, ought to be exempt by law from running for the legislatur. Tha are the strongest creeturs on earth, and heaviest, ackording tu their sise; I herd tell ov one who fell oph from the tow path, on the Eri kanawl, and sunk as soon as he touched bottom, but he kept rite on towing the boat tu the nex stashun, breathing thru his ears, which stuck out ov the water about 2 feet 6 inches; i did'nt see this did, but an auctioneer told me ov it, and i never knew an auctioneer tu lie unless it was absolutely convenient.

LAFFING

Anatomikally konsidered, laffing iz the sensation ov pheeling good all over, and showing it principally in one spot.

Morally konsidered, it iz the next best thing tew the 10 commandments. . . .

Theoretikally konsidered, it kan out-argy all the logik in existence. . . .

Pyroteknikally konsidered, it is the fire-works of the soul. . . .

But i don't intend this essa for laffing in the lump, but for laffing on the half-shell.

Laffing iz just az natral tew cum tew the surface az a rat iz tew cum out ov hiz hole when he wants tew.

Yu kant keep it back by swallowing enny more than yu kan the heekups.

If a man *kan't* laff there iz sum mistake made in putting him together, and if he *won't* laff he wants az mutch keeping away from az a bear-trap when it iz sot.

I have seen people who laffed altogether too mutch for their own good or for ennyboddy else's; they laft like a barrell ov nu sider with the tap pulled out, a perfekt stream.

This is a grate waste ov natral juice.

I have seen other people who didn't laff enuff tew giv themselfs vent; they waz like a barrell ov nu sider too, that waz bunged up tite, apt tew start a hoop and leak all away on the sly.

Thare ain't neither ov theze 2 ways right, and they never ought tew be pattented. . . .

Genuine laffing iz the vent ov the soul, the nostrils of the heart, and iz just az necessary for health and happiness az spring water iz for a trout.

Thare iz one kind ov a laff that i always did rekommend; it looks out ov the eye fust with a merry twinkle, then it kreeps down on its hands and kneze and plays around the mouth like a pretty moth around the blaze ov a kandle, then it steals over into the dimples ov the cheeks and rides around into thoze little whirlpools for a while, then it lites up the whole face like the mello bloom on a damask roze, then it swims oph on the air with a peal az klear and az happy az a dinner-bell, then it goes bak agin on golden tiptoze like an angel out for an airing, and laze down on its little bed ov violets in the heart where it cum from.

Thare iz another laff that nobody kan withstand; it iz just az honest and noisy az a distrikt skool let out tew play; it shakes a man up from hiz toze tew hiz temples, it dubbles and twists him like a whiskee phit, it lifts him oph from his cheer like feathers, and lets him bak agin like melted led; it goes all thru him like a pikpocket, and finally leaves him az weak and az krazy az tho he had bin soaking all day in a Rushing bath and forgot to be took out.

This kind ov a laff belongs tew jolly good phellows who are az healthy az quakers, and who are az eazy tew pleaze az a gall who iz going tew be married to-morrow.

In konclushion i say laff every good chance yu kan git, but don't laff unless yu feal like it, for there ain't nothing in this world more harty than a good honest laff, nor nothing more hollow than a hartless one.

When yu do laff open yure mouth wide enuff for the noize tew git out without squealing, thro yure hed bak az tho yu waz going tew be shaved, hold on tew yure false hair with both hands and then laff till yure soul gets thoroly rested.

ANSWERS TO CONTRIBUTORS

"*Lines tu a sleeping infant,* bi Alice," receaved. Tha are tender, dredful tender, almost tu tender, tu keep thru this hot spel; yu hav talons ov the highest order, but yu must kross yure t's, or yu kant suckceed in potri; good bi Alice!

"*Reverie ov a Bachelor,*" Anonimous. — Received, and kontents noted. Thare iz only one trubble with this produckshun, which time will correckt, and that iz, " it wont du at all for our collums," respekfully declined, (on the part ov the edditurs, by J. B.) on account ov its length and thickness.

"*The Sea, the roarin Sea.*" — A sublime standzas, wurth at least 7 dollars, intended, undoubtedly, for *The Atlantic Monthly*, and cent tu us bi mistake, we wud like tu accept it, but dassent, fur fere folks mite sa we stole it.

"*Will yu Kiss me Dearest,*" Bi Mary Ann. — Acksepted. We take all them kind ov chanses. The potri ain't fust rate, but we expect the kissin kan't be beat, till then, fair Maid ajew!

"*A gealogikal synopsorum ov the heavenly spears,*" Bi Paul Vernon — Will appere in our nex issu. This writer haz attaked a subjeck ov grate differkilty, with the biggest kind ov energee, and haz suckceeded; his thesis is admirable, hiz argyment iz clus, and his stile is camphene. We sa " Mount Vernon! on eagil wings, beyond the klouds, and paint yure name rite over the top ov the door that leads tu glory, Mount Vernon, mi boy!" We predick grate poplarity for this writer, if he aint kut oph by a frost.

"*A Prairie on fire,*" Bi Diogoneze. — Rejeckted to onst. Tu hot for the sezon — cool artikles take the best now. It made me swet tu rede the manuskrip. "Dont despair Diogoneze," if yu find literature aint yure stile, tri sawing wood; iv'e known hundreds ov men make a dust sawing wood, who want worth a cuss tu write for the nusepapirs.

"*Wait a little longer,*" Bi Eugene. — This potri wants greasing. Thare aint nothin so eaza tu rite az potri, if yu know how. Our advise tu this author iz tu take pills, and if tha dont release him ov his potri, he kan konklude he haz got the potri dizeaze the natral wa, and iz liable tu brake out at sumtime.

In konklusion, Fustly, we would sa tu moste writers, "write often, and publish seldom." Secondly, tu sum writers, "write seldom and publish seldemmer."

PIONEERS

God bless the pironeers — the whole ov them — inkluding the man who fust rode a mule. Hiz name was Stickfasst, he will be remembered az long az black wax will be, hiz posterity have aul bin good stickers, sum ov the best clothes-pins the world ever saw, cum from this familee. . . . I remember olde Buffaloo. He waz a sunsett pironeer; he started tew discover, "out west," 40 years ago, hiz property was a wife, with the side ake, 2 galls, just busting thru their clothes into womanhood, 2 boys, who kould kill a skunk at 3 paces, and dodge the smell, a one-hoss wagging, a rifle, and a brasskittle, he squat at Rock River, in the Illinoise, for 6 months, and then moved on more westly, the last that ware seen ov him, was the hind-board ov hiz wagging, just doubling the top ov the rocky mountains. . . . And thare waz Beltrigging, who fust diskovered the tempranse question, he had bin a suckcessful rumdrinker, and seller for 36 years, and had retired with a pile, he diskovered kold water one day, on the back side ov hiz farm, digging out foxes; he lektured nex day, in a 7-day babtiss church, and told his xperiense; he made 13 hundred dollars lekturing, and died 9 years afterwards, in grate agony, having drank 4 drops ov french brandee, on a lump ov brown sugar bi mistake. He begot Springwater, and Springwater begot Rainwater, and Rainwater begot Dewdrop, and Dewdrop begot Morning-Mist, awl ov them selebrated tempranse lekturers. . . . And there waz Solomon Saw-dust, the author ov bran-bred, and nailrod-soup; he waz a champion ov lite weights; he fit the dispepshee in aul its forms; he lived for 18 months, at one heat, on the smell ov a red herring, and gained 9 pounds in wind. He had menny admirers and immitaturs the moste grate ov which was Wet Pack and Water Kure. . . . And there waz Mehitable Saffron, the virgin-hero ov wimmins' rights; i herd her fust orashun, in the town hall; she spoke without notes, at arms' length. She ced, "woman had a destiny that man kould n't fill for her, and az for her, she could go it alone, she did n't want no he-creeter around her, she had on a pair of kowhide pegged boots, and closed up bi holding hi in the air, a pair ov corduroy breeches, which she swore bi the good olde Mozes, waz awl enny man had to brag ov. . . . She waz the first pironeer in the corduroy britches business, she died celibate, and haz had menny followers amung her sexes, but none that had the jism she had. . . . And then thare waz Old Perpetual; he got crazee at last, but not till he had invented a pitch-pine dog, with a bass-wood tail, that would bark and chase every wagging that cum along, clean down to the bridge over bean kreek. He got out a patent for a sorrel horse, and a nu milch cow, and lived till he was 90 years olde, and then died from a kold he had caught, down seller, trieing tew make soft sope, out ov bull's liver. On hiz grave stun waz these affekting paragraph.: "State, and county rights for sale, enquire ov — the widder."

FREDERICK SWARTOUT COZZENS

Frederick Swartout Cozzens, born in 1818, had become a successful wine merchant before he broke forth as a humorist with "The Sparrowgrass Papers", describing the experiences of a city man who retires to the country. They gained him immediate and wide popularity and he was obliged to supply his public with four later books which added nothing to his fame. He had a genuine vein and chose his first theme — the joys and woes of the suburbanite — at just the right moment. He died in 1869.

LIVING IN THE COUNTRY [1]

IT is a good thing to live in the country. To escape from the prison-walls of the metropolis — the great brickery we call "the city" — and to live amid blossoms and leaves, in shadow and sunshine, in moonlight and starlight, in rain, mist, dew, hoarfrost, and drought, out in the open campaign and under the blue dome that is bounded by the horizon only. It is a good thing to have a well with dripping buckets, a porch with honey-buds and sweet-bells, a hive embroidered with nimble bees, a sun-dial mossed over, ivy up to the eaves, curtains of dimity, a tumbler of fresh flowers in your bedroom, a rooster on the roof, and a dog under the piazza.

When Mrs. Sparrowgrass and I moved into the country, with our heads full of fresh butter, and cool, crisp radishes for tea; with ideas entirely lucid respecting milk, and a looseness of calculation as to the number in family it would take a good laying hen to supply with fresh eggs every morning; when Mrs. Sparrowgrass and I moved into the country, we found some preconceived notions had to be abandoned, and some departures made from the plans we had laid down in the little back parlor of Avenue G.

[1] From "The Sparrowgrass Papers."

One of the first achievements in the country is early rising! with the lark — with the sun — while the dew is on the grass, "under the opening eyelids of the morn," and so forth. Early rising! What can be done with five or six o'clock in town? What may not be done at those hours in the country? With the hoe, the rake, the dibble, the spade, the watering-pot? To plant, prune, drill, transplant, graft, train, and sprinkle! Mrs. S. and I agreed to rise *early* in the country. Early rising in the country is not an instinct; it is a sentiment, and must be cultivated.

A friend recommended me to send to the south side of Long Island for some very prolific potatoes — the real hippopotamus breed. Down went my man, and what, with expenses of horse-hire, tavern bills, toll-gates, and breaking a wagon, the hippopotami cost as much apiece as pineapples. They were fine potatoes, though, with comely features, and large, languishing eyes, that promised increase of family without delay. As I worked my own garden (for which I hired a landscape gardener at two dollars per day to give me instructions), I concluded that the object of my first experiment in early rising should be the planting of the hippopotamuses. I accordingly arose next morning at five, and it rained! I rose next day at five, and it rained! The next, and it rained! It rained for two weeks! We had splendid potatoes every day for dinner. "My dear," said I to Mrs. Sparrowgrass, "where did you get these fine potatoes?" "Why," said she, innocently, "out of that basket from Long Island!" The last of the hippopotamuses were before me, peeled, and boiled, and mashed, and baked, with a nice thin brown crust on the top.

I was more successful afterward. I did get some fine seed-potatoes in the ground. But something was the matter; at the end of the season I did not get as many out as I had put in.

Mrs. Sparrowgrass, who is a notable housewife, said to me one day, "Now, my dear, we shall soon have plenty of eggs, for I have been buying a lot of young chickens."

There they were, each one with as many feathers as a grass-hopper, and a chirp not louder. Of course, we looked forward with pleasant hopes to the period when the first cackle should announce the milk-white egg, warmly deposited in the hay which we had provided bountifully. They grew finely, and one day I ventured to remark that our hens had remarkably large combs, to which Mrs. S. replied, " Yes, indeed, she had observed that; but if I wanted to have a real treat I ought to get up early in the morning and hear them crow." "Crow!" said I, faintly, "our hens crowing! Then, by 'the cock that crowed in the morn, to wake the priest all shaven and shorn,' we might as well give up all hopes of having any eggs," said I; "for as sure as you live, Mrs. S., our hens are all roosters!" And so they were roosters! They grew up and fought with the neighbors' chickens, until there was not a whole pair of eyes on either side of the fence.

A *dog* is a good thing to have in the country. I have one which I raised from a pup. He is a good, stout fellow, and a hearty barker and feeder. The man of whom I bought him said he was thoroughbred, but he begins to have a mongrel look about him. He is a good watchdog, though; for the moment he sees any suspicious-looking person about the premises he comes right into the kitchen and gets behind the stove. First, we kept him in the house, and he scratched all night to get out. Then we turned him out, and he scratched all night to get in. Then we tied him up at the back of the garden, and he howled so that our neighbour shot at him twice before daybreak. Finally we gave him away, and he came back; and now he is just recovering from a fit, in which he has torn up the patch that has been sown for our spring radishes.

A good, strong gate is a necessary article for your garden. A good, strong, heavy gate, with a dislocated hinge, so that it will neither open nor shut. Such a one have I. The grounds before my fence are in common, and all the neighbors' cows pasture there. I remarked to Mrs. S., as we

stood at the window in a June sunset, how placid and
picturesque the cattle looked, as they strolled about, crop-
ping the green herbage. Next morning I found the innocent creatures in my garden. They had not left a green
thing in it. The corn in the milk, the beans on the poles,
the young cabbages, the tender lettuce, even the thriving
shoots on my young fruit trees had vanished. And there
they were, looking quietly on the ruin they had made. Our
watchdog, too, was foregathering with them. It was too
much; so I got a large stick and drove them all out, except
a young heifer, whom I chased all over the flower-beds,
breaking down my trellises, my woodbines and sweet-briers,
my roses and petunias, until I cornered her in the hotbed.
I had to call for assistance to extricate her from the sashes,
and her owner has sued me for damages. I believe I shall
move in town.

.   .   .   .

Mrs. Sparrowgrass and I have concluded to try it once
more; we are going to give the country another chance.
After all, birds in the spring are lovely. First come little
snowbirds, *avant-couriers* of the feathered army; then blue-
birds in national uniforms, just graduated, perhaps, from
the ornithological corps of cadets with high honors in the
topographical class; then follows a detachment of flying
artillery — swallows; sand-martens, sappers and miners,
begin their mines and countermines under the sandy para-
pets; then cedar birds, in trim jackets faced with yellow —
aha, dragoons! And then the great rank and file of infantry, robins, wrens, sparrows, chipping-birds; and lastly
— the band!

> From nature's old cathedral sweetly ring
> The wild bird choirs — burst of the woodland band,
>   — who mid the blossoms sing;
> Their leafy temple, gloomy, tall and grand,
> Pillared with oaks, and roofed with Heaven's own hand.

There, there, that is Mario, the celebrated tenor. Hear that magnificent chest note from the chestnuts! then a crescendo, falling in silence — *à plomb!*

Hush! he begins again with a low, liquid monotone, mounting by degrees and swelling into an infinitude of melody — the whole grove dilating, as it were, with exquisite epithalamium.

Silence now — and how still!

Hush! the musical monologue begins anew; up, up into the tree-tops it mounts, fairly lifting the leaves with its passionate effluence, it trills through the upper branches — and then dripping down the listening foliage, in a cadenza of matchless beauty, subsides into silence again.

"That's a he catbird," says my carpenter.

A catbird? Then Shakespeare and Shelley have wasted powder upon the skylark; for never such "profuse strains of unpremeditated art" issued from living bird before. Skylark! pooh! who would rise at dawn to hear the skylark if a catbird were about after breakfast?

.   .   .   .

I have bought me a boat. A boat is a good thing to have in the country, especially if there be any water near. There is a fine beach in front of my house. When visitors come I usually propose to give them a row. I go down — and find the boat full of water; then I send to the house for a dipper and prepare to bail; and, what with bailing and swabbing her with a mop and plugging up the cracks in her sides, and struggling to get the rudder in its place, and unlocking the rusty padlock, my strength is so much exhausted that it is almost impossible for me to handle the oars. Meanwhile the poor guests sit on stones around the beach with woe-begone faces.

"My dear," said Mrs. Sparrowgrass, "why don't you sell that boat?"

"Sell it? Ha! ha!"

One day a Quaker lady from Philadelphia paid us a visit. She was uncommonly dignified, and walked down to the water in the most stately manner, as is customary with Friends. It was just twilight, deepening into darkness, when I set about preparing the boat. Meanwhile our Friend seated herself upon *something* on the beach. While I was engaged in bailing, the wind shifted, and I became sensible of an unpleasant odor; afraid that our Friend would perceive it, too, I whispered Mrs. Sparrowgrass to coax her off and get her farther up the beach.

"Thank thee, no, Susan; I feel a smell hereabout and I am better where I am."

Mrs. S. came back and whispered mysteriously that our Friend was sitting on a dead dog, at which I redoubled the bailing and got her out in deep water as soon as possible.

Dogs have a remarkable scent. A dead setter one morning found his way to our beach, and I towed him out in the middle of the river; but the faithful creature came back in less than an hour — that dog's smell was remarkable indeed.

I have bought me a fyke! A fyke is a good thing to have in the country. A fyke is a fish-net, with long wings on each side; in shape like a nightcap with ear lappets; in mechanism like a rat-trap. You put a stake at the tip end of the nightcap, a stake at each end of the outspread lappets; there are large hoops to keep the nightcap distended, sinkers to keep the lower sides of the lappets under water, and floats as large as muskmelons to keep the upper sides above the water. The stupid fish come downstream, and, rubbing their noses against the wings, follow the curve toward the fyke and swim into the trap. When they get in they cannot get out. That is the philosophy of a fyke. I bought one of Conroy. "Now," said I to Mrs. Sparrowgrass, "we shall have fresh fish to-morrow for breakfast," and went out to set it. I drove the stakes in the mud, spread the fyke in the boat, tied the end of one wing to the stake, and cast the whole into the water. The tide carried it out in a straight line. I got the loose end fastened to the boat, and found it impossible to row back against the tide with the fyke. I then untied it, and it went downstream, stake and all. I got it into the boat, rowed up, and set the stake again. Then I tied one end to the stake and got out of the boat myself in shoal water. Then the boat got away in deep water; then I had to swim for the boat. Then I rowed back and untied the fyke. Then the fyke got away. Then I jumped out of the boat to save the fyke, and the boat got away. Then I had to swim again after the boat and row after the fyke, and finally was glad to get my net on dry land, where I left it for a week in the sun. Then I hired a man to set it, and he did, but he said it was "rotted." Nevertheless, in it I caught two small flounders and an eel. At last a brace of Irishmen came down to my beach for a swim at high tide. One of them, a stout, athletic fellow, after performing sundry aquatic gymnastics, dived under and disappeared for a fearful length of time. The truth is, he had dived into my net. After much turmoil in the water, he rose to the surface with the filaments hanging over his head, and cried out, as if he had found a bird's nest: " I say, Jimmy! begorra, here's a foike!" That unfeeling exclamation to Jimmy, who was not the owner of the net, made me almost wish that it had not been "rotted."

.   .   .   .

We are worried about our cucumbers. Mrs. S. is fond of cucumbers, so I planted enough for ten families. The more they are picked, the faster they grow; and if you do not pick them, they turn yellow and look ugly. Our neighbor has plenty, too. He sent us some one morning, by way of a present. What to do with them we did not know, with so many of our own. To give them away was not polite; to throw them away was sinful; to eat them was impossible. Mrs. S. said, " Save them for seed." So we did. Next day, our neighbor sent us a dozen more. We thanked the messenger grimly and took them in. Next morning another dozen came. It was getting to be a serious matter; so I rose betimes the following morning, and when my neighbor's cucumbers came I filled his man's basket with some of my own, by way of exchange. This bit of pleasantry was resented by my neighbor, who told his man to throw them to the hogs. His man told our girl, and our girl told Mrs. S., and in consequence, all intimacy between the two families has ceased; the ladies do not speak, even at church.

We have another neighbor, whose name is Bates; he keeps cows. This year our gate has been fixed; but my young peach trees near the fences are accessible from the road; and Bates's cows walk along that road morning and evening. The sound of a cow-bell is pleasant in the twilight. Sometimes, after dark, we hear the mysterious curfew tolling along the road, and then with a louder peal it stops before our fence and again tolls itself off in the distance. The result is, my peach trees are as bare as bean-poles. One day I saw Mr. Bates walking along, and I hailed him: "Bates, those are your cows there, I believe?" "Yes, sir; nice ones, ain't they?" "Yes," I replied, "they are *nice* ones. Do you see that tree there?"—and I pointed to a thrifty peach, with as many leaves as an exploded skyrocket. "Yes, sir." "Well, Bates, that red-and-white cow of yours yonder ate the top off that tree; I saw her do it." Then I thought I had made Bates ashamed of himself, and had wounded his feelings, perhaps, too much. I was afraid he would offer me money for the tree, which I made up my mind to decline at once. "Sparrowgrass," said he, "it don't hurt a tree a single mossel to chaw it if it's a young tree. For my part, I'd rather have my young trees chawed than not. I think it makes them grow a leetle better. I can't do it with mine, but you can, because you can wait to have good trees, and the only way to have good trees is to have 'em chawed."

.   .   .   .

We have put a dumb-waiter in our house. A dumb-waiter is a good thing to have in the country, on account of its convenience. If you have company, everything can be sent up from the kitchen without any trouble; and if the baby gets to be unbearable, on account of his teeth, you can dismiss the complainant by stuffing him in one of the shelves and letting him down upon the help. To provide for contingencies, we had all our floors deafened. In consequence, you cannot hear anything that is going on in the story below; and when you are in the upper room of the house there might be a democratic ratification meeting in the cellar and you would not know it. Therefore, if any one should break into the basement it would not disturb us; but to please Mrs. Sparrowgrass, I put stout iron bars in all the lower windows. Besides, Mrs. Sparrowgrass had bought a rattle when she was in Philadelphia; such a rattle as watchmen carry there. This is to alarm our neighbor, who, upon the signal, is to come to the rescue with his revolver. He is a rash man, prone to pull trigger first and make inquiries afterward.

One evening Mrs. S. had retired and I was busy writing, when it struck me a glass of icewater would be palatable. So I took the candle and a pitcher and went down to the pump. Our pump is in the kitchen. A country pump in the kitchen is more convenient; but a well with buckets is certainly more picturesque. Unfortunately, our well water has not been sweet since it was cleaned out. First I had to open a bolted door that lets you into the basement hall, and then I went to the kitchen door, which proved to be locked. Then I remembered that our girl always carried the key to bed with her and slept with it under her pillow. Then I retraced my steps, bolted the basement door, and went up into the dining-room. As is always the case, I found, when I could not get any water, I was thirstier than I supposed I was. Then I thought I would wake our girl up. Then I concluded not to do it. Then I thought of the well, but I gave that up on account of its flavor. Then I opened the closet doors: there was no water there; and then I thought of the dumb-waiter! The novelty of the idea made me smile. I took out two of the movable shelves, stood the pitcher on the bottom of the dumb-waiter, got in myself with the lamp;

let myself down, until I supposed I was within a foot of the floor below, and then let go!

We came down so suddenly that I was shot out of the apparatus as if it had been a catapult; it broke the pitcher, extinguished the lamp, and landed me in the middle of the kitchen at midnight, with no fire and the air not much above the zero point. The truth is, I had miscalculated the distance of the descent — instead of falling one foot, I had fallen five. My first impulse was to ascend by the way I came down, but I found that impracticable. Then I tried the kitchen door; it was locked. I tried to force it open; it was made of two-inch stuff, and held its own. Then I hoisted a window, and there were the rigid iron bars. If ever I felt angry at anybody it was at myself for putting up those bars to please Mrs. Sparrowgrass. I put them up, not to keep people in, but to keep people out.

I laid my cheek against the ice-cold barriers and looked out at the sky; not a star was visible; it was as black as ink overhead. Then I thought of Baron Trenck and the prisoner of Chillon. Then I made a noise. I shouted until I was hoarse, and ruined our preserving kettle with the poker. That brought our dogs out in full bark, and between us we made night hideous. Then I thought I heard a voice and listened — it was Mrs. Sparrowgrass calling to me from the top of the staircase. I tried to make her hear me, but the infernal dogs united with howl, and growl, and bark, so as to drown my voice, which is naturally plaintive and tender. Besides, there were two bolted doors and double-deafened floors between us; how could she recognize my voice, even if she did hear it? Mrs. Sparrowgrass called once or twice and then got frightened; the next thing I heard was a sound as if the roof had fallen in, by which I understood that Mrs. Sparrowgrass was springing the rattle! That called out our neighbor, already wide awake; he came to the rescue with a bull-terrier, a Newfoundland pup, a lantern, and a revolver. The moment he saw me at the window he shot at me, but fortunately just missed me. I threw myself under the kitchen table and ventured to expostulate with him, but he would not listen to reason. In the excitement I had forgotten his name, and that made matters worse. It was not until he had roused up everybody around, broken in the basement door with an ax, gotten into the kitchen with his cursed savage dogs and shooting-iron, and seized me by the collar, that he recognized me — and then he wanted me to explain it! But what kind of an explanation could I make to him? I told him he would have to wait until my mind was composed, and then I would let him understand the whole matter fully. But he never would have had the particulars from me, for I do not approve of neighbors that shoot at you, break in your door, and treat you, in your own house, as if you were a jailbird. He knows all about it, however — somebody has told him — *somebody* tells everybody everything in our village.

Exaggeration.

MAX ADELER

Charles Heber Clark was the real name of "Max Adeler", who was a widely read humorist of the popular type in the early seventies. He was born in Maryland, in 1841, and died about twenty years ago. Although most of his work was contributed originally to periodicals, there was a nation-wide demand for his books. "Out of the Hurly-Burly", his most popular work, is said to have sold more than a quarter of a million copies. Almost equally popular was "Elbow-Room." Others were "Random Shots" and "Fortunate Island." He turned out a steady stream of work for twenty years and was the popular humorist of the masses when Mark Twain's star was just beginning to rise — but he is now forgotten.

THE OBITUARY POET [1]

A RATHER unusual sensation has been excited in the village by the *Morning Argus* within a day or two; and while most of the readers of that wonderful sheet have thus been supplied with amusement, the soul of the editor has been filled with gloom and wrath and despair. Colonel Bangs recently determined to engage an assistant to take the place made vacant by the retirement of the eminent art-critic, Mr. Murphy, and he found in one of the lower counties of the State a person who appeared to him to be suitable. The name of the new man is Slimmer. He has often contributed to the *Argus* verses of a distressing character, and I suppose Bangs must have become acquainted with him through the medium of the correspondence thus begun. No one in the world but Bangs would ever have selected such a poet for an editorial position. But Bangs is singular — he is exceptional. He never operates in accordance with any known laws, and he is more than likely to do

[1] From "Out of the Hurly-Burly."

any given thing in such a fashion as no other person could possibly have adopted for the purpose. As the *Argus* is also *sui generis*, perhaps Bangs does right to conduct it in a peculiar manner. But he made a mistake when he employed Mr. Slimmer.

The colonel, in his own small way, is tolerably shrewd. He had observed the disposition of persons who have been bereaved of their relatives to give expression to their feelings in verse, and it occurred to him that it might be profitable to use Slimmer's poetical talent in such a way as to make the *Argus* a very popular vehicle for the conveyance to the public of notices of deaths. That kind of intelligence, he well knew, is especially interesting to a very large class of readers, and he believed that if he could offer to each advertiser a gratuitous verse to accompany the obituary paragraph, the *Argus* would not only attract advertisements of that description from the country round about the village, but it would secure a much larger circulation.

When Mr. Slimmer arrived, therefore, and entered upon the performance of his duties, Colonel Bangs explained his theory to the poet, and suggested that whenever a death-notice reached the office, he should immediately write a rhyme or two which should express the sentiments most suitable to the occasion.

"You understand, Mr. Slimmer," said the colonel, "that when the death of an individual is announced I want you, as it were, to cheer the members of the afflicted family with the resources of your noble art. I wish you to throw yourself, you may say, into their situation, and to give them, f'r instance, a few lines about the deceased which will seem to be the expression of the emotion which agitates the breasts of the bereaved."

"To lighten the gloom in a certain sense," said Mr. Slimmer, "and to —"

"Precisely," exclaimed Colonel Bangs. "Lighten the gloom. Do not mourn over the departed, but rather take a joyous view of death, which, after all, Mr. Slimmer, is, as it were, but the entrance to a better life. Therefore, I wish you to touch the heart-strings of the afflicted with a tender hand, and to endeavor, f'r instance, to divert their minds from contemplation of the horrors of the tomb." *People.*

"Refrain from despondency, I suppose, and lift their thoughts to — "

"Just so! And at the same time combine elevating sentiment with such practical information as you can obtain from the advertisement. Throw a glamour of poesy, f'r instance, over the commonplace details of the every-day life of the deceased. People are fond of minute descriptions. Some facts useful for this purpose may be obtained from the man who brings the notice to the office; others you may perhaps be able to supply from your imagination."

"I think I can do it first rate," said Mr. Slimmer.

"But, above all," continued the colonel, "try always to take a bright view of the matter. Cause the sunshine of smiles, as it were, to burst through the tempest of tears; and if we don't make the *Morning Argus* hum around this town, it will be queer."

Mr. Slimmer had charge of the editorial department the next day during the absence of Colonel Bangs in Wilmington. Throughout the afternoon and evening death-notices arrived; and when one would reach Mr. Slimmer's desk, he would lock the door, place the fingers of his left hand among his hair and agonize until he succeeded in completing a verse that seemed to him to accord with instructions.

The next morning Mr. Slimmer proceeded calmly to the office for the purpose of enbalming in sympathetic verse the memories of other departed ones. As he came near to the establishment he observed a crowd of people in front of it, struggling to get into the door. Ascending some steps upon the other side of the street, he overlooked the crowd, and could see within the office the clerks selling papers as fast as they could handle them, while the mob pushed and yelled in frantic efforts to obtain copies, the presses in the cellar meanwhile clanging furiously. Standing upon the curbstone in front of the office there was a long row of men, each of whom was engaged in reading *The Morning Argus* with an earnestness that Mr. Slimmer had never before seen displayed by the patrons of that sheet. The bard concluded that either his poetry had touched a sympathetic chord in the popular heart, or that an appalling disaster had occurred in some quarter of the globe.

He went around to the back of the office and ascended to the editorial rooms. As he approached the sanctum, loud voices were heard within. Mr. Slimmer determined to ascertain the cause before entering. He obtained a chair, and placing it by the side door, he mounted and peeped over the door through the transom. There sat Colonel Bangs, holding *The Morning Argus* in both hands, while the fringe which grew in a semicircle around the edge of his bald head stood straight out, until he seemed to resemble a gigantic gun-swab. Two or three persons stood in front of him in threatening attitudes. Slimmer heard one of them say:

"My name is McGlue, sir! — William McGlue! I am a brother of the late Alexander McGlue. I picked up your paper this morning, and perceived in it an outrageous insult to my deceased relative, and I have come around to demand, sir, WHAT YOU MEAN by the following infamous language:

"' The death-angel smote Alexander McGlue,
    And gave him protracted repose;
He wore a checked shirt and a Number Nine shoe,
    And he had a pink wart on his nose.
No doubt he is happier dwelling in space
    Over there on the evergreen shore.
His friends are informed that his funeral takes place
    Precisely at quarter-past four.'

"This is simply diabolical! My late brother had no wart on his nose, sir. He had upon his nose neither a pink wart nor a green wart, nor a cream-colored wart, nor a wart of any other color. It is a slander! It is a gratuitous insult to my family, and I distinctly want you to say *what do you mean* by such conduct?"

"Really, sir," said Bangs, "it is a mistake. This is the horrible work of a miscreant in whom I reposed perfect confidence. He shall be punished by my own hand for this outrage. A pink wart! Awful! sir — awful! The miserable scoundrel shall suffer for this — he shall, indeed!"

"How could I know," murmured Mr. Slimmer to the foreman, who with him was listening, "that the corpse had n't a pink wart? I used to know a man named McGlue, and *he* had one, and I thought *all* the McGlues had. This comes of irregularities in families."

"And who," said another man, addressing the editor, "authorized you to print this hideous stuff about my deceased son? Do you mean to say, Bangs, that it was not with your authority that your low comedian inserted with my advertisement the following scandalous burlesque? Listen to this:

" ' Willie had a purple monkey climbing on a yellow stick,
And when he sucked the paint all off it made him deathly sick;
And in his latest hours he clasped that monkey in his hand,
And bade good-bye to earth and went into a better land.

" ' Oh! no more he 'll shoot his sister with his little wooden gun;
And no more he 'll twist the pussy's tail and make her yowl, for fun.
The pussy's tail now stands out straight; the gun is laid aside;
The monkey does n't jump around since little Willie died.'

"The atrocious character of this libel will appear when I say that my son was twenty years old, and that he died of liver complaint."

"Infamous! — utterly infamous!" groaned the editor as he cast his eyes over the lines. "And the wretch who did this still remains unpunished! It is too much!"

"And yet," whispered Slimmer to the foreman, "he told me to lighten the gloom and to cheer the afflicted family with the resources of my art; and I certainly thought that idea about the monkey would have that effect, somehow. Bangs is ungrateful!"

Just then there was a knock at the door, and a woman entered, crying.

"Are you the editor?" she inquired of Colonel Bangs.

Bangs said he was.

"W-w-well!" she said, in a voice broken by sobs, "wh-what d'you mean by publishing this kind of poetry about m-my child? M-my name is Sm-Smith; and wh-when I looked this m-morning for the notice of Johnny's d-death in your paper, I saw this scandalous verse:

> "'Four doctors tackled Johnny Smith—
>   They blistered and they bled him;
> With squills and anti-bilious pills
>   And ipecac, they fed him.
> They stirred him up with calomel,
>   And tried to move his liver;
> But all in vain—his little soul
>   Was wafted o'er The River.'

"It's false! false! and mean! Johnny only had *one* doctor. And they d-did n't bl-bleed him and b-blister him. It's a wicked falsehood, and you're a hard-hearted brute f-f-for printing it!"

"Madam, I shall go crazy!" exclaimed Bangs. "This is not my work. It is the work of a villain whom I will slay with my own hand as soon as he comes in. Madam, the miserable outcast shall die!"

"Strange! strange!" said Slimmer. "And this man told me to combine elevating sentiment with practical information. If the information concerning the squills and ipecac is not practical, I have misunderstood the use of that word. And if young Smith did n't have four doctors, it was an outrage. He ought to have had them, and they ought to have excited his liver. Thus it is that human life is sacrificed to carelessness."

At this juncture the sheriff entered, his brow clothed with thunder. He had a copy of *The Morning Argus* in his hand. He approached the editor, and pointing to a death-notice, said, " Read that outrageous burlesque, and tell me the name of the writer, so that I can chastise him."

The editor read as follows:

" We have lost our little Hanner in a very painful manner,
    And we often asked, How can her harsh sufferings be borne?
When her death was first reported, her aunt got up and snorted
    With the grief that she supported, for it made her feel forlorn.

" She was such a little seraph that her father, who is sheriff,
    Really doesn 't seem to care if he ne'er smiles in life again.
She has gone, we hope, to heaven, at the early age of seven
    (Funeral starts off at eleven), where she 'll nevermore have pain."

" As a consequence of this, I withdraw all the county advertising from your paper. A man who could trifle in this manner with the feelings of a parent is a savage and a scoundrel!"

As the sheriff went out, Colonel Bangs placed his head upon the table and groaned. *just then*

" Really," Mr. Slimmer said, " that person must be deranged. I tried, in his case, to put myself in his place, and to write as if I was one of the family, according to instructions. The verses are beautiful. That allusion to the grief of the aunt, particularly, seemed to me to be very happy. It expresses violent emotion with a felicitous combination of sweetness and force. These people have no soul — no appreciation of the beautiful in art."

While the poet mused, hurried steps were heard upon the stairs, and in a moment a middle-aged man dashed in abruptly, and seizing the colonel's scattered hair, bumped his prostrate head against the table three or four times with considerable force. Having expended the violence of his emotion in this manner, he held the editor's head down with one hand, shaking it occasionally by way of emphasis, and with the other hand seized the paper and said,

"You disgraceful old reprobate! You disgusting vampire! You hoary-headed old ghoul! What d'you mean by putting such stuff as this in your paper about my deceased son? What d'you mean by printing such awful doggerel as this, you depraved and dissolute ink-slinger — you imbecile quill-driver, you!

"'Oh! bury Bartholomew out in the woods,
    In a beautiful hole in the ground,
Where the bumble-bees buzz and the woodpeckers sing,
    And the straddle-bugs tumble around;
So that, in winter, when the snow and the slush
    Have covered his last little bed,
His brother Artemas can go out with Jane
    And visit the place with his sled.'

"I'll teach you to talk about straddle-bugs! I'll instruct you about slush! I'll enlighten your insane old intellect on the subject of singing woodpeckers! What do *you* know about Jane and Artemas, you wretched buccaneer, you despicable butcher of the English language? Go out with a sled! I'll carry you out in a hearse before I'm done with you, you deplorable lunatic!"

At the end of every phrase the visitor gave the editor's head a fresh knock against the table. When the exercise was ended, Colonel Bangs explained and apologized in the humblest manner, promising at the same time to give his assailant a chance to flog Mr. Slimmer, who was expected to arrive in a few moments.

"The treachery of this man," murmured the poet to the foreman, "is dreadful. Didn't he desire me to throw a glamour of poesy over commonplace details? But for that I should never have thought of alluding to woodpeckers and bugs, and other children of Nature. The man objects to the remarks about the sled. Can the idiot know that it was necessary to have a rhyme for 'bed'? Can he suppose that I could write poetry without rhymes? The man is a lunatic! He ought not to be at large!"

Hardly had the indignant and energetic parent of Bartholomew departed when a man with red hair and a ferocious glare in his eyes entered, carrying a club and accompanied by a savage-looking dog.

" I want to see the editor," he shouted.

A ghastly pallor overspread the colonel's face, and he said,

" The editor is not in."

" Well, when *will* he be in, then?"

" Not for a week — for a month — for a year — for ever! He will never come in any more!" screamed Bangs. " He has gone to South America, with the intention to remain there during the rest of his life. He has departed. He has fled. If you want to see him, you had better follow him to the equator. He will be glad to see you. I would advise you, as a friend, to take the next boat — to start at once."

" That is unfortunate," said the man; " I came all the way from Delaware City for the purpose of battering him up a lot with this club."

" He will be sorry," said Bangs, sarcastically. " He will regret missing you. I will write to him, and mention that you dropped in."

" My name is McFadden," said the man. " I came to break the head of the man who wrote that obituary poetry about my wife. If you don't tell me who perpetrated the following, I 'll break *yours* for you. Where 's the man who wrote this? Pay attention:

" ' Mrs. McFadden has gone from this life;
　　She has left all its sorrows and cares;
　She caught the rheum*a*tics in both of her legs
　　While scrubbing the cellar and stairs.
　They put mustard-plasters upon her in vain;
　　They bathed her with whisky and rum;
　But Thursday her spirit departed, and left
　　Her body entirely numb.' "

" The man who held the late Mrs. McFadden up to the scorn of an unsympathetic world in that shocking manner,"

said the editor, " is named James B. Slimmer. He boards
in Blank Street, fourth door from the corner. I would advise you to call on him and avenge Mrs. McFadden's
wrongs with an intermixture of club and dog-bites."

" And this," sighed the poet, outside the door, " is the
man who told me to divert McFadden's mind from contemplation of the horrors of the tomb. It was this monster
who counseled me to make the sunshine of McFadden's
smiles burst through the tempest of McFadden's tears. If
that red-headed monster couldn't smile over that allusion
to whisky and rum, if those remarks about the rheumatism
in her legs could not divert his mind from the horrors of
the tomb, was it *my* fault? McFadden grovels! He knows
no more about poetry than a mule knows about the Shorter
Catechism."

The poet determined to leave before any more criticisms
were made upon his performances. He jumped down from
his chair and crept softly toward the back staircase.

The story told by the foreman relates that Colonel Bangs
at the same instant resolved to escape any further persecu-
tion, and he moved off in the direction taken by the poet.
The two met upon the landing, and the colonel was about
to begin his quarrel with Slimmer, when an enraged old
woman who had been groping her way up stairs suddenly
plunged her umbrella at Bangs, and held him in the corner
while she handed a copy of the *Argus* to Slimmer, and
pointing to a certain stanza, asked him to read it aloud.
He did so in a somewhat tremulous voice and with frightened glances at the enraged colonel. The verse was as follows:

> " Little Alexander 's dead;
>   Jam him in a coffin;
> Don't have as good a chance
>   For a fun'ral often.
> Rush his body right around
>   To the cemetery;
> Drop him in the sepulchre
>   With his Uncle Jerry."

The colonel's assailant accompanied the recitation with such energetic remarks as these:

"Oh, you willin! D' you hear that, you wretch? What d' you mean by writin' of my grandson in that way? Take that, you serpint! Oh, you wiper, you! tryin' to break a lone widder's heart with such scand'lus lies as them! There, you willin! I kemmere to hammer you well with this here umbreller, you owdacious wiper, you! Take that, and that, you wile, indecent, disgustin' wagabone! When you know well enough that Aleck never had no Uncle Jerry, and never had no uncle in no sepulchre anyhow, you wile wretch, you!"

When Mr. Slimmer had concluded his portion of the entertainment, he left the colonel in the hands of the enemy and fled. He has not been seen in New Castle since that day, and it is supposed that he has returned to Sussex county for the purpose of continuing in private his dalliance with the Muses. Colonel Bangs appears to have abandoned the idea of establishing a department of obituary poetry, and the *Argus* has resumed its accustomed aspect of dreariness.

It may fairly boast, however, that once during its career it has produced a profound impression upon the community.

Exaggeration

EDWARD EGGLESTON

There are still living some who can remember that literary event, the publication of "The Hoosier School-master", in 1871, the first genuine folk-story out of the middle west. Edward Eggleston was born, in 1837, among the scenes he depicted. Coming east to New York, as most literary lions of that day did, he followed his first success with "The Circuit Rider", "Roxy", "The Graysons", etc. and he became the acknowledged historical romancer of his own time and scene. His literary life was long and busy; he produced more than a score of volumes, but his fame will rest on his first works. How genuine a humorist he was this extract from "The Hoosier School-master" will bear witness.

THE SPELLING-BEE [1]

I 'LOW," said Mrs. Means, as she stuffed the tobacco into her cob pipe after supper on that eventful Wednesday evening, "I 'low they'll appint the Squire to gin out the words to-night. They mos' always do, you see, kase he's the peartest *ole* man in this deestrick; and I 'low some of the young fellers would have to git up and dust ef they would keep up to him. And he uses sech remarkable smart words. He speaks so polite, too. But laws! don't I remember when he was poarer nor Job's turkey? Twenty year ago, when he come to these 'ere diggins, that air Squire Hawkins was a poar Yankee school-master, that said 'pail' instid of bucket, and that called a cow a 'caow', and that couldn't tell to save his gizzard what we meant by *'low* and by *right smart*. But he's larnt our ways now, an' he's jest as civilized as the rest of us. You would-n know he'd ever been a Yankee. He didn't stay poar long. Not he. He jest married a right

[1] From "The Hoosier School-master." Reprinted by permission of Stanton & Van Vliet Company, Edward Eggleston and Orange Judd Company.

rich girl! He! he! . . . He didn't stay poar, you bet a hoss!" and with this the coal was deposited on the pipe, and the lips began to crack like parchment as each puff of smoke escaped. "He married rich, you see. . . . His wife hadn't no book-larnin'. She'd been through the spellin'-book wunst, and had got as fur as 'asperity' on it a second time. But she couldn't read a word when she was married, and never could. She warn't overly smart. She hadn't hardly got the sense the law allows. But schools was skase in them air days, and, besides, book-larnin' don't do no good to a woman. Makes her stuck up. I never knowed but one gal in my life as had ciphered into fractions, and she was so dog-on stuck up that she turned up her nose one night at a apple-peelin' bekase I tuck a sheet off the bed to splice out the table-cloth, which was ruther short. And the sheet was mos' clean, too. Had-n been slep on more'n wunst or twicet. But I was goin fer to say that when Squire Hawkins married Virginny Gray he got a heap o' money, or, what's the same thing mostly, a heap o' good land. And that's better'n book-larnin', says I. Ef a girl had gone clean through all eddication, and got to the rule of three itself, that would-n buy a feather-bed. Squire Hawkins jest put eddication agin the gal's farm, and traded even, an' ef ary one of 'em got swindled, I never heerd no complaints."

.   .   .   .

"Hanner, you kin come along, too, ef you're a mind, when you git the dishes washed," said Mrs. Means to the bound girl, as she shut and latched the back door. The Means family had built a new house in front of the old one, as a sort of advertisement of bettered circumstances, an eruption of shoddy feeling; but when the new building was completed, they found themselves unable to occupy it for anything else than a lumber-room, and so, except a parlor which Mirandy had made an effort to furnish a little (in hope of the blissful time when somebody should "set up" with her of evenings), the new building was almost

unoccupied, and the family went in and out through the
back door, which, indeed, was the front door also, for, according to a curious custom, the "front" of the house was
placed toward the south, though the "big road" (Hoosier
for *highway*) ran along the north-west side, or, rather, past
the north-west corner of it.

When the old woman had spoken thus to Hannah and
had latched the door, she muttered, "That gal don't never
show no gratitude fer favors;" to which Bud rejoined that
he did n't think she had no great sight to be pertickler thankful fer. To which Mrs. Means made no reply, thinking it
best, perhaps, not to wake up her dutiful son on so interesting a theme as her treatment of Hannah. Ralph felt
glad that he was this evening to go to another boarding
place. He should not hear the rest of the controversy.

. . . .

Every family furnished a candle. There were yellow
dips and white dips, burning, smoking, and flaring. There
was laughing, and talking, and giggling, and simpering,
and ogling, and flirting, and courting. What a dress party
is to Fifth Avenue, a spelling-school is to Hoopole County.
It is an occasion which is metaphorically inscribed with this
legend, "Choose your partners." Spelling is only a blind in
Hoopole County, as is dancing on Fifth Avenue. But as
there are some in society who love dancing for its own sake,
so in Flat Creek district there were those who loved spelling
for its own sake, and who, smelling the battle from afar,
had come to try their skill in this tournament, hoping to
freshen the laurels they had won in their school-days.

"I 'low," said Mr. Means, speaking as the principal school
trustee, "I 'low our friend the Square is jest the man to boss
this ere consarn to-night. Ef nobody objects, I 'll appint
him. Come, Square, don't be bashful. Walk up to the
trough, fodder or no fodder, as the man said to his donkey."

There was a general giggle at this, and many of the
young swains took occasion to nudge the girls alongside

them, ostensibly for the purpose of making them see the joke, but really for the pure pleasure of nudging. The Greeks figured Cupid as naked, probably because he wears so many disguises that they could not select a costume for him.

The Squire came to the front. Ralph made an inventory of the agglomeration which bore the name of Squire Hawkins, as follows:

1. A swallow-tail coat of indefinite age, worn only on state occasions when its owner was called to figure in his public capacity. Either the Squire had grown too large or the coat too small.

2. A pair of black gloves, the most phenomenal, abnormal, and unexpected apparition conceivable in Flat Creek district, where the preachers wore no coats in the summer, and where a black glove was never seen except on the hands of the Squire.

3. A wig of that dirty, waxy color so common to wigs. This one showed a continual inclination to slip off the owner's smooth, bald pate, and the Squire had frequently to adjust it. As his hair had been red, the wig did not accord with his face, and the hair ungrayed was sadly discordant with a face shriveled by age.

4. A semicircular row of whiskers hedging the edge of the jaw and chin. These were dyed a frightful dead black, such as no natural hair or beard ever had. At the roots there was a quarter of an inch of white, giving the whiskers the appearance of having been stuck on.

5. A pair of spectacles "with tortoise-shell rim." Wont to slip off.

6. A glass eye, purchased of a peddler, and differing in color from its natural mate, perpetually getting out of focus by turning in or out.

7. A set of false teeth, badly fitted, and given to bobbing up and down.

8. The Squire proper, to whom these patches were loosely attached.

It is an old story that a boy wrote home to his father begging him to come West, because "mighty mean men got in office out here." But Ralph concluded that some Yankees had taught school in Hoopole County who would not have held a high place in the educational institutions of Massachusetts. Hawkins had some New England idioms, but they were well overlaid by a Western pronunciation.

"Ladies and gentlemen," he began, shoving up his spectacles, and sucking his lips over his white teeth to keep them in place, "ladies and gentlemen, young men and maidens, raley I'm obleeged to Mr. Means fer this honor," and the Squire took both hands and turned the top of his head round several inches. Then he adjusted his spectacles. Whether he was obliged to Mr. Means for the honor of being compared to a donkey, was not clear. "I feel in the inmost compartments of my animal spirits a most happifying sense of the success and futility of all my endeavors to sarve the people of Flat Crick deestrick, and the people of Tomkins township, in my weak way and manner." This burst of eloquence was delivered with a constrained air and an apparent sense of a danger that he, Squire Hawkins, might fall to pieces in his weak way and manner, and of the success and futility (especially the latter) of all attempts at reconstruction. For by this time the ghastly pupil of the left eye, which was black, was looking away round to the left, while the little blue one on the right twinkled cheerfully toward the front. The front teeth would drop down so that the Squire's mouth was kept nearly closed, and his words whistled through.

"I feel as if I could be grandiloquent on this interesting occasion," twisting his scalp round, "but raley I must forego any such exertions. It is spelling you want. Spelling is the cornerstone, the grand, underlying subterfuge of a good eddication. I put the spellin'-book prepared by the great Daniel Webster alongside the Bible. I do, raley. I think I may put it ahead of the Bible. For if it wurnt fer spellin'-books and sich occasions as these, where would the

Bible be? I should like to know. The man who got up, who compounded this little work of inextricable valoo was a benufactor to the whole human race or any other." Here the spectacles fell off. The Squire replaced them in some confusion, gave the top of his head another twist, and felt of his glass eye, while poor Shocky stared in wonder, and Betsey Short rolled from side to side at the point of death from the effort to suppress her giggle. Mrs. Means and the other old ladies looked the applause they could not speak.

"I appint Larkin Lanham and Jeems Buchanan fer captings," said the Squire. And the two young men thus named took a stick and tossed it from hand to hand to decide which should have the "first chice." One tossed the stick to the other, who held it fast just where he happened to catch it. Then the first placed his hand above the second, and so the hands were alternately changed to the top. The one who held the stick last without room for the other to take hold had gained the lot. This was tried three times. As Larkin held the stick twice out of three times, he had the choice. He hesitated a moment. Everybody looked toward tall Jim Phillips. But Larkin was fond of a venture on unknown seas, and so he said, " I take the master," while a buzz of surprise ran around the room, and the captain of the other side, as if afraid his opponent would withdraw the choice, retorted quickly, and with a little smack of exultation and defiance in his voice: "And *I* take Jeems Phillips."

And soon all present, except a few of the old folks, found themselves ranged in opposing hosts, the poor spellers lagging in, with what grace they could, at the foot of the two divisions. The Squire opened his spelling-book and began to give out the words to the two captains, who stood up and spelled against each other. It was not long until Larkin spelled "really" with one *l*, and had to sit down in confusion, while a murmur of satisfaction ran through the ranks of the opposing forces. His own side bit their lips. The slender figure of the young teacher took the place of the fallen leader, and the excitement made the house very quiet.

Ralph dreaded the loss of influence he would suffer if he should be easily spelled down. And at the moment of rising he saw in the darkest corner the figure of a well-dressed young man sitting in the shadow. It made him tremble. Why should his evil genius haunt him? But by a strong effort he turned his attention away from Dr. Small, and listened carefully to the words which the Squire did not pronounce very distinctly, spelling them with extreme deliberation. This gave him an air of hesitation which disappointed those on his own side. They wanted him to spell with a dashing assurance. But he did not begin a word until he had mentally felt his way through it. After ten minutes of spelling hard words Jeems Buchanan, the captain on the other side, spelled "atrocious" with an *s* instead of a *c*, and subsided, his first choice, Jeems Phillips, coming up against the teacher. This brought the excitement to fever-heat. For though Ralph was chosen first, it was entirely on trust, and most of the company were disappointed. The champion who now stood up against the school-master was a famous speller. Jim Phillips was a tall, lank, stoop-shouldered fellow, who had never distinguished himself in any other pursuit than spelling. Except in this one art of spelling he was of no account. He could not catch well or bat well in ball. He could not throw well enough to make his mark in that famous Western game of bull-pen. He did not succeed well in any study but that of Webster's Elementary. But in that he was— to use the usual Flat Creek locution — in that he was "a hoss." This genius for spelling is in some people a sixth sense, a matter of intuition. Some spellers are born and not made, and their facility reminds one of the mathematical prodigies that crop out every now and then to bewilder the world. Bud Means, foreseeing that Ralph would be pitted against Jim Phillips, had warned his friend that Jim could "spell like thunder and lightning," and that it "took a powerful smart speller" to beat him, for he knew "a heap of spelling-book." To have "spelled down the master" is the next thing to having whipped the biggest bully in Hoopole County, and Jim had "spelled down" the last three masters. He divided the hero-worship of the district with Bud Means.

For half an hour the Squire gave out hard words. What a blessed thing our crooked orthography is! Without it there could be no spelling-schools. As Ralph discovered his opponent's mettle he became more and more cautious. He was now satisfied that Jim would eventually beat him. The fellow evidently knew more about the spelling-book than old Noah Webster himself. As he stood there, with his dull face and long sharp nose, his hands behind his back, and his voice spelling infallibly, it seemed to Hartsook that his superiority must lie in his nose. Ralph's cautiousness answered a double purpose: it enabled him to tread surely, and it was mistaken by Jim for weakness. Phillips was now confident that he should carry off the scalp of the fourth school-master before the evening was over. He spelled eagerly, confidently, brilliantly. Stoop-shouldered as he was, he began to straighten up. In the minds of all the company the odds were in his favor. He saw this, and became ambitious to distinguish himself by spelling without giving the matter any thought.

Ralph always believed that he would have been speedily defeated by Phillips had it not been for two thoughts which braced him. The sinister shadow of young Dr. Small sitting in the dark corner by the water-bucket nerved him. A victory over Phillips was a defeat to one who wished only ill to the young school-master. The other thought that kept his pluck alive was the recollection of Bull. He approached a word as Bull approached the raccoon. He did not take hold until he was sure of his game. When he took hold, it was with a quiet assurance of success. As Ralph spelled in this dogged way for half an hour the hardest words the Squire could find, the excitement steadily rose in all parts of the house, and Ralph's friends even ventured to whisper that "may be Jim had cotched his match after all!"

But Phillips never doubted of his success.

" Theodolite," said the Squire.

" T-h-e, the, o-d, od, theod, o, theodo, l-y-t-e, theodolite," spelled the champion.

"Next," said the Squire, nearly losing his teeth in his excitement.

Ralph spelled the word slowly and correctly, and the conquered champion sat down in confusion. The excitement was so great for some minutes that the spelling was suspended. Everybody in the house had shown sympathy with one or the other of the combatants, except the silent shadow in the corner. *It* had not moved during the contest, and did not show any interest now in the result.

" Gewhilliky crickets! Thunder and lightning! Licked him all to smash!" said Bud, rubbing his hands on his knees. "That beats my time all holler!"

And Betsey Short giggled until her tuck-comb fell out, though she was on the defeated side.

Shocky got up and danced with pleasure. . . .

" He's powerful smart, is the master," said old Jack to Mr. Pete Jones. " He'll beat the whole kit and tuck of 'em afore he's through. I know'd he was smart. That's the reason I tuck him," proceeded Mr. Means.

" Yaas, but he don't lick enough. Not nigh," answered Pete Jones. " No lickin', no larnin', says I."

It was now not so hard. The other spellers on the opposite side went down quickly under the hard words which the Squire gave out. The master had mowed down all but a few, his opponents had given up the battle, and all had lost their keen interest in a contest to which there could be but one conclusion, for there were only the poor spellers left. But Ralph Hartsook ran against a stump where he was least expecting it. It was the Squire's custom, when one of the smaller scholars or poorer spellers rose to spell against the master, to give out eight or ten easy words that they might have some breathing spell before being slaughtered, and then to give a poser or two which soon settled them. He let them run a little, as a cat does a doomed mouse. There was now but one person left on the opposite side, and as she rose in her blue calico dress, Ralph recognized Hannah, the bound girl at old Jack Means's. She had not attended school in the district, and had never spelled in spelling-school before, and was chosen last as an uncertain quantity. The Squire began with easy words of two syllables, from that page of Webster, so well known to all who ever thumbed it, as " Baker," from the word that stands at the top of the page. She spelled these words in an absent and uninterested manner. As everybody knew that she would have to go down as soon as this preliminary skirmishing was over, everybody began to get ready to go home, and already there was the buzz of preparation. Young men were timidly asking girls if " they could see them safe home," which is the approved formula, and were trembling in mortal fear of " the mitten." Presently the Squire, thinking it time to close the contest, pulled his scalp forward, adjusted his glass eye, which had been examining his nose long enough, and turned over the leaves of the book to the great words at the place known to spellers as " Incomprehensibility," and began to give out those "words of eight syllables with the accent on the sixth." Listless scholars now turned round, and ceased to whisper in order to be in at the master's final triumph. But to their surprise, " ole Miss Meanses' white nigger," as some of them called her, in allusion to her slavish life, spelled these great words with as perfect ease as the master. Still, not doubting the result, the Squire turned from place to place and selected all the hard words he could find. The school became utterly quiet, the excitement was too great for the ordinary buzz. Would " Meanses' Hanner" beat the master? Beat the master that had laid out Jim Philips? Everybody's sympathy was now turned to Hannah. Ralph noticed that even Shocky had deserted him, and that his face grew brilliant every time Hannah spelled a word. In fact, Ralph deserted himself. As he saw the fine, timid face of the girl so long oppressed flush and shine with interest, as he looked at the rather low but broad and intelli-

gent brow and the fresh, white complexion, and saw the
rich, womanly nature coming to the surface under the influence of applause and sympathy, he did not want to beat.
If he had not felt that a victory given would insult her, he
would have missed intentionally. The bull-dog, the stern,
relentless setting of the will, had gone, he knew not whither.
And there had come in its place, as he looked in that face,
a something which he did not understand. You did not,
gentle reader, the first time it came to you.

The Squire was puzzled. He had given out all the hard
words in the book. He again pulled the top of his head
forward. Then he wiped his spectacles and put them on.
Then out of the depths of his pocket he fished up a list of
words just coming into use in those days — words not in the
spelling-book. He regarded the paper attentively with his
blue right eye. His black left eye meanwhile fixed itself in
such a stare on Mirandy Means that she shuddered and hid
her eyes in her red silk handkerchief.

"Daguerreotype," sniffled the Squire. It was Ralph's
turn.

"D-a-u, dau —"

"Next."

And Hannah spelled it right.

Such a buzz followed that Betsey Short's giggle could
not be heard, but Shocky shouted, "Hanner beat! my
Hanner spelled down the master!" And Ralph went over
and congratulated her. . . .

And then the Squire called them to order, and said: "As
our friend Hanner Thomson is the only one left on her
side, she will have to spell against nearly all on t'other side.
I shall, therefore, take the liberty of procrastinating the com-
pletion of this interesting and exacting contest until to-
morrow evening. I hope our friend Hanner may again
carry off the cypress crown of glory. There is nothing
better for us than healthful and kindly simulation."

MARK TWAIN

Samuel Langhorne Clemens (Mark Twain) is unquestionably the representative American humorist, by right both of the quality and the quantity of his output. We seriously question whether any authority would care to dispute his position. He was born in Missouri, in 1835 — under a lucky star — and from his twentieth year to the close of a long life, in 1910, was a successful and celebrated man of letters. Humor was unquestionably his greatest gift — and he had many — and the flame of it never burned more brightly than in his younger years. "The Jumping Frog" is a prime example.

THE JUMPING FROG[1]

In English. Then in French. Then Clawed Back into a Civilized Language Once More by Patient, Unrenumerated Toil.

EVEN a criminal is entitled to fair play; and certainly when a man who has done no harm has been unjustly treated, he is privileged to do his best to right himself. My attention has just been called to an article some three years old in a French Magazine entitled, "Revue des Deux Mondes" (Review of Some Two Worlds), wherein the writer treats of "Les Humoristes Americaines" (These Humorists Americans). I am one of these humorists Americans dissected by him, and hence the complaint I am making.

This gentleman's article is an able one (as articles go, in the French, where they always tangle up everything to that degree that when you start into a sentence you never know whether you are going to come out alive or not). It is a very good article, and the writer says all manner of kind and complimentary things about me — for which I am sure

---

[1] From "Sketches New and Old." Reprinted by permission of the Trustees of the Estate of Samuel L. Clemens, the Mark Twain Company and Harper and Brothers. Copyright, 1875, 1903, by Samuel L. Clemens.

I thank him with all my heart; but then why should he go and spoil all his praise by one unlucky experiment? What I refer to is this: he says my Jumping Frog is a funny story, but still he can't see why it should ever really convulse any one with laughter — and straightway proceeds to translate it into French in order to prove to his nation that there is nothing so very extravagantly funny about it. Just there is where my complaint originates. He has not translated it at all: he has simply mixed it all up; it is no more like the Jumping Frog when he gets through with it than I am like a meridian of longitude. But my mere assertion is not proof; wherefore I print the French version, that all may see that I do not speak falsely; furthermore, in order that even the unlettered may know my injury and give me their compassion, I have been at infinite pains and trouble to re-translate this French version back into English; and to tell the truth I have well nigh worn myself out at it, having scarcely rested from my work during five days and nights. I cannot speak the French language, but I can translate very well, though not fast, I being self-educated. I ask the reader to run his eye over the original English version of the Jumping Frog, and then read the French or my re-translation, and kindly take notice how the Frenchman has riddled the grammar. I think it is the worst I ever saw; and yet the French are called a polished nation. If I had a boy that put sentences together as they do, I would polish him to some purpose. Without further introduction, the Jumping Frog, as I originally wrote it, was as follows [after it will be found the French version, and after the latter my re-translation from the French]:

THE NOTORIOUS JUMPING FROG OF CALAVERAS[1] COUNTY

In compliance with the request of a friend of mine, who wrote me from the East, I called on good-natured, garrulous old Simon Wheeler, and inquired after my friend's friend,

[1] Pronounced Cal-e-*va*-ras.

Leonidas W. Smiley, as requested to do, and I hereunto append the result. I have a lurking suspicion that *Leonidas W*. Smiley is a myth; that my friend never knew such a personage; and that he only conjectured that if I asked old Wheeler about him, it would remind him of his infamous *Jim* Smiley, and he would go to work and bore me to death with some exasperating reminiscence of him as long and as tedious as it should be useless to me. If that was the design, it succeeded.

I found Simon Wheeler dozing comfortably by the barroom stove of the dilapidated tavern in the decayed mining camp of Angel's, and I noticed that he was fat and baldheaded, and had an expression of winning gentleness and simplicity upon his tranquil countenance. He roused up, and gave me good-day. I told him a friend of mine had commissioned me to make some inquiries about a cherished companion of his boyhood named *Leonidas W*. Smiley — *Rev. Leonidas W*. Smiley, a young minister of the Gospel, who he had heard was at one time a resident of Angel's Camp. I added that if Mr. Wheeler could tell me anything about this Rev. Leonidas W. Smiley, I would feel under many obligations to him.

Simon Wheeler backed me into a corner and blockaded me there with his chair, and then sat down and reeled off the monotonous narrative which follows this paragraph. He never smiled, he never frowned, he never changed his voice from the gentle-flowing key to which he tuned his initial sentence, he never betrayed the slightest suspicion of enthusiasm; but all through the interminable narrative there ran a vein of impressive earnestness and sincerity, which showed me plainly that, so far from his imagining that there was anything ridiculous or funny about his story, he regarded it as a really important matter, and admired its two heroes as men of transcendent genius in *finesse*. I let him go on in his own way, and never interrupted him once.

Rev. Leonidas W. H'm, Reverend Le — well, there was a feller here once by the name of *Jim* Smiley, in the winter of '49 — or may be it was the spring of '50 — I don't recollect exactly, somehow, though what makes me think it was one or the other is because I remember the big flume warn't finished when he first come to the camp; but any way, he was the curiousest man about always betting on anything that turned up you ever see, if he could get anybody to bet on the other side; and if he could n't he 'd change sides. Any way that suited the other man would suit *him* — any way just so 's he got a bet, *he* was satisfied. But still he was lucky, uncommon lucky; he most always come out winner. He was always ready and laying for a chance; there couldn't be no solit'ry thing mentioned but that feller'd offer to bet on it, and take ary side you please, as I was just telling you. If there was a horse-race, you'd find him flush or you'd find him busted at the end of it; if there was a dog-fight, he'd bet on it; if there was a cat-fight, he'd bet on it; if there was a chicken-fight, he'd bet on it; why, if there was two birds setting on a fence, he would bet you which one would fly first; or if there was a camp-meeting, he would be there reg'lar to bet on Parson Walker, which he judged to be the best exhorter about here, and so he was too, and a good man. If he even see a straddle-bug start to go anywheres, he would bet you how long it would take him to get to — to wherever he was going to, and if you took him up, he would foller that straddle-bug to Mexico but what he would find out where he was bound for and how long he was on the road. Lots of the boys here has seen that Smiley, and can tell you about him. Why, it never made no difference to *him* — he'd bet on *any* thing — the dangdest feller. Parson Walker's wife laid very sick once, for a good while, and it seemed as if they warn't going to save her; but one morning he come in, and Smiley up and asked him how she was, and he said she was considable better — thank the Lord for his inf'nite mercy — and coming on so smart that with the blessing of Prov'dence she'd get well yet; and Smiley, before he thought, says, "Well, I'll resk two-and-a-half she don't anyway."

Thish-yer Smiley had a mare — the boys called her the fifteen-minute nag, but that was only in fun, you know, because of course she was faster than that — and he used to win money on that horse, for all she was so slow and always had the asthma, or the distemper, or the consumption, or something of that kind. They used to give her two or three hundred yards start, and then pass her under way; but always at the fag end of the race she'd get excited and desperate like, and come cavorting and straddling up, and scattering her legs around limber, some-times in the air, and sometimes out to one side among the fences, and kicking up m-o-r-e dust and raising m-o-r-e racket with her coughing and sneezing and blowing her nose — and *always* fetch up at the stand just about a neck ahead, as near as you can cipher it down.

And he had a little small bull-pup, that to look at him you'd think he warn't worth a cent but to set around and look ornery and lay for a chance to steal something. But as soon as money was up on him he was a different dog; his under-jaw 'd begin to stick out like the fo'castle of a steamboat, and his teeth would uncover and shine like the furnaces. And a dog might tackle him and bully-rag him, and bite him, and throw him over his shoulder two or three times, and Andrew Jackson — which was the name of the pup — Andrew Jackson would never let on but what *he* was satisfied, and had n't expected nothing else — and the bets being doubled and doubled on the other side all the time, till the money was all up; and then all of a sudden he would grab that other dog jest by the j'int of his hind leg and freeze to it — not chaw, you understand, but only just grip and hang on till they throwed up the sponge, if it was a year. Smiley always come out winner on that pup, till he harnessed a dog once that did n't have no hind legs, because they 'd been sawed off in a circular saw, and when the thing had gone along far enough, and the money was all up, and he come to make a snatch for his pet holt, he see in a minute how he 'd been imposed on, and how the other dog had him in the door, so to speak, and he 'peared surprised, and then he looked sorter discouraged-like, and did n't try no more to win the fight, and so he got shucked out bad. He give Smiley a look, as much as to say his heart was broke, and it was *his* fault, for putting up a dog that had n't no hind legs for him to take holt of, which was his main dependence in a fight, and then he limped off a piece and laid down and died. It was a good pup, was that Andrew Jackson, and would have made a name for hisself if he 'd lived, for the stuff was in him and he had genius — I know it, because he had n't no opportunities to speak of, and it don't stand to reason that a dog could make such a fight as he could under them circumstances if he had n't no talent. It always makes me feel sorry when I think of that last fight of his'n, and the way it turned out.

Well, thish-yer Smiley had rat-tarriers, and chicken cocks, and tom-cats and all them kind of things, till you could n't rest, and you could n't fetch nothing for him to bet on but he 'd match you. He ketched a frog one day, and took him home, and said he cal'lated to educate him; and so he never done nothing for three months but set in his back yard and learn that frog to jump. And you bet you he *did* learn him, too. He 'd give him a little punch behind, and the next minute you 'd see that frog whirling in the air like a doughnut — see him turn one summerset, or may be a couple, if he got a good start, and come down flat-footed and all right, like a cat. He got him up so in the matter of ketching flies, and kep' him in practice so constant, that he'd nail a fly every time as fur as he could see him. Smiley said all a frog wanted was education, and he could do 'most anything — and I believe him. Why, I 've seen him set Dan'l Webster down here on this floor — Dan'l Webster was the name of the frog — and sing out, "Flies, Dan'l, flies!" and quicker'n you could wink he 'd spring straight up and snake a fly off'n the counter there, and flop down on the floor ag'in as solid as a gob of mud, and fall to scratching the side of his head with his hind foot as indifferent as if he had n't no idea he 'd been doin' any more'n any frog might do. You never see a frog so modest and straightfor'ard as he was, for all he was so gifted. And when it come to fair and square jumping on a dead level, he could get over more ground at one straddle than any animal of his breed you ever see. Jumping on a dead level was his strong suit, you understand; and when it come to that, Smiley would ante up money on him as long as he had a red. Smiley was monstrous proud of his frog, and well he might be, for fellers that had traveled and been everywheres all said he laid over any frog that ever *they* see.

Well, Smiley kep' the beast in a little lattice box, and he used to fetch him down town sometimes and lay for a bet. One day a feller — a stranger in the camp, he was — come acrost him with his box, and says:

"What might it be that you 've got in the box?"

And Smiley says, sorter indifferent-like, "It might be a parrot, or it might be a canary, maybe, but it ain't — its only just a frog."

And the feller took it, and looked at it careful, and turned it round this way and that, and says, "H'm — so 'tis. Well, what 's *he* good for?"

"Well," Smiley says, easy and careless, "he 's good enough for *one* thing, I should judge — he can outjump any frog in Calaveras county."

The feller took the box again, and took another long, particular look, and give it back to Smiley, and says, very deliberate, "Well," he says, "I don't see no p'ints about that frog that 's any better'n any other frog."

"Maybe you don't," Smiley says. "Maybe you understand frogs and maybe you don't understand 'em; maybe you 've had experience, and maybe you ain't only a amature, as it were. Anyways, I 've got *my* opinion, and I 'll resk forty dollars that he can outjump any frog in Calaveras county."

And the feller studied a minute, and then says, kinder sad like, " Well, I 'm only a stranger here, and I ain't got no frog; but if I had a frog, I 'd bet you."

And then Smiley says, "That 's all right — that 's all right — if you 'll hold my box a minute, I 'll go and get you a frog." And so the feller took the box, and put up his forty dollars along with Smiley's, and set down to wait.

So he set there a good while thinking and thinking to hisself, and then he got the frog out and prized his mouth open and took a teaspoon and filled him full of quail shot — filled him pretty near up to his chin — and set him on the floor. Smiley he went to the swamp and slopped around in the mud for a long time, and finally he ketched a frog, and fetched him in, and give him to this feller, and says:

" Now, if you 're ready, set him alongside of Dan'l, with his fore-paws just even with Dan'l's, and I 'll give the word." Then he says, " One — two — three — *git!* " and him and the feller touched up the frogs from behind, and the new frog hopped off lively, but Dan'l give a heave, and hysted up his shoulders — so — like a Frenchman, but it warn't no use — he could n't budge; he was planted as solid as a church, and he could n't no more stir than if he was anchored out. Smiley was a good deal surprised, and he was disgusted too, but he did n't have no idea what the matter was, of course.

The feller took the money and started away; and when he was going out at the door, he sorter jerked his thumb over his shoulder — so — at Dan'l, and says again, very deliberate, " Well," he says, *"I* don't see no p'ints about that frog that 's any better'n any other frog."

Smiley he stood scratching his head and looking down at Dan'l a long time, and at last he says, " I do wonder what in the nation that frog throw'd off for — I wonder if there ain't something the matter with him — he 'pears to look mighty baggy, somehow." And he ketched Dan'l by the nap of the neck, and hefted him, and says, " Why blame my cats if he don't weigh five pound! " and turned him upside down and he belched out a double handful of shot. And then he see how it was, and he was the maddest man — he set the frog down and took out after that feller, but he never ketched him. And —— "

[Here Simon Wheeler heard his name called from the front yard, and got up to see what was wanted.] And turning to me as he moved away, he said: "Just set where you are, stranger, and rest easy — I ain't going to be gone a second."

But, by your leave, I did not think that a continuation of the history of the enterprising vagabond *Jim* Smiley would be likely to afford me much information concerning the Rev. *Leonidas W.* Smiley, and so I started away.

At the door I met the sociable Wheeler returning, and he buttonholed me and re-commenced:

"Well, thish-yer Smiley had a yaller one-eyed cow that did n't have ᴐ tail, only just a short stump like a bannanner, and——"

However, lacking both time and inclination, I did not wait to hear about the afflicted cow, but took my leave.

Now let the learned look upon this picture and say if iconoclasm can further go:

[From the *Revue des Deux Mondes,* of July 15th, 1872.]

LA GRENOUILLE SAUTEUSE DU COMTE DE CALAVERAS

" — Il y avait une fois ici un individu connu sous le nom de Jim Smiley: c'était dans l'hiver de 49, peut-être bien au printemps de 50, je ne me rappelle pas exactement. Ce qui me fait croire que c'était l'un ou l'autre, c'est que je me souviens que le grand bief n'était pas achevé lorsqu'il arriva au camp pour la premiére fois, mais de toutes façons il était l'homme le plus friand de paris qui se pût voir, pariant sur tout ce qui se présentait, quand il pouvait trouver un adversaire, et, quand il n'en trouvait pas il passait du côté opposé. Tout ce qui convenait á l'autre lui convenait; pourvu qu'il eût un pari, Smiley était satisfait. Et il avait une chance! une chance inouï: presque toujours il gagnait. Il faut dire qu'il était toujours prêt à s'exposer, qu'on ne pouvait mentionner la moindre chose sans que ce gaillard offrît de parier ládessus n'importe quoi et de prendre le côté que l'on voudrait, comme je vous le disais tout à l'heure. S'il y avait des courses, vous le trouviez riche ou ruiné â la fin; s'il y avait un combat de chiens, il apportait son enjeu; il l'apportait pour un combat de chats, pour un combat de coqs; — parbleu! si vous aviez vu deux oiseaux sur une haie, il vous aurait offert de parier lequel s'envolerait le premier, et, s'il y avait *meeting* au camp, il venait parier régulièrement pour le curé Walker, qu'il jugeait être le meilleur prédicateur des environs, et qui l'était en effet, et un brave homme. Il aurait rencontré une punaise de bois en chemin, qu'il aurait parié sur le temps qu'il lui faudrait pour aller où elle voudrait aller, et, si vous l'aviez pris au mot, il aurait suivi la punaise jusqu'au Mexique, sans se soucier d'aller si loin, ni du temps qu'il y perdrait. Une fois la femme du curé Walker fut très malade pendant longtemps, il semblait qu'on ne la sauverait pas; mais un matin le curé arrive, et Smiley lui demande comment ella va, et il dit qu'elle est bien mieux, grâce à l'infinie miséricorde, tellement mieux qu'avec la bénédiction de la Providence elle s'en tirerait, et voila que. sans y penser, Smiley répond: — Eh bien! ye gage deux et demi qu'elle mourra tout de même.

"Ce Smiley avait une jument que les gars appelaient le bidet du quart d'heure, mais seulement pour plaisenter, vous comprenez, parce que, bien entendu, elle était plus *vite* que ça! Et il avait coutume de gagner de l'argent avec cette bête, quoiqu'elle fût poussive, cornarde, toujours prise d'asthme, de coliques ou de consomption, ou de quelque chose d'approchant. On lui donnait 2 ou 300 *yards* au départ, puis on la dépassait sans peine; mais jamais à la fin elle ne manquait de s'échauffer, de s'exaspérer, et elle arrivait, s'écartant, se défendant, ses jambes grêles en l'air devant les obstacles, quelquefois les évitant et faisant avec cela plus de poussière qu'aucum cheval, plus de bruit surtout avec ses éternumens et reniflemens, — crac! elle arrivait donc toujours première d'une tête, aussi juste qu'on peut le mesurer. Et il avait un petit bouledogue qui, à le voir, ne valait pas un sou; on aurait cru que parier contre lui c'était voler, tant il était ordinaire; mais aussitôt les enjeux faits, il devenait un autre chien. Sa mâchoire inférieure commençait à ressortir comme un gaillard d'avant, ses dents se découvraient brillantes commes des fournaises, et un chien pouvait le taquiner, l'exciter, le mordre, le jeter deux ou trois fois pardessus son épaule, André Jackson, c'était le nom du chien, André Jackson prenait cela tranquillement, comme s'il ne se fût jamais attendu à autre chose, et quand les paris étaient doublés et redoublés contre lui, il vous saisissait l'autre chien juste à l'articulation de la jambe de derrière, et il ne la lâchait plus, non pas qu'il la mâchât, vous concevez, mais il s'y serait tenu pendu jusqu'à ce qu'on jetât l'éponge en l'air, fallût-il attendre un an. Smiley gagnait toujours avec cette bête-là; malheureusement ils ont fini par dresser un chien qui n'avait pas de pattes de derrière, parce qu'on les avait sciées, et quand les choses furent au point qu'il voulait, et qu'il en vint à se jeter sur son morceau favori, le pauvre chien comprit en un instant qu'on s'était moqué de lui, et que l'autre le tenait. Vous n'avez jamais vu personne avoir l'air plus penaud et plus découragé; il ne fit aucun effort pour gagner le combat et fut

rudement secoué, de sorte que, regardant Smiley comme pour
lui dire : — Mon cœur est brisé, c'est ta faute ; pourquoi m'avoir
livré à un chien qui n'a pas de pattes de derriére, puisque c'est
par là que je les bats ? — il s'en alla en clopinant, et se coucha
pour mourir. Ah! c'était un bon chien, cet André Jackson, et
il se serait fait un nom, s'il avait vécu, car il y avait de l'etoffe
en lui, il avait du génie, je la sais, bien que de grandes occasions lui aient manqué ; mais il est impossible de supposer
qu'un chien capable de se battre comme lui, certaines circon-
stances étant données, ait manqué de talent. Je me sens triste
toutes les fois que je pense à son dernier combat et au dé-
noûment qu'il a eu. Eh bien! ce Smiley nourrissait des
terriers à rats, et des coqs de combat, et des chats, et toute
sorte de choses, au point qu'il était toujours en mesure de vous
tenir tête, et qu'avec sa rage de paris on n'avait plus de repos.
Il attrapa un jour une grenouille et l'emporta chez lui, disant
qu'il prétendait faire son éducation ; vous me croirez si vous
voulez, mais pendant trois mois il n'a rien fait que lui apprendre à sauter dans une cour retirée de sa maison. Et je vous
réponds qu'il avait réussi. Il lui donnait un petit coup par derrière, et l'instant d'après vous voyiez la grenouille tourner en
l'air comme un beignet au-dessus de la poêle, faire une culbute,
quelquefois deux, lorsqu'elle était bien partie, et retomber sur
ses pattes comme un chat. Il l'avait dressée dans l'art de
gober des mouches, et l'y exerçait continuellement, si bien
qu'une mouche, du plus loin qu'elle apparaissait, était une
mouche perdue. Smiley avait coutume de dire que tout ce qui
manquait à une grenouille, c'était l'éducation, qu'avec l'éducation elle pouvait faire presque tout, et je le crois. Tenez, je
l'ai vu poser Daniel Webster la sur se plancher, — Daniel
Webster était le nom de la grenouille, — et lui chanter : — Des
mouches! Daniel, des mouches! — En un clin d'œil, Daniel
avait bondi et saisi une mouche ici sur le comptoir, puis sauté
de nouveau par terre, où il restait vraiment à se gratter la tête
avec sa patte de derrière, comme s'il n'avait pas eu la moindre
idée de sa supériorité. Jamais vous n'avez grenouille vu de
aussi modeste, aussi naturelle, douée comme elle l'était! Et
quand il s'agissait de sauter purement et simplement sur terrain
plat, elle faisait plus de chemin en un saut qu'aucune bête de
son espèce que vous puissiez connaître. Sauter à plat, c'était
son fort! Quand il s'agaissait de cela, Smiley entassait les
enjeux sur elle tant qu'il lui, restait un rouge liard. Il faut le
reconnaître, Smiley était monstrueusement fier de sa grenouille,
et il en avait le droit, car des gens qui avaient voyagé, qui

avaient tout vu, disaient qu'on lui ferait injure de la comparer à une autre; de façon que Smiley gardait Daniel dans une petite boîte à clairevoie qu'il emporta it parfois à la ville pour quelque pari.

"Un jour, un individu étranger au camp l'arrête avec sa boîte et lui dit:— Qu'est-ce que vous avez donc serré là dedans?

"Smiley dit d'un air indifférent:— Cela pourrait être un perroquet ou un serin, mais ce n'est rien de pareil, ce n'est qu'une grenouille.

"L'individu la prend, la regarde avec soin, la tourne d'un côté et de l'autre puss il dit. — Tiens! en effet! A quoi est-elle bonne?

" — Mon Dieu! répond Smiley, toujours d'un air dégagé, elle est bonne pour une chose à mon avis, elle peut battre en sautant toute grenouille du comté de Calaveras.

"L'individu reprend la boîte, l'examine de nouveau longuement, et la rend à Smiley en disant d'un air délibéré:— Eh bien! je ne vois pas que cette grenouille ait rien de mieux qu'aucune grenouille.

" — Possible que vous ne le voyiez paz, dit Smiley, possible que vous vous entendiez en grenouilles, possible que vous ne vous y entendez point, possible que vous ayez de l'expérience, et possible que vous ne soyez qu'un amateur. De toute manière, je parie quarante dollars qu'elle battra en sautant n'importe quelle grenouille du comté de Calaveras.

"L'individu réfléchit une seconde et dit comme attristé:— Je ne suis qu'un étranger ici, je n'ai pas de grenouille; mais, si j'en avais une, je tiendrais le pari.

" — Fort bien! répond Smiley. Rien de plus facile. Si vous voulez tenir ma boîte une minute, j'irai vous chercher une grenouille. — Voilà donc l'individu qui garde la boîte, qui met ses quarante dollars sur ceux de Smiley et qui attend. Il attend assez longtemps, réfléchissant tout seul, et figurez vous qu'il prend Daniel, lui ouvre la bouche de force et avec une cuiller à thé l'emplit de menu plomb de chasse, mais l'emplit jusqu'au menton, puis il le pose par terre. Smiley pendant ce temps était à barboter dans une mare. Finalement il attrape une grenouille, l'apporte à cet individu et dit:— Maintenant, si vous étes prêt, mettez-la tout contre Daniel, avec leurs pattes de devant sur la même ligne, et je donnerai le signal; — puis il ajoute:— Un, deux, trois, sautez!

"Lui et l'individu touchent leurs grenouilles par derrière, et la grenouille neuve se met à sautiller, mais Daniel se soulève lourdement, hausse les épaules ainsi, comme un Français; à quoi bon? il ne pouvait bouger, il était planté solide comme une enclume, il n'avançait pas puls que si on l'eût mis á l'ancre. Smiley fut surpris et dégoûté mais il ne se doutait pas du tour, bien entendu. L'individu empoche l'argent, s'en va, et en s'en allant est-ce qu'il ne donne pas un coup de pouce par-dessus lé'paule, comme ça, au pauvre Daniel, en disant de son air délibéré:— Eh bien! je ne vois pas que cette grenouille ait rien de mieux qu'une autre.

"Smiley se gratta longtemps la tête, les yeux fixés sur Daniel, jusqu'à ce qu'enfin il dit:— Je me demande comment diable il se fait que cette bête ait refusé. . . Est-ce qu'elle aurait quelque chose? . . On croirait qu'elle est enflée.

"Il empoigne Daniel par la peau du cou, le souléve et dit:— Le loup me croque, s'il ne pèse pas cinq livres.

"Il le retourne, et le malheureux crache deux poignées de plomb. Quand Smiley reconnut ce qui en était, il fut comme fou. Vous le voyez d'ici poser sa grenouille par terre et courir aprés cet individu, mais il ne le rattrapa jamais, et." . . .

[Translation of the above back from the French.]

THE FROG JUMPING OF THE COUNTY OF CALAVERAS.

It there was one time here an individual known under the name of Jim Smiley; it was in the winter of '49, possibly well at the spring of '50, I no me recollect not exactly. This which me makes to believe that it was the one or the other, it is that I shall remember that the grand flume is not achieved when he arrives at the camp for the first time, but of all sides he was the man the most fond of to bet which one have seen, betting upon all that which is presented, when he could find an adversary; and when he not of it could not, he passed to the side opposed. All that which convenienced to the other, to him convenienced also; seeing that he had a bet, Smiley was satisfied. And he had a chance! a chance even worthless; nearly always he gained. It must to say that he was always near to himself expose, but one no could mention the least thing without that this gaillard offered to bet the bottom, no matter what, and to take the side that one him would, as I you it said all at the hour (tout à l'heure). If it there was of races, you him find rich or ruined at the end; if it there is a combat of dogs, he bring his bet; he himself laid always for a combat of cats, for a combat of cocks;—by-blue! If you have see two birds upon a fence, he you should have offered of to bet which of those birds shall fly the first; and if there is *meeting* at the camp (*meeting* au camp) he comes to bet regularly for the curé Walker, which he judged to be the best predicator of the neighborhood (prédicateur des environs) and which he was in effect, and a brave man. He would encounter a bug of wood in the road, whom he will bet upon the time which he shall take to go where she would go — and if you him have take at the word, he will follow the bug as far as Mexique, without himself caring to go so far; neither of the time which he there lost. One time the woman of the curé Walker is very sick during long time, it seemed that one not her saved not; but one morning the curé arrives, and Smiley him demanded how she goes, and he said that she is well better, grace to the infinite misery (lui demande comment elle va, et il dit qu'elle est bien mieux, grâce à l'infinie misèricorde) so much better that with the benediction of the Providence she herself of it would pull out (elle s'en tirerait); and behold that without there thinking Smiley responds: "Well, I gage two-and-half that she will die all of same."

This Smiley had an animal which the boys called the nag of the quarter of hour, but solely for pleasantry, you comprehend, because, well understood, she was more fast as that! [Now why that exclamation?—M. T.] And it was custom of to gain of the silver with this beast, notwithstanding she was poussive, cornarde, always taken of asthma, of colics or of consumption, or something of approaching. One him would give two or three hundred yards at the departure, then one him passed without pain; but never at the last she not fail of herself èchauffer, of

herself exasperate, and she arrives herself écartant, se dè-
fendant, her legs grêles in the air before the obstacles, sometimes them elevating and making with this more of dust
than any horse, more of noise above with his éternumens
and reniflemens — crac! she arrives then always first by
one head, as just as one can it measure. And he had a small
bull dog (boule dogue!) who, to him see, no value, not a
cent; one would believe that to bet against him it was to
steal, so much he was ordinary; but as soon as the game
made, she becomes another dog. Her jaw inferior com-
mence to project like a deck of before, his teeth themselves
discover brilliant like some furnaces, and a dog could him
tackle (le taquiner), him excite, him murder (le mordre),
him throw two or three times over his shoulder, André
Jackson — this was the name of the dog — André Jackson
takes that tranquilly, as if he not himself was never expecting other thing, and when the bets were doubled and redoubled against him, he you seize the other dog just at
the articulation of the leg behind, and he not it leave
more, not that he it masticate, you conceive, but he himself
there shall be holding during until that one throws the
sponge in the air, must he wait a year. Smiley gained always with this beast-là; unhappily they have finished by
elevating a dog who no had not of feet of behind, because
one them had sawed; and when things were at the point
that he would, and that he came to himself throw upon
his morsel favorite, the poor dog comprehended in
an instant that he himself was deceived in him, and
that the other dog him had. You no have never see person having the air more penaud and more discouraged;
he not made no effort to gain the combat, and was rudely
shocked.

Eh bien! this Smiley nourished some terriers à rats, and
some cocks of combat, and some cats, and all sorts of
things; and with his rage of betting one no had more of
repose. He trapped one day a frog and him imported with
him (et l'emporta chez lui) saying that he pretended to make

his education. You me believe if you will, but during three months he not has nothing done but to him apprehend to jump (apprendre à sauter) in a court retired of her mansion (de sa maison). And I you respond that he have succeeded. He him gives a small blow by behind, and the instant after you shall see the frog turn in the air like a grease-biscuit, make one summersault, sometimes two, when she was well started, and re-fall upon his feet like a cat. He him had accomplished in the art of to gobble the flies (gober des mouches), and him there exercised continually — so well that a fly at the most far that she appeared was a fly lost. Smiley had custom to say that all which lacked to a frog it was the education, but with the education she could do nearly all — and I him believe. Tenez, I him have seen pose Daniel Webster there upon this plank — Daniel Webster was the name of the frog — and to him sing, "Some flies, Daniel, some flies!" — in a flash of the eye Daniel had bounded and seized a fly here upon the counter, then jumped anew at the earth, where he rested truly to himself scratch the head with his behind foot, as if he no had not the least idea of his superiority. Never you not have seen frog as modest, as natural, sweet as she was. And when he himself agitated to jump purely and simply upon plain earth, she does more ground in one jump than any beast of his species than you can know. To jump plain — this was his strong. When he himself agitated for that, Smiley multiplied the bets upon her as long as there to him remained a red. It must to know, Smiley was monstrously proud of his frog, and he of it was right, for some men who were traveled, who had all seen, said that they to him would be injurious to him compare to another frog. Smiley guarded Daniel in a little box latticed which he carried by-times to the village for some bet.

One day an individual stranger at the camp him arrested with his box and him said:

"What is this that you have then shut up there within?"

Smiley said, with an air indifferent:

"That could be a paroquet, or a syringe (ou un serin), but this no is nothing of such, it not is but a frog."

The individual it took, it regarded with care, it turned from one side and from the other, then he said:

"Tiens! in effect!—At what is she good?"

"My God!" responded Smiley, always with an air disengaged, "she is good for one thing, to my notice (à mon avis), she can batter in jumping (elle peut batter en sautant) all frogs of the county of Calaveras."

The individual re-took the box, it examined of new longly, and it rendered to Smiley in saying with an air deliberate:

"Eh bien! I no saw not that that frog had nothing of better than each frog." (Je ne vois pas que cette grenouille ait rien de mieux qu'aucune grenouille.) [If that is n't grammar gone to seed, then I count myself no judge.— M. T.]

"Possible that you not it saw not," said Smiley, "possible that you—you comprehend frogs; possible that you not you there comprehend nothing; possible that you had of the experience, and possible that you not be but an amateur. Of all manner (De toute manière) I bet forty dollars that she batter in jumping no matter which frog of the county of Calaveras."

The individual reflected a second, and said like sad:

"I not am but a stranger here, I no have not a frog; but if I of it had one, I would embrace the bet."

"Strong well!" respond Smiley; "nothing of more facility. If you will hold my box a minute, I go you to search a frog (j' irai vous chercher)."

Behold, then, the individual, who guards the box, who puts his forty dollars upon those of Smiley, and who attends (et qui attend). He attended enough longtimes, reflecting all solely. And figure you that he takes Daniel, him opens the mouth by force and with a teaspoon him fills with shot of the hunt, even him fills just to the chin, then he him puts by the earth. Smiley during these times was

at slopping in a swamp. Finally he trapped (attrape) a
frog, him carried to that individual, and said:

"Now if you be ready, put him all against Daniel, with
their before feet upon the same line, and I give the signal"
— then he added: "One, two, three — advance!"

Him and the individual touched their frogs by behind,
and the frog new put to jump smartly, but Daniel himself
lifted ponderously, exalted the shoulders thus, like a Frenchman — to what good? he not could budge, he is planted
solid like a church, he not advance no more than if one
him had put at the anchor.

Smiley was surprised and disgusted, but he not himself
doubted not of the turn being intended (mais il ne se doutait pas du tour, bien entendu). The individual empocketed
the silver, himself with it went, and of it himself in going
is it that he no gives not a jerk of thumb over the shoulder
— like that — at the poor Daniel, in saying with his air
deliberate — (L'individu empoche l'argent, s'en va et en
s'en allant est ce qu'il ne donne pas un coup de pouce par-
dessus l'épaule, comme ca, au pauvre Daniel, endisant de
son air délibéré):

"Eh bien! *I no see not that that frog has nothing of
better than another.*"

Smiley himself scratched longtimes the head, the eyes
fixed upon Daniel, until that which at last he said:

"I me demand how the devil it makes itself that this
beast has refused. Is it that she had something? One
would believe that she is stuffed."

He grasped Daniel by the skin of the neck, him lifted
and said:

"The wolf me bite if he no weigh not five pounds."

He him reversed and the unhappy belched two handfuls
of shot (et le malhereus, etc.). When Smiley recognized
how it was, he was like mad. He deposited his frog by the
earth and ran after that individual, but he not him caught
never.

Such is the Jumping Frog, to the distorted French eye.

I claim that I never put together such an odious mixture of bad grammar and delirium tremens in my life. And what has a poor foreigner like me done, to be abused and misrepresented like this? When I say, "Well, I don't see no p'ints about that frog that's any better'n any other frog," is it kind, is it just, for this Frenchman to try to make it appear that I said, "Eh bien! I no saw not that that frog had nothing of better than each frog?" I have no heart to write more. I never felt so about anything before.

BILL NYE

New England, which from her constituency and character, became the national nursery of American literary genius from its beginning, has given us a number of our best humorists down to this day. "Bill Nye" (Edgar Wilson Nye), who for thirty years enjoyed a strong nation-wide vogue, was born in the same section that gave us Artemus Ward and Josh Billings and the author of "The Biglow Papers." He was a native of Maine, but his parents moved to northern Wisconsin when he was but two years old. Humor seems to have been his birthright, for soon after he was admitted to the bar in Laramie, Wyoming, he began writing humorous articles and in 1881 he founded the *Laramie Boomerang*, which he had made a household word when he was barely thirty. From the time he was thirty-five up to his untimely death in 1896, he was in great demand as a lecturer, and the public was at the same time delighted with book after book in his characteristic vein — to the number of half a score. Of all the humorists of his period, he seems to have possessed the soundest philosophy.

SKIMMING THE MILKY WAY [1]

THE COMET

THE comet is a kind of astronomical parody on the planet. Comets look some like planets, but they are thinner and do not hurt so hard when they hit anybody as a planet does. The comet was so called because it had hair on it, I believe, but late years the bald-headed comet is giving just as good satisfaction everywhere.

The characteristic features of a comet are: A nucleus, a nebulous light or coma, and usually a luminous train or tail worn high. Sometimes several tails are observed on one comet, but this occurs only in flush times.

When I was young I used to think I would like to be a comet in the sky, up above the world so high, with nothing to do but loaf around and play with the little new-laid

[1] From "Bill Nye's Red Book."

planets and have a good time, but now I can see where I was wrong. Comets also have their troubles, their peri-hilions, their hyperbolas and their parabolas. A little over 300 years ago Tycho Brahe discovered that comets were extraneous to our atmosphere, and since then times have improved. I can see that trade is steadier and potatoes run less to tows than they did before.

Soon after that they discovered that comets all had more or less periodicity. Nobody knows how they got it. All the astronomers had been watching them day and night and didn't know when they were exposed, but there was no time to talk and argue over the question. There were two or three hundred comets all down with it at once. It was an exciting time.

Comets sometimes live to a great age. This shows that the night air is not so injurious to the health as many people would have us believe. The great comet of 1780 is sup-posed to have been the one that was noticed about the time of Cæsar's death, 44 B.C., and still, when it appeared in New-ton's time, seventeen hundred years after its first grand fare-well tour, Ike said that it was very well preserved, indeed, and seemed to have retained all its faculties in good shape.

Astronomers say that the tails of all comets are turned from the sun. I do not know why they do this, whether it is etiquette among them or just a mere habit.

A later writer on astronomy said that the substance of the nebulosity and the tail is of almost inconceivable tenuity. He said this and then death came to his relief. Another writer says of the comet and its tail that "the curvature of the latter and the acceleration of the periodic time in the case of Encke's comet indicate their being affected by a resisting medium which has never been observed to have the slightest influence on the planetary periods."

I do not fully agree with the eminent authority, though he may be right. Much fear has been the result of the comet's appearance ever since the world began, and it is as good a thing to worry about as anything I know of. If we could get close to a comet without frightening it away, we would find that we could walk through it anywhere as we could through the glare of a torchlight procession. We should so live that we will not be ashamed to look a comet in the eye, however. Let us pay up our newspaper subscription and lead such lives that when the comet strikes we will be ready.

Some worry a good deal about the chances for a big comet to plow into the sun some dark, rainy night, and thus bust up the whole universe. I wish that was all I had to worry about. If any respectable man will agree to pay my taxes and funeral expenses, I will agree to do his worrying about the comet's crashing into the bosom of the sun and knocking its daylights out.

The Sun

This luminous body is 92,000,000 miles from the earth, though there have been mornings this winter when it seemed to me that it was further than that. A railway train going at the rate of 40 miles per hour would be 263 years going there, to say nothing of stopping for fuel or water, or stopping on side tracks to wait for freight trains to pass. Several years ago it was discovered that a slight error had been made in the calculations of the sun's distance from the earth, and, owing to a misplaced logarithm, or something of that kind, a mistake of 3,000,000 miles was made in the result. People cannot be too careful in such matters. Supposing that, on the strength of the information contained in the old time-table, a man should start out with only provisions sufficient to take him 89,000,000 miles and should then find that 3,000,000 miles still stretched out ahead of him. He would then have to buy fresh figs of the train boy in order to sustain life. Think of buying nice fresh figs on a train that had been en route 250 years! Imagine a train boy starting out at ten years of age, and perishing at the age of 60 years with only one-fifth of his journey accomplished. Think of five train boys, one after the other, dying of old age on the way, and the train at last pulling slowly into the depot with not a living thing on board except the worms in the " nice eating apples ! "

The sun cannot be examined through an ordinary telescope with impunity. Only one man ever tried that, and he is now wearing a glass eye that cost him $9.

If you examine the sun through an ordinary solar microscope, you discover that it has a curdled or mottled appearance, as though suffering from biliousness. It is also marked here and there by long streaks of light, called faculæ, which look like foam flecks below a cataract. The spots on the sun vary from minute pores the size of an ordinary school district to spots 100,000 miles in diameter, visible to the nude eye. The center of these spots is as black as a brunette cat, and is called the umbra, so called because it resembles an umbrella. The next circle is less dark, and called the penumbra, because it so closely resembles the numbra.

There are many theories regarding these spots, but, to be perfectly candid with the gentle reader, neither Prof. Proctor nor myself can tell exactly what they are. If we could get a little closer, we flatter ourselves that we could speak more definitely. My own theory is they are either, first, open air caucuses held by the colored people of the sun; or, second, they may be the dark horses in the campaign; or, third, they may be the spots knocked off the defeated candidate by the opposition.

Frankly, however, I do not believe either of these theories to be tenable. Prof. Proctor sneers at these theories also on the ground that these spots do not appear to revolve so fast as the sun. This, however, I am prepared to explain upon the theory that this might be the result of delays in the returns. However, I am free to confess that speculative science is filled with the intangible.

The sun revolves upon his or her axletree, as the case

may be, once in 25 to 28 of our days, so that a man living there would have almost two years to pay a 30-day note. We should so live that when we come to die we may go at once to the sun.

Regarding the sun's temperature, Sir John Herschel says that it is sufficient to melt a shell of ice covering its entire surface to a depth of 40 feet. I do not know whether he made this experiment personally or hired a man to do it for him.

The sun is like the star spangled banner — it is " still there." You get up to-morrow morning just before sunrise and look away toward the east, and keep on looking in that direction, and at last you will see a fine sight, if what I have been told is true. If the sunrise is as grand as the sunset, it indeed must be one of nature's most sublime phenomena.

The sun is the great source of light and heat for our earth. If the sun were to go somewhere for a few weeks for relaxation and rest, it would be a cold day for us. The moon, too, would be useless, for she is largely dependent on the sun. Animal life would soon cease and real estate would become depressed in price. We owe very much of our enjoyment to the sun, and not many years ago there were a large number of people who worshipped the sun. When a man showed signs of emotional insanity, they took him up on the observatory of the temple and sacrificed him to the sun. They were a very prosperous and happy people. If the conqueror had not come among them with civilization and guns and grand juries they would have been very happy, indeed.

The Stars

There is much in the great field of astronomy that is discouraging to the savant who hasn't the time nor the means to rummage around through the heavens. At times I am almost hopeless, and feel like saying to the great yearnful, hungry world: " Grope on forever. Do not ask me for another scientific fact. Find it out yourself. Hunt up your own new-laid planets, and let me have a rest. Never ask me again to sit up all night and take care of a new-born world, while you lie in bed and reck not."

I get no salary for examining the trackless void night after night when I ought to be in bed. I sacrifice my health in order that the public may know at once of the presence of a red-hot comet, fresh from the factory. And yet, what thanks do I get?

Is it surprising that every little while I contemplate withdrawing from scientific research, to go and skin an eight-mule team down through the dim vista of relentless years?

Then, again, you take a certain style of star, which you learn from Professor Simon Newcomb is such a distance that it takes 50,000 years for its light to reach Boston. Now, we will suppose that after looking over the large stock of new and second-hand stars, and after examining the spring catalogue and price list, I decide that one of the smaller size will do me, and I buy it. How do I know that it was there when I bought it? Its cold and silent rays may have ceased 49,000 years before I was born and the intelligence be still on the way. There is too much margin between sale and delivery. Every now and then another astronomer comes to me and says: " Professor, I have discovered another new star and intend to file it. Found it last night about a mile and a half south of the zenith, running loose. Haven't heard of anybody who has lost a star of the fifteenth magnitude, about thirteen hands high, with light mane and tail, have you?" Now, how do I know that he has discovered a brand new star? How can I discover whether he is or is not playing an old, threadbare star on me for a new one?

We are told that there has been no perceptible growth or decay in the star business since man began to roam around through space, in his mind, and make figures on the barn door with red chalk showing the celestial time table.

No serious accidents have occurred in the starry heavens since I began to observe and study their habits. Not a star has waxed, not a star has waned to my knowledge. Not a planet has season-cracked or shown any of the injurious effects of our rigorous climate. Not a star has ripened prematurely or fallen off the trees. The varnish on the very oldest stars I find on close and critical examination to be in splendid condition. They will all no doubt wear as long as we need them, and wink on long after we have ceased to wink back.

In 1866 there appeared suddenly in the northern crown a star of about the third magnitude and worth at least $250. It was generally conceded by astronomers that this was a brand new star that had never been used, but upon consulting Argelander's star catalogue and price list it was found that this was not a new star at all, but an old, faded star of the ninth magnitude, with the front breadths turned wrong side out and trimmed with moonlight along the seams. After a few days of phenomenal brightness, it gently ceased to draw a salary as a star of the third magnitude, and walked home with an Uncle Tom's Cabin company.

It is such things as this that make the life of the astronomer one of constant and discouraging toil. I have long contemplated, as I say, the advisability of retiring from this field of science and allowing others to light the northern lights, skim the milky way and do the other celestial chores. I would do them myself cheerfully if my health would permit, but for years I have realized, and so has my wife, that my duties as an astronomer kept me up too much at night, and my wife is certainly right about it when she says if I insist on scanning the heavens night after night, coming home late with the cork out of my telescope and my eyes red and swollen with these exhausting night vigils, I will be cut down in my prime. So I am liable to abandon the great labor to which I had intended to devote my life, my dazzling genius and my princely income. I hope that other savants will spare me the pain of another refusal, for my mind is fully made up that unless another skimmist is at once secured, the milky way will henceforth remain unskum.

JAMES WHITCOMB RILEY

James Whitcomb Riley, the beloved "Hoosier poet", was born in Greenfield, Indiana, in 1852, in circumstances that obliged him to begin life's struggle in his 'teens. His first venture was as a singer and reciter with a traveling patent-medicine wagon. Afterwards he became a roving sign painter. But as all his biographies show, the breath of romance was ever in him, and the breath of song soon followed. He was little more than twenty-five when he had won the approval of Longfellow and other famous poets. He settled down to the lyre and became the acclaimed and honored bard of Hoosierdom and the humble. Humor constantly displays itself throughout his work and a characteristic example in prose is the story herewith presented. Riley was the American "Pied Piper." He died in 1916.

THE CHAMPION CHECKER–PLAYER [1]

OF course as fur as Checker-playin''s concerned, you can't jest adzactly claim 'at lots makes fortunes and lots gits bu'sted at it — but still, it's on'y simple jestice to acknowledge 'at there're absolute p'ints in the game 'at takes scientific principles to figger out, and a mighty level-headed feller to *dim*onstrate, don't you understand!

Checkers is a' *old* enough game, ef age is any rickommendation; and it's a' evident fact, too, 'at "the tooth of time," as the feller says, which fer the last six thousand years has gained some reputation fer a-eatin' up things in giner'l, don't 'pear to 'a' gnawed much of a hole in Checkers — jedgin' from the checker-board of to-day and the ones 'at they're uccasionally shovellin' out at *Pom*p'y-*i*, er whatever its name is. Turned up a checker-board there not long ago, I wuz readin' 'bout, 'at still had the spots on — as plain and fresh

[1] From the Biographical Edition of the Complete Works of James Whitcomb Riley. Reprinted by special permission of the publishers, The Bobbs-Merrill Company. Copyright, 1913, by The Bobbs-Merrill Company.

as the modern white-pine board o' our'n, squared off with
pencil-marks and pokeberry-juice. These is facts 'at history herself has dug out, and of course it ain't fer me ner
you to turn our nose up at Checkers, whuther we ever
tamper with the fool-game er not. Fur's that's concerned,
I don't p'tend to be no checker-player *myse'f*,—but I knowed
a feller onc't 'at *could* play, and sort o' made a business of
it; and *that* man, in my opinion, wuz a geenyus! Name wuz
Wesley Cotterl — John Wesley Cotterl — just plain Wes,
as us fellers round the shoe-shop ust to call him; ust to
allus make the shoe-shop his headquarters-like; and, rain
er shine, wet er dry, you'd allus find *Wes* on hands,
ready to banter some feller fer a game, er jest a-settin'
humped up there over the checker-board all alone, a-cipherin'
out some new move er 'nuther, and whistlin' low and solem'
to hisse'f-like and a-payin' no attention to nobody.

And *I'll* tell *you*, Wes Cotterl wuz no man's fool, as sly as
you keep it! He wuz a deep thinker, Wes wuz; and ef he'd
'a' jest turned that mind o' his loose on *preachin'*, fer in-
stunce, and the 'terpertation o' the Bible, don't you know,
Wes 'ud 'a' worked p'ints out o' there 'at no livin' expound-
erers ever got in gunshot of!

But Wes he didn't 'pear to be cut out fer nothin' much
but jest Checker-playin'. Oh, of course, he *could* knock
around his own wood-pile some, and garden a little, more
er less; and the neighbers ust to find Wes purty handy
'bout trimmin' fruit-trees, you understand, and workin'
in among the worms and cattapillers in the vines and
shrubbery, and the like. And handlin' bees!—They
wuzn't no man under the heavens 'at knowed more 'bout
handlin' bees 'n Wes Cotterl!—"Settlin'" the blame
things when they wuz a-swarmin'; and a-robbin' hives,
and all sich fool-resks. W'y, I've saw Wes Cotterl, 'fore
now, when a swarm of bees 'ud settle in a' orchard,—like
they will sometimes, you know,—I've saw Wes Cotterl jest
roll up his shirt-sleeves and bend down a' apple tree limb
'at wuz jest kivvered with the pesky things, and scrape 'em

back into the hive with his naked hands, by the quart and
gallon, and never git a scratch! You could n't *hire* a bee
to sting Wes Cotterl! But *lazy?* — I think that man had
railly ort to 'a' been a' Injun! He wuz the fust and on'y
man 'at ever I laid eyes on 'at wuz too lazy to drap a
checker-man to p'int out the right road fer a feller 'at ast
him onc't the way to Burke's Mill; and Wes 'ithout ever
a-liftin' eye er finger, jest sort o' crooked out that mouth
o' his'n in the direction the feller wanted, and says:
"*H-yonder!*" and went on with his whistlin'. But all this
hain't Checkers, and that's what I started out to tell ye.

Wes had a way o' jest natchurally a-cleanin' out anybody
and ever'body 'at 'ud he'p hold up a checker-board! Wes
wuz n't what you 'd call a *lively* player at all, ner a competiter 'at talked much 'crost the board er made much furse
over a game whilse he *wuz* a-playin'. He had his faults, o'
course, and *would* take back moves 'casion'ly, er inch up on
you ef you did n't watch him, mebby. But, *as a rule*, Wes
had the insight to grasp the idy of whoever wuz a-playin'
ag'in' him, and *his* style o' game, you understand, and wuz
on the lookout continual'; and under sich circumstances
could play as *honest* a game o' Checkers as the babe unborn.

One thing in *Wes's* favor allus wuz the feller's temper.
— Nothin' 'peared to aggervate Wes, and nothin' on earth
could break his slow and lazy way o' takin' his own time
fer ever'thing. You jest *could n't crowd Wes* er git him
rattled anyway. — Jest 'peared to have one fixed principle,
and that wuz to take plenty o' time, and never make no
move 'ithout a-ciphern'n' ahead on the prob'ble conse-
quences, don't you understand! "Be shore you 're right,"
Wes 'ud say, a-lettin' up fer a second on that low and sorry-
like little wind-through-the-keyhole whistle o' his, and
a-nosin' out a place whur he could swap one man fer two. —
"Be shore you 're right" — and somep'n' after this style
wuz Wes's way: "Be shore you 're right" — (whistling
a long, lonesome bar of "Barbara Allen") — "and then"
— (another long, retarded bar) — "go ahead!" — and

by the time the feller 'ud git through with his whistlin',
and a-stoppin' and a-startin' in ag'in, he 'd be about three
men ahead to your one. And then he 'd jest go on with his
whistlin' 'sef nothin' had happened, and mebby you a-jest
a-rearin' and a-callin' him all the mean, outlandish, ornry
names 'at you could lay tongue to.

But Wes's good nature, I reckon, wuz the thing 'at he'ped
him out as much as any other p'ints the feller had. And
Wes' 'ud allus win, in the long run! — I don't keer *who*
played ag'inst him! It was on'y a question o' time with
Wes o' waxin' it to the best of 'em. Lots o' players has
tackled Wes, and right at the *start* 'ud mebby give him
trouble, — but in the *long run,* now mind ye — *in the long
run,* no mortal man, I reckon, had any business o' rubbin'
knees with Wes Cotterl under no airthly checker-board in
all this vale o' tears!

I mind onc't th' come along a high-toned feller from in
around In'i'nop'lus som'er's. — Wuz a *lawyer,* er some *p'fes-
sional* kind o' man. Had a big yaller, luther-kivvered book
under his arm, and a bunch o' these-'ere big en*velop*'s and
a lot o' suppeenies stickin' out o' his breast-pocket. Mighty
slick-lookin' feller he wuz; wore a stovepipe hat, sort o' set
'way back on his head — so 's to show off his Giner'l Jackson forr'ed, don't you know! Well-sir, this feller struck
the place, on some business er other, and then missed the
hack 'at *ort* to 'a' tuk him out o' here sooner'n it *did* take
him out! — And whilse he wuz a-loafin' round, sort o' lonesome — like a feller allus *is* in a strange place, you know —
he kind o' drapped in on our crowd at the shoe-shop, osten-
chably to git a boot-strop stitched on, but *I* knowed, the
minute he set foot in the door, 'at *that* feller wanted
comp'ny wuss'n *cobblin'.*

Well, as good luck would have it, there set Wes, as usual,
with the checker-board in his lap, a-playin' all by hisse'f,
and a-whistlin' so low and solem'-like and sad it railly made
the crowd seem like a *religious* getherun' o' some kind er
other, we wuz all so quiet and still-like, as the man come in.

Well, the stranger stated his business, set down, tuk off his boot, and set there nussin' his foot and talkin' weather fer ten minutes, I reckon, 'fore he ever 'peared to notice Wes at all. We wuz all back'ard, anyhow, 'bout talkin' much; besides, we knowed, long afore he come in, all about how hot the weather wuz, and the pore chance there wuz o' rain, and all that; and so the subject had purty well died out, when jest then the feller's eyes struck Wes and the checker-board,—and I'll never fergit the warm, salvation smile 'at flashed over him at the promisin' discovery. "*What!*" says he, a-grinnin' like a' angel and a-edgin' his cheer to'rds Wes, "have we a checker-board and checkers here?"

"We hev," says I, knowin' 'at Wes would n't let go o' that whistle long enough to answer—more'n to mebby nod his head.

"And who is your best player?" says the feller, kindo' pitiful-like, with another inquirin' look at Wes.

"Him," says I, a-pokin' Wes with a peg-float. But Wes on'y spit kind o' absent-like, and went on with his whistlin'.

"Much of a player, is he?" says the feller, with a sort o' doubtful smile at Wes ag'in.

"Plays a purty good hick'ry," says I, a-pokin' Wes ag'in. "Wes," says I, "here's a gentleman 'at 'ud mebby like to take a hand with you there, and give you a few idies," says I.

"Yes," says the stranger, eager-like, a-settin' his plug-hat keerful' up in the empty shelvin', and a-rubbin' his hands and smilin' as confident-like as old Hoyle hisse'f.—"Yes, indeed, I'd be glad to give the gentleman" (meanin' Wes) "a' idy er two about Checkers—ef *he'd* jest as lief,— 'cause I reckon ef there're any one thing 'at I *do* know more about 'an another, it's Checkers," says he; "and there're no game 'at delights me more—*pervidin'*, o' course, I find a competiter 'at kin make it anyways in-te*rest*in'."

"Got much of a rickord on Checkers?" says I.

"Well," says the feller, "I don't like to brag, but I've

never *be'n* beat — in any *legitimut* contest," says he, "and I 've played more'n one o' *them*," he says, "here and there round the country. Of course, *your friend* here," he went on, smilin' sociable at Wes, "*he'll* take it all in good part ef I should happen to lead him a little — jest as *I 'd* do," he says, "ef it wuz possible fer him to lead *me*."

"*Wes*," says I, "*has* warmed the wax in the yeers of some mighty good checker-players," says I, as he squared the board around, still a-whistlin' to hisse'f-like, as the stranger tuk his place, a-smilin'-like and roachin' back his hair.

"Move," says Wes.

"No," says the feller, with a polite flourish of his hand; "the first move shall be your'n." And, by jucks! fer all he would n't take even the advantage of a starter, he flaxed it to Wes the fust game in less'n fifteen minutes.

"Right shore you 've given me your best player?" he says, smilin' round at the crowd, as Wes set squarin' the board fer another game and whistlin' as onconcerned-like as ef nothin' had happened more'n ordinary.

"'S your move," says Wes, a-squintin' out into the game 'bout forty foot from shore, and a-whistlin' purt' nigh in a whisper.

"Well-sir, it 'peared-like the feller railly did n't *try* to play; and you could see, too, 'at Wes knowed he 'd about met his match, and played accordin'. He did n't make no move at all 'at he did n't give keerful thought to; whilse the feller — ! Well, as I wuz sayin', it jest 'peared-like *Checkers* wuz *child's-play* fer him! Putt in most o' the time 'long through the game a-sayin' things calkilated to kind o' bore a' ordinary man. But Wes helt hisse'f purty level, and did n't show no signs, and kep' up his *whistlin'*, mighty well — considerin'.

"Reckon you play the *fiddle*, too, as well as *Checkers?*" says the feller, laughin', as Wes come a-whistlin' out of the little end of the second game and went on a-fixin' fer the next round.

"'S my move!" says Wes, 'thout seemin' to notice the feller's tantalizin' words whatsomever.

"'Ll! *this* time," thinks I, "Mr. Smarty from the *metrol-opin* deestricts, *you're* liable to git *waxed — shore!*" But the *feller* did n't 'pear to think so at all, and played right ahead as glib-like and keerless as ever — 'casion'ly a-throwin' in them sircastic remarks o' his'n, — 'bout bein' "slow and shore" 'bout things in gineral — "Liked to *see* that," he said: — "Liked to see fellers do things with plenty o' *deliberation*, and even ef a feller *wuz n't* much of a checker-player, liked to see him *die* slow *anyhow!* — and then 'tend his own funeral," he says, — "and march in the p'session — to his own *music*," says he. — And jest then his remarks wuz brung to a close by Wes a-jumpin' two men, and a-lightin' square in the king-row. . . . "Crown that," says Wes, a-droppin' back into his old tune. And fer the rest o' *that* game Wes helt the feller purty level, but had to finally knock under — but by jest the clos'test kind o' shave o' winnin'.

"They ain't much use," says the feller, "o' keepin' *this* thing up — 'less I could manage, *some* way er other, to git beat *onc't 'n a while!*"

"Move," says Wes, a-drappin' back into the same old whistle and a-*settlin'* there.

"'Music has charms,' as the Good Book tells us," says the feller, kind o' nervous-like, and a-roachin' his hair back as ef some sort o' p'tracted headache wuz a-settin' in.

"Never wuz 'skunked,' wuz ye?" says Wes, kind o' sud-dent-like, with a fur-off look in them big white eyes o' his — and then a-whistlin' right on 'sef he had n't said *nothin'.*

"*Not much!*" says the feller, sort o' s'prised-like, as ef such a' idy as that had never struck him afore. — "Never was 'skunked' *myse'f;* but I 've saw fellers in my time 'at *wuz!*" says he.

But from that time on I noticed the feller 'peared to play more keerful, and railly la'nched into the game with some-pin' like inter'st. Wes, he seemed to be jest a-limberin'-up-like; and-sir, blame me! ef he did n't walk the feller's log fer him *that* time, 'thout no 'pearent trouble at all!

"And *now*," says Wes, all quiet-like, a-squarin' the board fer another'n, — "we 're kind o' gittin' at things *right*. Move." And away went that little unconcerned whistle o' his ag'in, and *Mr. Cityman* jest gittin' white and sweaty too — he wuz so nervous. Ner he did n't 'pear to find much to laugh at in the *next* game — ner the next *two* games nuther! Things wuz a-gettin' mighty inter*est*in' 'bout them times, and I guess the feller wuz ser'ous-like a-wakin' up to the solem' fact 'at it tuk 'bout all *his* spare time to keep up his end o' the row, and even that state o' 'pore satisfaction wuz a-creepin' furder and furder away from him ever' new turn he undertook. Whilse *Wes* jest 'peared to git more deliber't' and certain ever' game; and that unendin' se'f-satisfied and comfortin' little whistle o' his never drapped a stitch, but toed out ever' game alike, — to'rds the *last*, and, fer the *most* part, disaster 's to the feller 'at had started in with sich confi*dence* and actchul promise, don't you know.

Well-sir, the feller stuck the whole *forenoon* out, and then the *afternoon;* and then knuckled down to it 'way into the night — yes, and plum *midnight!* — And he buckled into the thing bright and airly *next morning!* And-sir, fer *two long days* and nights, a-hardly a-stoppin' long enough to *eat*, the feller stuck it out, — and Wes a-jest a-warpin' it to him hand-over-fist, and leavin' him furder behind, ever' game! — till finally, to'rds the last, the feller got so blame-don worked up and excited-like, he jes' 'peared act-chully purt' nigh plum crazy and histurical as a woman!

It was a-gittin' late into the shank of the second day, and the boys hed jest lit a candle fer 'em to finish out one of the clos'test games the feller 'd played Wes fer some time. But, Wes wuz jest as cool and ca'm as ever, and still a-whistlin' consolin' to hisse'f-like, whilse the feller jest 'peared wore out and ready to drap right in his tracks any minute.

"*Durn you!*" he snarled out at Wes, "hain't you never goern to move?" And there set Wes, a-balancin' a checker-man above the board, a-studyin' whur to set it, and a-fillin' in the time with that-air whistle.

"*Flames and flashes!*" says the feller ag'in, "will you *ever* stop that death-seducin' tune o' your'n long enough to move?"—And as Wes deliber't'ly set his man down whur the feller see he'd haf to jump it and lose two men and a king, Wes wuz a-singin', low and sad-like, as ef all to hisse'f :

> "*O we'll move that man, and leave him there.*—
> *Fer the love of B-a-r-b—bry Al-len!*"

Well-sir! the feller jest jumped to his feet, upset the board, and tore out o' the shop stark-starin' crazy—blame ef he wuz n't!—'cause some of us putt out after him and overtook him 'way beyent the 'pike-bridge, and hollered to him;—and he shuk his fist at us and hollered back and says, says he : "Ef you fellers over here," says he, "'ll agree to *muzzle* that durn checker-player o' your'n, I'll bet fifteen hundred dollars to fifteen cents 'at I kin beat him 'leven games out of ever' dozen!—But there're *no money*," he says, "'at kin hire me to play him ag'in, on this aboundin' airth, on'y on them conditions—'cause that durn, eternal, infernal, dad-blasted whistle o' his 'ud beat the oldest man in Ameriky!"

dialect — queer word

EUGENE FIELD

No writer who has ever come out of the West is more honored among his people to-day than Eugene Field. Riley, his contemporary, is personally dearer to a narrower circle, but Field's fame — as the singer of childhood — is much wider in the West. Schools are named for him in many cities, towns and villages and a "Field" day is an annual holiday. Field had two great gifts — the inheritance of his Yankee ancestors (he was born in St. Louis in 1850) — a perfect sense of humor, and a vein of sentiment that was inimitable — a combination simply irresistible to the West of his day, where it was much needed. The flavor of the true Attic salt was in Field and a vast uncultured people received his gospel and heard him gladly. He was the miracle of literary culture among the barbarians. He ought to be one of our immortals. He published a dozen books and became an American classic. "The Cyclopeedy" is a fine example of his humor in prose. He died in 1895.

THE CYCLOPEEDY [1]

HAVIN' lived next door to the Hobart place f'r goin' on thirty years, I calc'late that I know jest about ez much about the case ez anybody else now on airth, exceptin' perhaps it's ol' Jedge Baker, and he's so plaguey old 'nd so powerful feeble that *he* don't know nothin'.

It seems that in the spring uv '47 — the year that Cy Watson's oldest boy wuz drownded in West River — there come along a book agent sellin' volyumes 'nd tracks f'r the diffusion uv knowledge, 'nd havin' got the recommend of the minister 'nd uv the select men, he done an all-fired big business in our part uv the county. His name wuz Lemuel Higgins, 'nd he wuz ez likely a talker ez I ever heerd, barrin' Lawyer Conkey, 'nd everybody allowed that when Conkey

---

[1] From "A Little Book of Profitable Tales." Reprinted by permission of the publishers, Charles Scribner's Sons. Copyright, 1889, by Eugene Field.

wuz round he talked so fast that the town pump ud have to be greased every twenty minutes.

One of the first uv our folks that this Lemuel Higgins struck wuz Leander Hobart. Leander had jest marr'd one uv the Peasley girls 'nd had moved into the old homestead on the Plainville road, — old Deacon Hobart havin' give up the place to him, the other boys havin' moved out West (like a lot o' darned fools that they wuz!). Leander wuz feelin' his oats jest about this time, 'nd nuthin' wuz too good f'r him.

"Hattie," sez he, "I guess I'll have to lay in a few books f'r readin' in the winter time, 'nd I've half a notion to subscribe f'r a cyclopeedy. Mr. Higgins here says they're invalerable in a family, and that we orter have 'em, bein' as how we're likely to have the fam'ly bime by."

"Lor's sakes, Leander, how you talk!" sez Hattie, blushin' all over, ez brides allers does to heern tell uv sich things.

Waal, to make a long story short, Leander bargained with Mr. Higgins for a set uv them cyclopeedies, 'nd he signed his name to a long printed paper that showed how he agreed to take a cyclopeedy oncet in so often, which wuz to be ez often ez a new one uv the volyumes wuz printed. A cyclopeedy is n't printed all at oncet, because that would make it cost too much; consekently the man that gets it up has it strung along fur apart, so as to hit folks oncet every year or two, and gin-rally about harvest time. So Leander kind uv liked the idee, and he signed the printed paper 'nd made his affidavit to it afore Jedge Warner.

The fust volyume of the cyclopeedy stood on a shelf in the old seckertary in the settin'-room about four months before they had any use f'r it. One night 'Squire Turner's son come over to visit Leander 'nd Hattie, and they got to talkin' about apples, 'nd the sort uv apples that wuz the best. Leander allowed that the Rhode Island greenin' wuz the best, but Hattie and the Turner boy stuck up f'r the Roxbury russet, until at last a happy idee struck Leander, and sez he: " We'll leave it to the cyclopeedy, b'gosh! Whichever one the cyclopeedy sez is the best will settle it."

" But you can't find out nothin' 'bout Roxbury russets nor Rhode Island greenin's in *our* cyclopeedy," sez Hattie.

" Why not, I'd like to know?" sez Leander, kind uv indignant like.

" 'Cause ours haint got down to the R yet," sez Hattie. " All ours tells about is things beginnin' with A."

" Well, aint we talkin' about Apples?" sez Leander. " You aggervate me terrible, Hattie, by insistin' on knowin' what you don't know nothin' 'bout."

Leander went to the seckertary 'nd took down the cyclopeedy 'nd hunted all through it f'r Apples, but all he could find wuz " Apple — See Pomology."

" How in thunder kin I see Pomology," sez Leander, " when there aint no Pomology to see? Gol durn a cyclopeedy, anyhow!"

And he put the volyume back onto the shelf 'nd never sot eyes into it agin.

That's the way the thing run f'r years 'nd years. Leander would 've gin up the plaguey bargain, but he couldn't; he had signed a printed paper 'nd had swore to it afore a justice of the peace. Higgins would have had the law on him if he had throwed up the trade.

The most aggervatin' feature uv it all wuz that a new one uv them cussid cyclopeedies wuz allus sure to show up at the wrong time, — when Leander wuz hard up or had jest been afflicted some way or other. His barn burnt down two nights afore the volyume containin' the letter B arrived, and Leander needed all his chink to pay f'r lumber, but Higgins sot back on that affidavit and defied the life out uv him.

" Never mind, Leander," sez his wife, soothin' like, " it's a good book to have in the house, anyhow, now that we've got a baby."

" That's so," sez Leander, " babies does begin with B, don't it?"

You see their fust baby had been born; they named him Peasley, — Peasley Hobart, — after Hattie's folks. So, seein' as how it wuz payin' f'r a book that told about babies, Leander did n't begredge that five dollars so very much after all.

"Leander," sez Hattie one forenoon, "that B cyclopeedy aint no account. There aint nothin' in it about babies except 'See Maternity'!"

"Waal, I 'll be gosh durned!" sez Leander. That wuz all he said, and he could n't do nothin' at all, f'r that book agent, Lemuel Higgins, had the dead wood on him, — the mean, sneakin' critter!

So the years passed on, one of them cyclopeedies showin' up now 'nd then, — sometimes every two years 'nd sometimes every four, but allus at a time when Leander found it pesky hard to give up a fiver. It warn't no use cussin' Higgins; Higgins just laffed when Leander allowed that the cyclopeedy wuz no good 'nd that he wuz bein' robbed. Meantime Leander's family wuz increasin' and growin'. Little Sarey had the hoopin' cough dreadful one winter, but the cyclopeedy did n't help out at all, 'cause all it said wuz: "Hoopin' Cough—See Whoopin' Cough"—and uv course, there warn't no Whoopin' Cough to see, bein' as how the W had n't come yet!

Oncet when Hiram wanted to dreen the home pasture, he went to the cyclopeedy to find out about it, but all he diskivered wuz: "Drain— See Tile." This wuz in 1859, and the cyclopeedy had only got down to G.

The cow wuz sick with lung fever one spell, and Leander laid her dyin' to that cussid cyclopeedy, 'cause when he went to readin' 'bout cows it told him to "See Zoölogy."

But what 's the use uv harrowin' up one's feelin's talkin' 'nd thinkin' about these things? Leander got so after a while that the cyclopeedy did n't worry him at all: he grew to look at it ez one uv the crosses that human critters has to bear without complainin' through this vale uv tears. The only thing that bothered him wuz the fear that mebbe he would n't live to see the last volume — to tell the truth, this kind uv got to be his hobby, and I 've heern him talk 'bout it many a time settin' round the stove at the tarvern 'nd squirtin' tobacco juice at the sawdust box. His wife, Hattie, passed away with the yaller janders the winter W come, and all that seemed to reconcile Leander to survivin' her wuz the prospect uv seein' the last volyume uv that cyclopeedy. Lemuel Higgins, the book agent, had gone to his everlastin' punishment; but his son, Hiram, had succeeded to his father's business 'nd continued to visit the folks his old man had roped in. By this time Leander's children had growed up; all on 'em wuz marr'd, and there wuz numeris grandchildren to amuse the ol' gentleman. But Leander wuz n't to be satisfied with the common things uv airth; he did n't seem to take no pleasure in his grandchildren like most men do; his mind wuz allers sot on somethin' else, — for hours 'nd hours, yes, all day long, he 'd set out on the front stoop lookin' wistfully up the road for that book agent to come along with a cyclopeedy. He did n't want to die till he 'd got all the cyclopeedies his contract called for; he wanted to have everything straightened out before he passed away.

When — oh, how well I recollect it — when Y come along he wuz so overcome that he fell over in a fit uv paralysis, 'nd the old gentleman never got over it. For the next three years he drooped 'nd pined, and seemed like he could n't hold out much longer. Finally he had to take to his bed, — he was so old 'nd feeble, — but he made 'em move the bed up aginst the winder so he could watch for that last volyume of the cyclopeedy.

The end come one balmy day in the spring uv '87. His life wuz a-ebbin' powerful fast; the minister wuz there, 'nd me, 'nd Dock Wilson, 'nd Jedge Baker, 'nd most uv the fam'ly. Lovin' hands smoothed the wrinkled forehead 'nd breshed back the long, scant, white hair, but the eyes of the dyin' man wuz sot upon that piece uv road down which the cyclopeedy man allus come.

All to oncet a bright 'nd joyful look come into them eyes, 'nd ol' Leander riz up in bed 'nd sez, "It's come!"

"What is it, Father?" asked his daughter Sarey, sobbin' like.

"Hush," sez the minister, solemnly; "he sees the shinin' gates uv the Noo Jerusalum."

"No, no," cried the aged man; "it is the cyclopeedy — the letter Z — it's comin'!"

And, sure enough! the door opened, and in walked Higgins. He tottered rather than walked, f'r he had growed old 'nd feeble in his wicked perfession.

"Here's the Z cyclopeedy, Mr. Hobart," says Higgins.

Leander clutched it; he hugged it to his pantin' bosom; then stealin' one pale hand under the piller he drew out a faded bank-note 'nd gave it to Higgins.

"I thank Thee for this boon," sez Leander, rollin' his eyes up devoutly; then he gave a deep sigh.

"Hold on," cried Higgins, excitedly, "you've made a mistake — it isn't the last —"

But Leander didn't hear him — his soul hed fled from its mortal tenement 'nd hed soared rejoicin' to realms uv everlastin' bliss.

"He is no more," sez Dock Wilson, metaphorically.

"Then who are his heirs?" asked that mean critter Higgins.

"We be," sez the family.

"Do you conjointly and severally acknowledge and assume the obligation of deceased to me?" he asked 'em.

"What obligation?" asked Peasley Hobart, stern like.

"Deceased died owin' me f'r a cyclopeedy!" sez Higgins.

"That's a lie!" sez Peasley. "We all seen him pay you for the Z!"

"But there's another one to come," sez Higgins.

"Another?" they all asked.

"Yes, the index!" sez he.

So there wuz, and I'll be eternally goll durned if he aint a-suin' the estate in the probate court now f'r the price uv it!

RUTH McENERY STUART

Ruth McEnery Stuart, born in Louisiana, in 1856, is a Southern writer who, in her novels and short stories, has upheld the best traditions of American literature. A humorous gift of genuine quality must be a part of such a writer's equipment and Mrs. Stuart has given us a number of tales of great merit in this genre. She died in 1917.

THE DEACON'S MEDICINE[1]

WHEN the doctor drove by the Gregg farm about dusk, and saw old Deacon Gregg perched cross-legged upon his own gate-post, he knew that something was wrong within, and he could not resist the temptation to drive up and speak to the old man.

It was common talk in the neighborhood that when Grandmother Gregg made things too warm for him indoors, the good man, her spouse, was wont to stroll out to the front gate and to take this exalted seat.

Indeed, it was said by a certain Mrs. Frequent, a neighbor of prying proclivities and ungentle speech, that the deacon's wife sent him there as a punishment for misdemeanors. Furthermore, this same Mrs. Frequent did even go so far as to watch for the deacon, and when she would see him laboriously rise and resignedly poise himself upon the narrow area, she would remark:

"Well, I see Grandma Gregg has got the old man punished again. Wonder what he's been up to now?"

Her constant repetition of the unkind charge finally gained for it such credence that the diminutive figure upon

[1] From "Moriah's Mourning." Copyright, 1898, by Harper and Brothers.

the gate-post became an object of mingled sympathy and mirth in the popular regard.

The old doctor was the friend of a lifetime, and he was sincerely attached to the deacon, and when he turned his horse's head towards the gate this evening, he felt his heart go out in sympathy to the old man in durance vile upon his lonely perch.

But he had barely started to the gate when he heard a voice which he recognized as the deacon's, whereupon he would have hurried away had not his horse committed him to his first impulse by unequivocally facing the gate.

"I know three's a crowd," he called out cheerily as he presently drew rein, "but I ain't a-goin' to stay; I jest — Why, where's grandma?" he added, abruptly, seeing the old man alone. "I'm shore I heard —"

"You jest heerd me a-talkin' to myself, doctor — or not to myself, exactly, neither — that is to say, when you come up I was addressin' my remarks to this here pill."

"Bill? I don't see no bill." The doctor drew his buggy nearer. He was a little deaf.

"No; I said this pill, doctor. I'm a-holdin' of it here in the pa'm o' my hand, a-studyin' over it."

"What's she a-dosin' you for now, Enoch?"

The doctor always called the deacon by his first name when he approached him in sympathy. He did not know it. Neither did the deacon, but he felt the sympathy, and it unlocked the portals of his heart.

"Well" — the old man's voice softened — "she thinks I stand in need of 'em, of co'se. The fact is, that yaller-spotted steer run ag'in her clo'esline twice-t to-day — drug the whole week's washin' onto the ground, an' then tromped on it. She's inside a-renchin' an' a-starchin' of 'em over now. An' right on top o' that, I come in lookin' sort o' puny an' peaked, an' I happened to choke on a muskitty jest ez I come in, an' she declared she wasn't a-goin' to have a consumpted man sick on her hands an' a clo'es-destroyin' steer at the same time. An' with that she up an' wiped her hands on her apron, an' went an' selected this here pill out of a bottle of assorted sizes, an' instructed me to take it. They never was a thing done mo' delib'rate an' kind — never on earth. But of co'se you an' she know how it plegs me to take physic. You could mould out ice-cream in little pill shapes an' it would gag me, even ef 'twas vanilly-flavored. An' so, when I received it, why, I jest come out here to meditate. You can see it from where you set, doctor. It's a purty sizeable one, and I'm mighty suspicious of it."

The doctor cleared his throat. "Yas, I can see it, Enoch — of co'se."

"Could you jedge of it, doctor? That is, of its capabilities, I mean?"

"Why, no, of co'se not — not less'n I'd taste it, an' you can do that ez well ez I can. If it's quinine, it'll be bitter; an' ef it's soggy an' — "

"Don't explain no mo', doctor. I can't stand it. I s'pose it's jest ez foolish to investigate the inwardness of a pill a person is bound to take ez it would be to try to lif' the veil of the future in any other way. When I'm obligated to swaller one of 'em, I jest take a swig o' good spring water and repeat a po'tion of Scripture and commit myself unto the Lord. I always seem foreordained to choke to death, but I notice thet ef I recover from the first spell o' suffocation, I always come through. But I 'ain't never took one yet thet I didn't in a manner prepare to die."

"Then I wouldn't take it, Enoch. Don't do it." The doctor cleared his throat again, but this time he had no trouble to keep the corners of his mouth down. His sympathy robbed him for the time of the humor in the situation. "No, I wouldn't do it — doggone ef I would."

The deacon looked into the palm of his hand and sighed. "Oh yas, I reckon I better take it," he said, mildly. "Ef I don't stand in need of it now, maybe the good Lord'll sto'e it up in my system, some way, 'g'inst a future attackt."

"Well"— the doctor reached for his whip—"well, *I* would n't do it — *steer or no steer!*"

"Oh yas, I reckon you would, doctor, ef you had a wife ez worrited over a wash-tub ez what mine is. An' I had a extry shirt in wash this week, too. One little pill ain't much when you take in how she's been tantalized."

The doctor laughed outright.

"Tell you what to do, Enoch. Fling it away and don't let on. She don't question you, does she?"

"No, she 'ain't never to say questioned me, but— Well, I tried that once-t. Sampled a bitter white capsule she gave me, put it down for quinine, an' flung it away. Then I chirped up an' said I felt a heap better — and that was n't no lie — which I suppose was on account o' the relief to my mind, which it always did seem to me capsules was jest constructed to lodge in a person's air-passages. Jest lookin' at a box of 'em 'll make me low-sperited. Well, I taken notice thet she'd look at me keen now an' ag'in, an' then look up at the clock, an' treckly I see her fill the gou'd dipper an' go to her medicine-cabinet, an' then she come to me an' she says, says she, ' Open yore mouth!' An' of co'se I opened it. You see that first capsule, ez well ez the one she had jest administered, was mostly morphine, which she had give me to ward off a 'tackt o' the neuraligy she see approachin', and here I had been tryin' to live up to the re-qui'ements of quinine, an' wrastlin' severe with a sleepy spell, which, ef I'd only knew it, would o' saved me. Of co'se, after the second dose-t, which I swallered, I jest let nature take its co'se, an' treckly I commenced to doze off, an' seemed like I was a feather-bed an' wife had hung me on the fence to sun, an' I remember how she seemed to be a-whuppin' of me, but it did n't hurt. Of co'se nothin' could n't hurt me an' me all benumbed with morphine. An' I s'pose what put the feather-bed in my head was on account of it bein' goose-pickin' time, an' she was werrited with windy weather, an' she tryin' to fill the feather-beds. No, I won't never try to deceive her ag'in. It never has seemed to me thet she could have the same respect for me after ketchin' me at it, though she 'ain't never referred to it but once-t, an' that was the time I was elected deacon, an' even then she did n't do it outspoke. She seemed mighty tender over it, an' did n't no mo'n remind me thet a officer in a Christian church ought to examine hisself mighty conscientious an' be sure he was free of deceit, which, seemed to me, showed a heap o' consideration. She 'ain't got a deceitful bone in her body, doctor."

"Why, bless her old soul, Enoch, you know thet I think the world an' all o' Grandma Gregg! She's the salt o' the earth — an' rock-salt at that. She's saved too many o' my patients by her good nursin', in spite o' my poor doctorin', for me not to appreciate her. But that don't reconcile me to the way she doses you for her worries."

"It took me a long time to see that myself, doctor. But I've reasoned it out this a-way: I s'pose when she feels her temper a-risin' she's 'feerd thet she might be so took up with her troubles thet she'd neglect my health, an' so she wards off any attackt thet might be comin' on. I taken notice that time her strawberry preserves all soured on her hands, an' she painted my face with iodine, a man did die o' the erysipelas down here at Battle Creek, an' likely ez not she'd heerd of it. Sir? No, I did n't mention it at the time for fear she'd think best to lay on another coat, an' I felt sort o' disfiggured with it. Wife ain't a scoldin' woman, I'm thankful for that. An' some o' the peppermints an' things she keeps to dole out to me when she's fretted with little things — maybe her yeast'll refuse to rise, or a thunder-storm'll kill a settin' of eggs — why, they're so disguised thet *'cep'n thet I know they're medicine* — "

"Well, Kitty, I reckon we better be a-goin'." The doctor tapped his horse. "Be shore to give my love to grandma, Enoch. An' ef you're bound to take that pill — of co'se I can't no mo'n speculate about it at this distance, but I'd advise you to keep clear o' sours an' acids for a day or so. Don't think, because your teeth are adjustable, thet none o'

yore other functions ain't open to salivation. *Good*-night,
Enoch."

"Oh, she always looks after that, doctor. She's mighty
attentive, come to withholdin' harmful temptations. Good-
bye, doctor. It's did me good to open my mind to you a
little."

"Yas," he added, looking steadily into his palm as the
buggy rolled away — "yas, it's did me good to talk to him;
but I ain't no more reconciled to you, you barefaced, high-
foreheaded little roly-poly, you. Funny how a pill thet 'ain't
got a feature on earth can look me out o' countenance the
way it can, and frustrate my speech. Talk about whited
sepulchures, an' ravenin' wolves! I don't know how come
I to let on thet I was feelin' puny to-night, nohow. I might
've knew — with all them clo'es bedaubled over — though I
can't, ez the doctor says, see how me a-takin' a pill is goin'
to help matters — but of co'se I wouldn't let on to him, an'
he a bachelor."

He stopped talking and felt his wrist.

"Maybe my pulse is obstropulous, an' ought to be sedated
down. Reckon I'll haf to kill that steer — or sell him, one
— though I swo'e I wouldn't. But of co'se I swo'e that in a
temper, an' temp'rate vows ain't never made 'cep'in' to be
repented of."

Several times during the last few minutes, while the deacon spoke, there had come to him across the garden from
the kitchen the unmistakable odor of fried chicken.

He had foreseen that there would be a good supper to-
night, and that the tiny globule within his palm would constitute for him a prohibition concerning it.

Grandmother Gregg was one of those worthy if difficult
women who never let anything interfere with her duty as she
saw it magnified by the lenses of pain or temper. It usually
pleased her injured mood to make waffles on wash-day, and
the hen-house owed many renovations, with a reckless
upsetting of nests and roosts, to one of her "splittin' headaches." She would often wash her hair in view of impend-

ing company, although she averred that to wet her scalp never failed to bring on the "neuraligy." And her "neuraligy" in turn meant medicine for the deacon.

It was probably the doctor's timely advice, augmented, possibly, by the potencies of the frying-pan, with a strong underlying sympathy with the worrying woman within — it was, no doubt, all these powers combined that suddenly surprised the hitherto complying husband into such unprecedented conduct that any one knowing him in his old character, and seeing him now, would have thought that he had lost his mind.

With a swift and brave fling he threw the pill far into the night. Then, in an access of energy born of internal panic, he slid nimbly from his perch and started in a steady jog-trot into the road, wiping away the tears as he went, and stammering between sobs as he stumbled over the ruts:

"No, I won't — yas, I will, too — doggone shame, and she frettin' her life out — of co'se I will — I'll sell 'im for anything he'll fetch — an' I'll be a better man, yas, yas I will — but I won't swaller another one o' them blame — not ef I die for it."

This report, taken in long-hand by an amused listener by the road-side, is no doubt incomplete in its ejaculatory form, but it has at least the value of accuracy, so far as it goes, which may be had only from a verbatim transcript.

It was perhaps three-quarters of an hour later when Enoch entered the kitchen, wiping his face, nervous, weary, embarrassed. Supper was on the table. The blue-bordered dish, heaped with side bones and second joints done to a turn, was moved to a side station, while in its accustomed place before Enoch's plate there sat an ominous bowl of gruel. The old man did not look at the table, but he saw it all. He would have realized it with his eyes shut. Domestic history, as well as that of greater principalities and powers, often repeats itself.

Enoch's fingers trembled as he came near his wife, and standing with his back to the table, began to untie a broad flat parcel that he had brought in under his arm. She paused in one of her trips between the table and stove, and regarded him askance.

"Reckon I 'll haf to light the lantern befo' I set down to eat, wife," he said, by way of introduction. "Isrul 'll be along d'rec'ly to rope that steer. I 've done sold him." The good woman laid her dish upon the table and returned to the stove.

"Pity you had n't 'a' sold 'im day befo' yesterday. I 'd 'a' had a heap less pain in my shoulder-blade." She sniffed as she said it; and then she added, "That gruel ought to be e't warm."

By this time the parcel was open. There was a brief display of colored zephyrs and gleaming card-board. Then Enoch began re-wrapping them.

"Reckon you can look these over in the mornin', wife. They 're jest a few new cross-stitch Bible texts, an' I knowed you liked Scripture motters. Where 'll I lay 'em, wife, while I go out an' tend to lightin' that lantern? I told Isrul I 'd set it in the stable door so 's he could git that steer out o' the way immejate."

The proposal to lay the mottoes aside was a master-stroke.

The aggrieved wife had already begun to wipe her hands on her apron. Still, she would not seem too easily appeased.

"I do hope you 'ain't gone an' turned that whole steer into perforated paper, Enoch, even ef 't is Bible-texted over."

Thus she guarded her dignity. But even as she spoke she took the parcel from his hands. This was encouragement enough. It presaged a thawing out. And after Enoch had gone out to light the lantern, it would have amused a sympathetic observer to watch her gradual melting as she looked over the mottoes:

"A VIRTUOUS WIFE IS FAR ABOVE RUBIES."

"A PRUDENT WIFE IS FROM THE LORD."

"BETTER A DINNER OF HERBS WHERE LOVE IS — "

She read them over and over. Then she laid them aside and looked at Enoch's plate. Then she looked at the chicken-dish, and now at the bowl of gruel which she had carefully set on the back of the stove to keep warm.

"Don't know ez it would hurt 'im any ef I'd thicken that gruel up into mush. He's took sech a distaste to soft food sense he's got that new set."

She rose as she spoke, poured the gruel back into the pot, sifted and mixed a spoonful of meal and stirred it in. This done, she hesitated, glanced at the pile of mottoes, and reflected. Then with a sudden resolve she seized the milk-pitcher, filled a cup from it, poured the milk into the little pot of mush, hastily whipped up two eggs with some sugar, added the mixture to the pot, returned the whole to the yellow bowl, and set it in the oven to brown.

And just then Enoch came in, and approached the water-shelf.

"Don't keer how you polish it, a brass lantern an' coal ile is like murder on a man's hands. It will out."

He was thinking of the gruel, and putting off the evil hour. It had been his intention to boldly announce that he had n't taken his medicine, that he never would again unless he needed it, and, moreover, that he was going to eat his supper to-night, and always, as long as God should spare him, etc., etc., etc.

But he had no sooner found himself in the presence of long-confessed superior powers than he knew that he would never do any of these things.

His wife was thinking of the gruel too when she encouraged delay by remarking that he would better rest up a bit before eating.

"And I reckon you better soak yo' hands good. Take a pinch o' that bran out o' the safe to 'em," she added, "and ef that don't do, the Floridy water is in on my bureau."

When finally Enoch presented himself, ready for his fate, she was able to set the mush pudding, done to a fine brown, before him, and her tone was really tender as she said:

"This ain't very hearty ef you're hungry; but you can

eat it all. There ain't no interference in it with anything you've took."

The pudding was one of Enoch's favorite dishes, but as he broke its brown surface with his spoon he felt like a hypocrite. He took one long breath, and then he blurted:

"By-the-way, wife, this reminds me, I reckon you'll haf to fetch me another o' them pills. I dropped that one out in the grass—that is, ef you think I still stand in need of it. I feel consider'ble better'n I did when I come in this evenin'."

The good woman eyed him suspiciously a minute. Then her eyes fell upon the words "ABOVE RUBIES" lying upon the table. Reaching over, she lifted the pudding-bowl aside, took the dish of fried chicken from its sub-station, and set it before her lord.

"Better save that pudd'n' for dessert, honey, an' help yo'self to some o' that chicken, an' take a potater an' a roll, and eat a couple o' them spring onions—they're the first we've had. Sence you're a-feelin' better, maybe it's jest ez well thet you mislaid that pill."

The wind blows sometimes from the east in Simkinsville, as elsewhere, and there are still occasional days when the deacon betakes himself to the front gate and sits like a nineteenth-century Simon Stylites on his pillar, contemplating the open palm of his own hand, while he enriches Mrs. Frequent's *répertoire* of gossip by a picturesque item.

But the reverse of the picture has much of joy in it; for, in spite of her various tempers, Grandmother Gregg is a warm-hearted soul—and she loves her man. And he loves her.

Listen to him to-night, for instance, as, having finished his supper, he remarks:

"An' I'm a-goin' to see to it, from this on, thet you ain't fretted with things ez you've been, ef I can help it, wife. Sometimes, the way I act, I seem like ez ef I forgit you're all I've got—on earth."

"Of co'se I reelize that, Enoch," she replies. "We're each one all the other's got—an' that's why I don't spare no pains to keep you in health."

FINLEY PETER DUNNE

The West awoke to a new birth of humor with the publication of the "Dooley" talks in the *Chicago Journal* in the late nineties, and their vogue soon became nation-wide and very soon after captured England. Humor, sarcasm, and a wonderful knowledge of human beings, for a young newspaper man not yet in his thirties, were revealed in the divagations of "The Philosopher of Archey Road." "Mr. Dooley" soon became a national, nay an international figure, and in connection with his contemporary, George Ade — although the vein is widely different in some respects — gave a new and vital impulse to the whole field of American humorous writing. Finley Peter Dunne was born in Chicago on July 10, 1867. His first book, "Mr. Dooley in Peace and War", was published in 1898.

ON NEW YEAR'S RESOLUTIONS [1]

MR. HENNESSY looked out at the rain dripping down in Archey Road, and sighed, "A-ha, 'tis a bad spell iv weather we're havin'."

"Faith, it is," said Mr. Dooley, "or else we mind it more thin we did. I can't remimber wan day fr'm another. Whin I was young, I niver thought iv rain or snow, cold or heat. But now th' heat stings an' th' cold wrenches me bones; an', if I go out in th' rain with less on me thin a ton iv rubber, I'll pay dear f'r it in achin' j'ints, so I will. That's what old age means; an' now another year has been put on to what we had befure, an' we're expected to be gay. 'Ring out th' old,' says a guy at th' Brothers' School. 'Ring out th' old, ring in th' new,' he says. 'Ring out th' false, ring in th' thrue,' says he. It's a pretty sintimint, Hinnissy; but how ar-re we goin' to do it? Nawthin'd please me betther thin to turn me back on th' wicked an' ingloryous

[1] From "Mr. Dooley In Peace and War." Copyright, 1899, by Small, Maynard & Company. Reprinted by permission of the publishers.

past, rayform me life, an' live at peace with th' wurruld to
th' end iv me days. But how th' divvle can I do it? As th'
fellow says, 'Can th' leopard change his spots,' or can't he?

"You know Dorsey, iv coorse, th' cross-eyed May-o-man
that come to this counthry about wan day in advance iv a
warrant f'r sheep-stealin'? Ye know what he done to me,
tellin' people I was caught in me cellar poorin' wather into
a bar'l? Well, last night says I to mesilf, thinkin' iv Dorsey,
I says: 'I swear that henceforth I'll keep me temper with
me fellow-men. I'll not let anger or jealousy get th' betther
iv me,' I says. 'I'll lave off all me old feuds; an' if I meet
me inimy goin' down th' sthreet, I'll go up an' shake him
be th' hand, if I'm sure he hasn't a brick in th' other hand.'
Oh, I was mighty compliminthry to mesilf. I set be th'
stove dhrinkin' hot wans, an' ivry wan I dhrunk made me
more iv a pote. 'T is th' way with th' stuff. Whin I'm in
dhrink, I have manny a fine thought; an', if I wasn't too
comfortable to go an' look f'r th' ink-bottle, I cud write
pomes that'd make Shakespeare an' Mike Scanlan think
they were wur-rkin' on a dredge. 'Why,' says I, 'carry
into th' new year th' hathreds iv th' old?' I says. 'Let th'
dead past bury its dead,' says I. 'Tur-rn ye'er lamps up to
th' blue sky,' I says. (It was rainin' like th' divvle, an' th'
hour was midnight; but I give no heed to that, bein' comfortable with th' hot wans.) An' I wint to th' dure, an',
whin Mike Duffy come by on number wan hundherd an' five,
ringin' th' gong iv th' ca-ar, I hollered to him: 'Ring out th'
old, ring in th' new.' 'Go back into ye'er stall,' he says, 'an'
wring ye'ersilf out,' he says. 'Ye'er wet through,' he says.

"Whin I woke up this mornin', th' pothry had all disappeared, an' I begun to think th' las' hot wan I took had
somethin' wrong with it. Besides, th' lumbago was grippin'
me till I cud hardly put wan foot befure th' other. But I
remimbered me promises to mesilf, an' I wint out on th'
sthreet, intindin' to wish ivry wan a 'Happy New Year,' an'
hopin' in me hear-rt that th' first wan I wished it to'd tell
me to go to th' divvle, so I cud hit him in th' eye. I hadn't

gone half a block befure I spied Dorsey acrost th' sthreet. I picked up a half a brick an' put it in me pocket, an' Dorsey done th' same. Thin we wint up to each other. ' A Happy New Year,' says I. ' Th' same to you,' says he, ' an' manny iv thim,' he says. ' Ye have a brick in ye'er hand,' says I. ' I was thinkin' iv givin' ye a New Year's gift,' says he. ' Th' same to you, an' manny iv thim,' says I, fondlin' me own ammunition. ' 'T is even all around,' says he. ' It is,' says I. ' I was thinkin' las' night I 'd give up me gredge again ye,' says he. ' I had th' same thought mesilf,' says I. ' But, since I seen ye'er face,' he says, ' I 've con-cluded that I 'd be more comfortable hatin' ye thin havin' ye f'r a frind,' says he. ' Ye 're a man iv taste,' says I. An' we backed away fr'm each other. He 's a Tip,[1] an' can throw a stone like a rifleman; an', Hinnissy, I 'm somethin' iv an amachoor shot with a half-brick mesilf.

" Well, I 've been thinkin' it over, an' I 've argied it out that life 'd not be worth livin' if we did n't keep our inimies. I can have all th' frinds I need. Anny man can that keeps a liquor sthore. But a rale sthrong inimy, specially a May-o inimy, — wan that hates ye ha-ard, an' that ye 'd take th' coat off yer back to do a bad tur-rn to, — is a luxury that I can't go without in me ol' days. Dorsey is th' right sort. I can't go by his house without bein' in fear he 'll spill th' chimbly down on me head; an', whin he passes my place, he walks in th' middle iv th' sthreet, an' crosses himsilf. I 'll swear off on annything but Dorsey. He 's a good man, an' I despise him. Here 's long life to him."

ON FIREMEN [2]

" I knowed a man be th' name iv Clancy wanst, Jawn. He was fr'm th' County May-o, but a good man f'r all that ; an', whin he 'd growed to be a big, sthrappin' fellow, he wint

---

[1] Tipperary man.
[2] From " Mr. Dooley In Peace and War." Copyright, 1899, by Small, Maynard & Company. Reprinted by permission of the publishers.

on to th' fire departmint. They 'se an Irishman 'r two on th' fire departmint an' in th' army, too, Jawn, though ye 'd think be hearin' some talk they was all runnin' prim'ries an' thryin' to be cinthral comitymen. So ye wud. Ye niver hear iv thim on'y whin they die; an' thin, murther, what funerals they have!

"Well, this Clancy wint on th' fire departmint, an' they give him a place in thruck twenty-three. All th' r-road was proud iv him, an' faith he was proud iv himsilf. He r-rode free on th' sthreet ca-ars, an' was th' champeen hand-ball player f'r miles around. Ye shud see him goin' down th' sthreet, with his blue shirt an' his blue coat with th' buttons on it, an' his cap on his ear. But ne'er a cap or coat 'd he wear whin they was a fire. He might be shiv'rin' be th' stove in th' ingine house with a buffalo robe over his head; but, whin th' gong sthruck, 't was off with coat an' cap an' buffalo robe, an' out come me brave Clancy, bare-headed an' bare hand, dhrivin' with wan line an' spillin' th' hose cart on wan wheel at ivry jump iv th' horse. Did anny wan iver see a fireman with his coat on or a polisman with his off? Why, wanst, whin Clancy was standin' up f'r Grogan's eighth, his son come runnin' in to tell him they was a fire in Vogel's packin' house. He dhropped th' kid at Father Kelly's feet, an' whipped off his long coat an' wint tearin' f'r th' dure, kickin' over th' poorbox an' buttin' ol' Mis' O'Neill that 'd come in to say th' stations. 'T was lucky 't was wan iv th' Grogans. They 're a fine family f'r falls. Jawn Grogan was wurrukin' on th' top iv Metzri an' O'Connell's brewery wanst, with a man be th' name iv Dorsey. He slipped an' fell wan hundherd feet. Whin they come to see if he was dead, he got up, an' says he: 'Lave me at him.' 'At who?' says they. 'He 's deliryous,' they says. 'At Dorsey,' says Grogan. 'He thripped me.' So it did n't hurt Grogan's eighth to fall four 'r five feet.

"Well, Clancy wint to fires an' fires. Whin th' big organ facthry burnt, he carrid th' hose up to th' fourth story an' was squirtin' whin th' walls fell. They dug him out with pick an' shovel, an' he come up fr'm th' brick an' boards an' saluted th' chief. 'Clancy,' says th' chief, 'ye betther go over an' get a dhrink.' He did so, Jawn. I heerd it. An' Clancy was that proud!

"Whin th' Hogan flats on Halsted Sthreet took fire, they got all th' people out but wan; an' she was a woman asleep on th' fourth flure. 'Who'll go up?' says Bill Musham. 'Sure, sir,' says Clancy, 'I'll go'; an' up he wint. His captain was a man be th' name iv O'Connell, fr'm th' County Kerry; an' he had his fut on th' ladder whin Clancy started. Well, th' good man wint into th' smoke, with his wife faintin' down below. 'He'll be kilt,' says his brother. 'Ye don't know him,' says Bill Musham. An' sure enough, whin ivry wan'd give him up, out comes me brave Clancy, as black as a Turk, with th' girl in his arms. Th' others wint up like monkeys, but he shtud wavin' thim off, an' come down th' ladder face forward. 'Where'd ye larn that?' says Bill Musham. 'I seen a man do it at th' Lyceem whin I was a kid,' says Clancy. 'Was it all right?' 'I'll have ye up before th' ol' man,' says Bill Musham. 'I'll teach ye to come down a laddher as if ye was in a quadhrille, ye horse-stealin', ham-sthringin' May-o man,' he says. But he did n't. Clancy wint over to see his wife. 'O Mike,' says she, "'t was fine,' she says. 'But why d'ye take th' risk?' she says. 'Did ye see th' captain?' he says with a scowl. 'He wanted to go. Did he think I'd follow a Kerry man with all th' ward lukkin' on?' he says.

"Well, so he wint dhrivin' th' hose-cart on wan wheel, an' jumpin' whin he heerd a man so much as hit a glass to make it ring. All th' people looked up to him, an' th' kids followed him down th' sthreet; an' 't was th' gr-reatest priv'lige f'r anny wan f'r to play dominos with him near th' joker. But about a year ago he come in to see me, an' says he, 'Well, I'm goin' to quit.' 'Why,' says I, 'ye'er a young man yet,' I says. 'Faith,' he says, 'look at me hair,' he says, — 'young heart, ol' head. I've been at it these twinty year, an' th' good woman's wantin' to see more iv me thin blowin' into a saucer iv coffee,' he says. 'I'm goin' to quit,' he says, 'on'y I want to see wan more good fire,' he says. 'A rale good ol' hot wan,' he says, 'with th' win' blowin' f'r it an' a good dhraft in th' ilivator-shaft, an' about two stories, with pitcher-frames an' gasoline an' excelsior, an' to hear th' chief yellin': "Play 'way, sivinteen. What th' hell an' damnation are ye standin' aroun' with that pipe f'r? Is this a fire 'r a dam' livin' pitcher? I'll break ivry man iv eighteen, four, six, an' chem'cal five to-morrah mornin' befure breakfast."' 'Oh,' he says, bringin' his fist down, 'wan more, an' I'll quit.'

"An' he did, Jawn. Th' day th' Carpenter Brothers' box factory burnt. 'T was wan iv thim big, fine-lookin' buildings that pious men built out iv celluloid an' plasther iv Paris. An' Clancy was wan iv th' men undher whin th' wall fell. I seen thim bringin' him home; an' th' little woman met him at th' dure, rumplin' her apron in her hands."

ON BOOKS[1]

"Ivry time I pick up me mornin' paper to see how th' scrap come out at Batthry D," said Mr. Dooley, "th' first thing I r-run acrost is somethin' like this: 'A hot an' handsome gift f'r Christmas is Lucy Ann Patzooni's "Jims iv Englewood Thought"'; or 'If ye wud delight th' hear-rt iv yer child, ye'll give him Dr. Harper's monymental histhry iv th' Jewish thribes fr'm Moses to Dhryfuss' or 'Ivrybody is r-readin' Roodyard Kiplin's "Busy Pomes f'r Busy People."' Th' idee iv givin' books f'r Christmas prisints whin th' stores are full iv tin hor-rns an' dhrums an' boxin' gloves an' choo-choo ca-ars! People must be crazy."

"They ar-re," said Mr. Hennessy. "My house is so full iv books ye cudden't tur-rn around without stumblin' over

[1] From "Mr. Dooley in Peace and War." Copyright, 1899, by Small, Maynard & Company. Reprinted by permission of the publishers.

thim. I found th' life iv an ex-convict, the 'Prisoner iv Zinders,' in me high hat th' other day, where Mary Ann was hidin' it fr'm her sister. Instead iv th' childher fightin' an' skylarkin' in th' evenin', they're settin' around th' table with their noses glued into books. Th' ol' woman doesn't read, but she picks up what's goin' on. 'Tis 'Honoria, did Lor-rd What's-his-name marry th' fair Aminta?' or 'But that Lady Jane was a case.' An' so it goes. There's no injymint in th' house, an' they're usin' me cravats f'r book-marks."

"'T is all wrong," said Mr. Dooley. "They're on'y three books in th' wurruld worth readin',—Shakespeare, th' Bible, an' Mike Ahearn's histhry iv Chicago. I have Shakes-peare on thrust, Father Kelly r-reads th' Bible f'r me, an' I didn't buy Mike Ahearn's histhry because I seen more thin he cud put into it. Books is th' roon iv people, specially novels. Whin I was a young man, th' parish priest used to preach again thim; but nobody knowed what he meant. At that time Willum Joyce had th' on'y library in th' Sixth Wa-ard. Th' mayor give him th' bound volumes iv th' council proceedings, an' they was a very handsome set. Th' on'y books I seen was th' kind that has th' life iv th' pope on th' outside an' a set iv dominos on th' inside. They're good readin'. Nawthin' cud be better f'r a man whin he's tired out afther a day's wurruk thin to go to his library an' take down wan iv th' gr-reat wurruks iv lithra-tchoor an' play a game iv dominos f'r th' dhrinks out iv it. Anny other kind iv r-readin', barrin' th' newspapers, which will niver hurt anny onedycated man, is desthructive iv morals.

"I had it out with Father Kelly th' other day in this very matther. He was comin' up fr'm down town with an ar-rmful iv books f'r prizes at th' school. 'Have ye th' Key to Heaven there?' says I. 'No,' says he, 'th' childher that'll get these books don't need no key. They go in under th' turnstile,' he says, laughin'. 'Have ye th' Lives iv th' Saints, or the Christyan Dooty, or th' Story iv Saint Rose iv Lima?' I says. 'I have not,' says he. 'I have some good story books. I'd rather th' kids'd r-read Char-les Dickens than anny iv th' tales iv thim holy men that was burned in ile or et up be lines,' he says. 'It does no good in these degin'rate days to prove that th' best that can come to a man f'r behavin' himself is to be cooked in a pot or di-gisted be a line,' he says. 'Ye're wrong,' says I. 'Beggin' ye'er riv-rince's pardon, ye're wrong,' I says. 'What ar-re ye goin' to do with thim young wans? Ye're goin' to make thim near-sighted an' round-shouldered,' I says. 'Ye're goin' to have thim believe that, if they behave thimsilves an' lead a virchous life, they'll marry rich an' go to Congress. They'll wake up some day, an' find out that gettin' money an' behavin' ye'ersilf don't always go together,' I says. 'Some iv th' wickedest men in th' wur-ruld have marrid rich,' I says. 'Ye're goin' to teach thim that a man does n't have to use an ax to get along in th' wur-ruld. Ye're goin' to teach thim that a la-ad with a curlin' black mustache an' smokin' a cigareet is always a villyan, whin he's more often a barber with a lar-rge family. Life, says ye! There's no life in a book. If ye want to show thim what life is, tell thim to look around thim. There's more life on a Satur-dah night in th' Ar-rchy Road thin in all th' books fr'm Shakespeare to th' rayport iv th' drainage thrustees. No man,' I says, 'iver wrote a book if he had annything to write about, except Shakespeare an' Mike Ahearn. Shakes-peare was all r-right. I niver read anny of his pieces, but they sound good; an' I know Mike Ahearn is all r-right.'"

"What did he say?" asked Mr. Hennessy.

"He took it all r-right," said Mr. Dooley. "He kind o' grinned, an' says he: 'What ye say is thrue, an' it's not thrue,' he says. 'Books is f'r thim that can't injye thim-silves in anny other way,' he says. 'If ye're in good health, an' ar-re atin' three squares a day, an' not ayether sad or very much in love with ye'er lot, but just lookin' on an' not carin' a'—he said a "rush"—'not carin' a "rush", ye don't need books,' he says. 'But if ye're a down-spirited thing an' want to get away an' can't, ye need books. 'T is betther to be comfortable at home thin to go to th' circus, an' 't is betther to go to th' circus thin to r-read anny book. But 't is betther to r-read a book thin to want to go to th' circus an' not be able to,' he says. 'Well,' says I, 'whin I was growin' up, half th' congregation heard mass with their prayer books tur-rned upside down, an' they were as pious as anny. Th' Apostles' Creed niver was as con-vincin' to me afther I larned to r-read it as it was whin I cudden't read it, but believed it.'"

Dialect —
    stuttering

ANNE VIRGINIA CULBERTSON

This writer of negro folk-tales, which for vitality and color rival even "Uncle Remus", seems to be wholly outside the ken of literary biographers. All that one can say — wholly on good faith — is that she was a Southern woman, probably of a generation ago. The basis of the last statement is that the accompanying tale is from a collection of humorous stories made some thirty years ago, which, however, throws no light on her career. The writer recalls with pathos the instance of another Southern woman writer, Eva Wilder McGlasson, of whom he can find not one trace biographically, but whose songs in the *Century Magazine* forty years ago were and continue to be a living inspiration to the few who know them.

HOW MR. TERRAPIN LOST HIS BEARD

THE "cook-house" stood at some little distance from the "big house," and every evening after supper it was full of light and noise and laughter. The light came from the fire on the huge hearth, above which hung the crane and the great iron pots which Eliza, the cook, declared were indispensable in the practice of her art. To be sure, there was a cook-stove, but 'Liza was wedded to old ways and maintained there was nothing "stove cooked" that could hope to rival the rich and nutty flavor of ash cake, or greens "b'iled slow an' long over de ha'th, wid a piece er bacon in de pot."

The noise and laughter came from a circle of dusky and admiring friends, for Aunt 'Liza was a great favorite with everybody on the plantation, and though hunchbacked and homely, had, nevertheless, had her pick, as she was fond of boasting, of the likeliest looking men on the place; and though she had been twice wedded and twice widowed, aspirants were not wanting for the position now vacant for a third time. Indeed, not long before, a member of the family, on going to the cook-house to see why dinner was so late, had discovered one Sam, the burly young ox-cart driver, on his knees, pleading very earnestly with the elderly and humpbacked little cook, while dinner simmered on and on, unnoticed and forgotten. When remonstrated with she said that she was " 'bleeged ter have co'tin' times ez well ez de res' er folks," and intimated that in affairs of the heart these things were apt to happen at any time or place, and that if a gentleman chose an inopportune moment " 't wan't her fault," and no one could, with any show of reason, expect her not to pay attention to him. She ruled everybody, her white folks included, though just how she did it no one could say, unless she was one of those commanding spirits and born leaders who sometimes appear even in the humblest walks of life. It is possible that her uncommonly strong will compelled the affections of her male admirers, but it is also possible that she condescended to flatter, and it is certain that she fed them well.

One night, between supper and bedtime, the children heard the sound of a banjo proceeding from the cook-house. They had never ventured into Aunt 'Liza's domain before, but the plinketty-plunk of the banjo, the sound of patting and the thud of feet keeping time to the music drew them irresistibly. Aunt Nancy was there, in the circle about the embers, as was also her old-time foe, Aunt 'Phrony, and the banjo was in the hands of Tim, a plowboy, celebrated as being the best picker for miles around. Lastly, there were Aunt 'Liza and her latest conquest, Sam, whose hopes she could not have entirely quenched or he would not have beamed so complacently on the assembled company.

There was a hush as the three little heads appeared in the doorway, but the children begged them to go on, and so Tim picked away for dear life and Sam did a wonderful double-shuffle with the pigeon-wing thrown in. Then

Tim sang a plantation song about "Cindy Ann" that ran something like this:

> I'se gwine down ter Richmond,
> I'll tell you w'at hit's for:
> I'se gwine down ter Richmond,
> Fer ter try an' end dis war.

Refrain: An'-a you good-by, Cindy, Cindy,
> Good-by, Cindy Ann;
> An'-a you good-by, Cindy, Cindy,
> I'se gwine ter Rappahan.

> I oon ma'y a po' gal,
> I'll tell de reason w'y:
> Her neck so long an' skinny
> I'se 'feared she nuver die.

> Refrain.

> I oon ma'y a rich gal,
> I'll tell de reason w'y:
> Bekase she dip so much snuff
> Her mouf is nuver dry.

> Refrain.

> I ru'rr ma'y a young gal,
> A apple in her han',
> Dan ter ma'y a widdy
> Wid a house an' a lot er lan'.

> Refrain.

At the reference to a "widdy" he winked at the others and looked significantly at Sam and Aunt 'Liza. Then he declared it was the turn of the ladies to amuse the gentlemen. Aunt Nancy and Aunt 'Phrony cried, "Hysh! Go 'way, man! W'at ken we-all do? Done too ol' fer foolishness; leave dat ter de gals!" But 'Liza was not inclined to leave the entertainment of gentlemen to "gals", whom she declared to be, for the most part, "wu'fless trunnel-baid trash."

"Come, come, Sis' 'Phrony, an' you, too, Sis' Nancy,"

said she, "you knows dar ain' nu'rr pusson on de place kin beat you bofe in der marter uv tellin' tales. I ain' nuver have de knack myse'f, but I knows a good tale w'en I years hit, an' I bin gittin' myse'f fixed fer one uver sence you comed in."

The children added their petitions, seconded by Tim and Sam. Aunt Nancy looked as if she were feeling around in the dusk of half-forgotten things for a dimly remembered story, perceiving which the nimbler-witted Aunt 'Phrony made haste to say that she believed she knew a story which might please the company if they were not too hard to suit. They politely protested that such was far from being the case, whereupon she began the story of how the Terrapin lost his beard.

"Um-umph!" snorted Aunt Nancy, "who uver year tell uv a tarr'pin wid a by'ud!"

"Look-a-yer, ooman," said 'Phrony, "who tellin' dis, me'er you? You s'pose I'se talkin' 'bout de li'l ol' no-kyount tarr'pins dey has dese days? Naw, suh! I'se tellin' 'bout de ol' time Tarr'pin whar wuz a gre't chieft an' a big fighter, an' w'ensomuver tu'rr creeturs come roun' an' try ter pay him back, he jes' drord his haid in his shell an' dar he wuz. Dish yer ain' no ol' nigger tale, neener, dish yer a Injun tale whar my daddy done tol' me w'en I wan't no bigger'n Miss Janey. He say dat sidesen de by'ud, Tarr'pin had big wattles hangin' down beneaf his chin, jes' lak de tukkey-gobblers has dese days. Him an' Mistah Wi'yum Wil'-tukkey wuz mighty good fren's dem times, an' Tukkey he thought Tarr'pin wuz a monst'ous good-lookin' man. He useter mek gre't 'miration an' say, 'Mistah Tarry-long Tarr'pin, you sut'n'y is a harnsum man. Dar ain' nu'rr creetur in dese parts got such a by'ud an' wattles ez w'at you is.'

"Den Tarr'pin he'd stroke down de by'ud an' swell out de wattles an' say, 'Sho! sho! Mistah Tukkey, you done praise dese yer heap mo'n w'at dey is wuf,' but all de same he wuz might'ly please', fer dar's nuttin' lak a li'l bit er flatt'ry fer ilin' up de j'ints an' mekin' folks limbersome in der feelin's.

"Tukkey git ter thinkin' so much 'bout de by'ud an' de wattles dat seem ter him ez ef he kain't git long nohows lessen he have some fer hisse'f, 'kase in dem days de gobblers ain' have none. He study an' he study, but he kain't see whar he kin git 'em, an' de mo' he study de mo' he hone atter 'em. Las' he git so sharp set atter 'em dat he ain' kyare how he git 'em, jes' so he git 'em, an' den he mek up his min' he gwine tek 'em 'way f'um Tarr'pin. So one day w'en he met up wid him in de road he stop him an' bob his haid an' mek his manners mighty p'litely, an' he say, sezee, 'Mawnin', Mistah Tarry-long, mawnin'. How you come on dis day? I ain' hatter ax you, dough, 'kase you done look so sprucy wid yo' by'ud all comb' out an' yo' wattles puff' up. I wish, suh, you lemme putt 'em on fer a minnit, so's't I kin see ef I becomes 'em ez good ez w'at you does.'

"Ol' man Tarr'pin mighty easy-goin' an' 'commodatin', so he say, 'W'y, sut'n'y, Mistah Tukkey, you kin tek 'em an' welcome fer a w'iles.' So Tukkey he putts 'em on an' moseys down ter de branch ter look at hisse'f in de water. 'Whoo-ee!' sezee ter hisse'f, 'ain' I de caution in dese yer fixin's! I'se saw'y fer de gals now, I sut'n'y is, 'kase w'at wid my shape an' dish yer by'ud an' wattles, dar gwine be some sho'-'nuff heart-smashin' roun' dese diggin's, you year me sesso!'

"Den he go struttin' back, shakin' de by'ud an' swellin' out de wattles an' jes' mo'n steppin' high an' prancin' w'ile he sing:

'Cle'r outen de way fer ol' Dan Tucker,
You'se too late ter git yo' supper.'

"Den he say, sezee, 'Mistah Tarr'pin, please, suh, ter lemme keep dese yer? I b'lieve I becomes 'em mo'n w'at you does, 'kase my neck so long an' thin seem lak I needs 'em ter set hit off mo'n w'at you does wid dat shawt li'l neck er yo'n whar you keeps tuck 'way in yo' shell half de time, anyways. Sidesen dat, you is sech a runt dat you g'long draggin' de by'ud on de groun', an' fus' news you know hits 'bleeged ter be wo' out. You bes' lemme have hit, 'kase I kin tek good kyare uv hit.'

"Den Tarr'pin say, sezee, 'I lak ter 'commodate you, Mistah Tukkey, but I ain' see how I kin. I done got so use ter runnin' my fingers thu de by'ud an' spittin' over hit w'en I'se settin' roun' thinkin' er talkin' dat I dunno how I kin do widout hit, an' I kain't git long, nohow, widout swellin' up de wattles w'en I git tetched in my feelin's. Sidesen dat, I kin tek kyare er de by'ud, ef I *is* a runt; I bin doin' it a good w'ile, an' she ain' wo' out yit. So please, suh, ter han' me over my fixin's.'

"'Not w'iles I got any wind lef' in me fer runnin',' sez de Tukkey, sezee, an' wid dat he went a-scootin', ol' man Tarr'pin atter him, hot-foot. Dey went scrabblin' up de mountains an' down de mountains, an' 't wuz pull Dick, pull devil, fer a w'ile. Dey kain't neener one uv 'em climb up ve'y fas', but w'en dey git ter de top, Tukkey he fly down an' Tarr'pin he jes' natchully turn over an' roll down. But Tukkey git de start an' keep hit. W'en Tarr'pin roll to de bottom uv a mountain den he'd see Tukkey at de top er de nex' one. Dey kep' hit up dis-a-way 'cross fo' ridges, an' las' Tarr'pin he plumb wo' out an' he see he wan't gwine ketch up at dat rate, so he gin up fer dat day. Den he go an' hunt up de cunjerers an' ax 'em fer ter he'p him. He say, 'Y'all know dat by'ud an' wattles er mine? Well, I done loan 'em to Mistah Wi'yum Wil'-tukkey, 'kase he wuz my fren' an' he done ax me to. An' now he turn out ter be no-kyount trash, an' w'at I gwine do? You bin knowin' I is a slow man, an' if I kain't git some he'p, I hatter say good-by by'ud an' wattles.'"

"What are 'cunjerers,' Aunt 'Phrony?" said Ned.

"Well now, honey," said she, "I dunno ez I kin jes' rightly tell you, but deys w'at de Injuns calls 'medincin'-men,' an' dey doctors de sick folks an' he'ps de hunters ter git game an' de gals ter git beaux, an' putts spells on folks an' mek 'em do jes' 'bout w'at dey want 'em to. An' so dese yer cunjerers dey goes off by derse'fs an' has a confab an' den dey come back an' tell Mistah Tarr'pin dat dey reckon dey done fix Mistah Tukkey dis time.

"'W'at you done wid him?' sezee.

"'We ain' ketch 'im,' dey ses, 'we lef' dat fer you, dat ain' ow' bizness, but we done fix him up so 't you kin do de ketchin' yo'se'f.'

"'W'at has you done to him, den?' sezee.

"'Son', dey ses, 'we done putt a lot er li'l bones in his laigs, an' dat gwine slow him up might'ly, an' we 'pends on you ter do de res', 'kase we knows dat you is a gre't chieft.'

"Den Tarr'pin amble long 'bout his bizness an' neener stop ner res' ontwel he met up wid Tukkey onct mo'. He ax fer his by'ud an' wattles ag'in, but Tukkey jes' turnt an' stept out f'um dat, Tarr'pin atter him. But seem lak de cunjerers thought Mistah Tarr'pin wuz faster'n w'at he wuz, er dat Mistah Tukkey 'z slower'n w'at *he* wuz, 'kase Tarr'pin ain' nuver ketch up wid him yit, an' w'ats mo', de tarr'pins is still doin' widout by'uds an' wattles an' de gobblers is still wearin' 'em an' swellin' roun' showin' off ter de gals, steppin' ez high ez ef dem li'l bones w'at de cunjerers putt dar wan't still in der laigs, an' struttin' lak dey wuz sayin' ter ev'y pusson dey meets:

'Cle'r outen de way fer ol' Dan Tucker,
You'se too late ter git yo' supper.'

GEORGE HORACE LORIMER

George Horace Lorimer, who has for long years wielded the Jovian sceptre of the *Saturday Evening Post*, is perhaps the most powerful editor in the country to-day. One can readily recall the thrill of his popular success, "The Letters of a Self-Made Merchant to his Son", which the whole country was reading in 1902 and for two or three years after. He followed it up with three more books, two of them in the same vein, and then settled down to the editorial collar. Mr. Lorimer's place among our humorists is indisputable, although he is really more of a philosopher. Still he has abundance of feeling and an unassailable technique. He was born in Louisville, Kentucky, October 6, 1868, the son of a famous Baptist minister, Dr. George C. Lorimer, whose portrait is the sole ornament of his editorial rooms in Philadelphia to-day.

THE BEGINNING OF WISDOM [1]

CHICAGO, April 15, 189—

Dear Pierrepont: Don't ever write me another of those sad, sweet, gentle sufferer letters. It's only natural that a colt should kick a trifle when he's first hitched up to the break wagon, and I'm always a little suspicious of a critter that stands too quiet under the whip. I know it's not meekness, but meanness, that I've got to fight, and it's hard to tell which is the worst.

The only animal which the Bible calls patient is an ass, and that's both good doctrine and good natural history. For I had to make considerable of a study of the Missouri mule when I was a boy, and I discovered that he's not really patient, but that he only pretends to be. You can cuss him out till you've nothing but holy thoughts left in you to draw

---

[1] From "Letters of a Self-Made Merchant to his Son." Copyright, 1902, by Small, Maynard & Company. Reprinted by permission of the author and publishers.

on, and you can lay the rawhide on him till he's striped like a circus zebra, and if you're cautious and reserved in his company he will just look grieved and pained and re-signed. But all the time that mule will be getting meaner and meaner inside, adding compound cussedness every thirty days, and practicing drop kicks in his stall after dark.

Of course, nothing in this world is wholly bad, not even a mule, for he is half horse. But my observation has taught me that the horse half of him is the front half, and that the only really safe way to drive him is hind-side first. I suppose that you could train one to travel that way, but it really doesn't seem worth while when good roadsters are so cheap.

That's the way I feel about these young fellows who lazy along trying to turn in at every gate where there seems to be a little shade, and sulking and balking whenever you say "git-ap" to them. They are the men who are always howl-ing that Bill Smith was promoted because he had a pull, and that they are being held down because the manager is jealous of them. I've seen a good many "pulls" in my time, but I never saw one strong enough to lift a man any higher than he could raise himself by his boot straps, or long enough to reach through the cashier's window for more money than its owner earned.

When a fellow brags that he has a "pull", he's a liar or his employer's a fool. And when a fellow whines that he's being held down, the truth is, as a general thing, that his boss can't hold him up. He just picks a nice, soft spot, stretches out flat on his back, and yells that some heartless brute has knocked him down and is sitting on his chest.

A good man is as full of bounce as a cat with a small boy and a bull terrier after him. When he's thrown to the dog from the second-story window, he fixes while he's sail-ing through the air to land right, and when the dog jumps for the spot where he hits, he isn't there, but in the top of the tree across the street. He's a good deal like the little red-headed cuss that we saw in the football game you took me to. Every time the herd stampeded it would start in to trample and paw and gore him. One minute the whole bunch would be on top of him and the next he would be loping off down the range, spitting out hair and pieces of canvas jacket, or standing on one side as cool as a hog on ice, watching the mess unsnarl and the removal of the cripples.

I didn't understand football, but I understood that little sawed-off. He knew his business. And when a fellow knows his business, he doesn't have to explain to people that he does. It isn't what a man knows, but what he thinks he knows that he brags about. Big talk means little knowledge.

There's a vast difference between having a carload of miscellaneous facts sloshing around loose in your head and getting all mixed up in transit, and carrying the same assortment properly boxed and crated for convenient handling and immediate delivery. A ham never weighs so much as when it's half cured. When it has soaked in all the pickle that it can, it has to sweat out most of it in the smoke-house before it is any real good; and when you've soaked up all the information you can hold, you will have to forget half of it before you will be of any real use to the house. If there's anything worse than knowing too little, it's knowing too much. Education will broaden a narrow mind, but there's no known cure for a big head. The best you can hope is that it will swell up and bust; and then, of course, there's nothing left. Poverty never spoils a good man, but prosperity often does. It's easy to stand hard times, because that's the only thing you can do, but in good times the fool-killer has to do night-work.

I simply mention these things in a general way. A good many of them don't apply to you, no doubt, but it won't do any harm to make sure. Most men get cross-eyed when they come to size themselves up, and see an angel instead of what they're trying to look at. There's nothing that tells the truth to a woman like a mirror, or that lies harder to a man.

What I am sure of is that you have got the sulks too quick. If you knew all that you'll have to learn before you'll be a big, broad-gauged merchant, you might have something to be sulky about.

When you've posted yourself properly about the business you'll have taken a step in the right direction — you will be able to get your buyer's attention. All the other steps are those which lead you into his confidence.

Right here you will discover that you are in the fix of the young fellow who married his best girl and took her home to live with his mother. He found that the only way in which he could make one happy was by making the other mad, and that when he tried to make them both happy he only succeeded in making them both mad. Naturally, in the end, his wife divorced him and his mother disinherited him, and left her money to an orphan asylum, because, as she sensibly observed in the codicil, "orphans can not be ungrateful to their parents." But if the man had had a little tact he would have kept them in separate houses, and have let each one think that she was getting a trifle the best of it, without really giving it to either.

Tact is the knack of keeping quiet at the right time; of being so agreeable yourself that no one can be disagreeable to you; of making inferiority feel like equality. A tactful man can pull the stinger from a bee without getting stung.

Some men deal in facts, and call Bill Jones a liar. They get knocked down. Some men deal in subterfuges, and say that Bill Jones' father was a kettle-rendered liar, and that his mother's maiden name was Sapphira, and that any one who believes in the Darwinian theory should pity rather than blame their son. They get disliked. But your tactful man says that since Baron Munchausen no one has been so chuck full of bully reminiscences as Bill Jones; and when that comes back to Bill he is half tickled to death, because he doesn't know that the higher criticism has hurt the Baron's reputation. That man gets the trade.

There are two kinds of information: one to which everybody's entitled, and that is taught at school; and one which nobody ought to know except yourself, and that is what you think of Bill Jones. Of course, where you feel a man is not square you will be armed to meet him, but never on his own ground. Make him be honest with you if you can, but don't let him make you dishonest with him.

When you make a mistake, don't make the second one — keeping it to yourself. Own up. The time to sort out rotten eggs is at the nest. The deeper you hide them in the case the longer they stay in circulation, and the worse impression they make when they finally come to the breakfast-table. A mistake sprouts a lie when you cover it up. And one lie breeds enough distrust to choke out the prettiest crop of confidence that a fellow ever cultivated.

Of course, it's easy to have the confidence of the house, or the confidence of the buyer, but you've got to have both. The house pays you your salary, and the buyer helps you earn it. If you skin the buyer you will lose your trade; and if you play tag with the house you will lose your job. You've simply got to walk the fence straight, for if you step to either side you'll find a good deal of air under you.

Even after you are able to command the attention and the confidence of your buyers, you've got to be up and dressed all day to hold what trade is yours, and twisting and turning all night to wriggle into some of the other fellow's. When business is good, that is the time to force it, because it will come easy; and when it is bad, that is the time to force it, too, because we will need the orders.

Speaking of making trade naturally calls to my mind my old acquaintance, Herr Doctor Paracelsus Von Munsterberg, who, when I was a boy, came to our town "fresh from his healing triumphs at the Courts of Europe", as his handbills ran, "not to make money, but to confer on

suffering mankind the priceless boon of health; to make the
sick well, and the well better."

Munsterberg wasn't one of your common, coarse,
county-fair barkers. He was a pretty high-toned article.
Had nice, curly black hair and didn't spare the bear's
grease. Wore a silk hat and a Prince Albert coat all the
time, except when he was orating, and then he shed the
coat to get freer action with his arms. And when he talked
he used the whole language, you bet.

Of course, the Priceless Boon was put up in bottles,
labeled Munsterberg's Miraculous Medical Discovery, and,
simply to introduce it, he was willing to sell the small size
at fifty cents and the large one at a dollar. In addition to
being a philanthropist the Doctor was quite a hand at card
tricks, played the banjo, sang coon songs and imitated a
saw going through a board very creditably. All these ac-
complishments, and the story of how he cured the Emperor
of Austria's sister with a single bottle, drew a crowd, but
they didn't sell a drop of the Discovery. Nobody in town
was really sick, and those who thought they were had
stocked up the week before with Quackenboss' Quick Quinine Kure from a fellow that made just as liberal promises
as Munsterberg and sold the large size at fifty cents, including a handsome reproduction of an "old master" for the
parlor.

Some fellows would just have cussed a little and have
moved on to the next town, but Munsterberg made a beautiful speech, praising the climate, and saying that in his
humble capacity he had been privileged to meet the strength
and beauty of many Courts, but never had he been in any
place where strength was stronger or beauty beautifuller
than right here in Hoskins' Corners. He prayed with all
his heart, though it was almost too much to hope, that the
cholera, which was raging in Kentucky, would pass this
Eden by; that the yellow fever, which was devastating Ten-
nessee, would halt abashed before this stronghold of health,
though he felt bound to add that it was a peculiarly malig-

nant and persistent disease; that the smallpox, which was creeping southward from Canada, would smite the next town instead of ours, though he must own that it was no respecter of persons; that the diphtheria and scarlet-fever, which were sweeping over New England and crowding the graveyards, could be kept from crossing the Hudson, though they were great travelers and it was well to be prepared for the worst; that we one and all might providentially escape chills, headaches, coated tongue, pains in the back, loss of sleep and that tired feeling, but it was almost too much to ask, even of such a generous climate. In any event, he begged us to beware of worthless nostrums and base imitations. It made him sad to think that to-day we were here and that to-morrow we were running up an undertaker's bill, all for the lack of a small bottle of Medicine's greatest gift to Man.

I could see that this speech made a lot of women in the crowd powerful uneasy, and I heard the Widow Judkins say that she was afraid it was going to be "a mighty sickly winter", and she didn't know as it would do any harm to have some of that stuff in the house. But the Doctor didn't offer the Priceless Boon for sale again. He went right from his speech into an imitation of a dog, with a tin can tied to his tail, running down Main Street and crawling under Si Hooper's store at the far end of it — an imitation, he told us, to which the Sultan was powerful partial, "him being a cruel man and delighting in torturing the poor dumb beasts which the Lord has given us to love, honor and cherish."

He kept this sort of thing up till he judged it was our bedtime, and then he thanked us "one and all for our kind attention", and said that as his mission in life was to amuse as well as to heal, he would stay over till the next afternoon and give a special matinée for the little ones, whom he loved for the sake of his own golden-haired Willie, back there over the Rhine.

Naturally, all the women and children turned out the

next afternoon, though the men had to be at work in the fields and the stores, and the Doctor just made us roar for half an hour. Then, while he was singing an uncommon funny song, Mrs. Brown's Johnny let out a howl.

The Doctor stopped short. "Bring the poor little sufferer here, Madam, and let me see if I can soothe his agony," says he.

Mrs. Brown was a good deal embarrassed and more scared, but she pushed Johnny, yelling all the time, up to the Doctor, who began tapping him on the back and looking down his throat. Naturally, this made Johnny cry all the harder, and his mother was beginning to explain that she "reckoned she must have stepped on his sore toe", when the Doctor struck his forehead, cried "Eureka!", whipped out a bottle of the Priceless Boon, and forced a spoonful of it into Johnny's mouth. Then he gave the boy three slaps on the back and three taps on the stomach, ran one hand along his windpipe, and took a small button-hook out of his mouth with the other.

Johnny made all his previous attempts at yelling sound like an imitation when he saw this, and he broke away and ran toward home. Then the Doctor stuck one hand in over the top of his vest, waved the button-hook in the other, and cried: "Woman, your child is cured! Your button-hook is found!"

Then he went on to explain that when baby swallowed safety-pins, or pennies, or fish-bones, or button-hooks, or any little household articles, that all you had to do was to give it a spoonful of the Priceless Boon, tap it gently fore and aft, hold your hand under its mouth, and the little article would drop out like chocolate from a slot machine.

Every one was talking at once, now, and nobody had any time for Mrs. Brown, who was trying to say something. Finally she got mad and followed Johnny home. Half an hour later the Doctor drove out of the Corners, leaving his stock of the Priceless Boon distributed — for the usual consideration — among all the mothers in town.

It was not until the next day that Mrs. Brown got a chance to explain that while the Boon might be all that the Doctor claimed for it, no one in her house had ever owned a button-hook, because her old man wore jack-boots and she wore congress shoes, and little Johnny wore just plain feet.

I simply mention the Doctor in passing, not as an example in morals, but in methods. Some salesmen think that selling is like eating — to satisfy an existing appetite; but a good salesman is like a good cook — he can create an appetite when the buyer is n't hungry.

I don't care how good old methods are, new ones are better, even if they're only just as good. That's not so Irish as it sounds. Doing the same thing in the same way year after year is like eating a quail a day for thirty days. Along toward the middle of the month a fellow begins to long for a broiled crow or a slice of cold dog.

Your affectionate father,
JOHN GRAHAM.

ANNE WARNER

Anne Warner (Anne Warner French) born in 1869, appeared in the early nineteen hundreds at a very opportune time to heighten and continue the tradition of American woman humorists. "Susan Clegg" (1904) literally captivated the American public, and the author's popularity increased with her subsequent character stories. Mrs. French died in 1913. Her work is an almost incomparable addition to our general tradition.

MISS CLEGG'S ADOPTED [1]

IT was an evening in early October, — one of those first frosty nights when a bright wood fire is so agreeable to contemplate and so more than agreeable to sit in front of. Susan Clegg sat in front of hers, and doubtless thoroughly appreciated its cheerful warmth, but it cannot be said that she took any time to contemplate it, for her gaze was altogether riveted upon the stocking which she was knitting, and which appeared — for the time being — to absorb completely that persevering energy which was the dominant note of her character.

But still the beauty and brilliancy of the leaping flames were not altogether lost upon un unseeing world, for there was another present beside Susan, and that other was full to overflowing with the power of silent admiration. Her little black beady eyes stared at the dancing lights that leapt from each burning log in a species of rapt absorption, and it was only semi-occasionally that she turned them back upon the work which lay upon her lap. Mrs. Lathrop (for of course it was Mrs. Lathrop) was matching scraps for a

[1] From "Susan Clegg and Her Friend, Mrs. Lathrop." Copyright, 1904, by Little, Brown, and Company.

"crazy" sofa-pillow, and there was something as touchingly characteristic in the calmness and deliberation of her matching as there was in the wild whirl which Susan's stocking received whenever that lady felt the moment had come to alter her needles. For Susan, when she knit, knit fast and furiously, whereas Mrs. Lathrop's main joy in relation to labor lay in the sensation that she was preparing to undertake it.

. . . .

The former altered her needles with a fierce fling, and began:

"I must go on 'n' tell you what's on my mind. I'd be a fool not to tell you, havin' got you over here just for the purpose o' bein' told, 'n' yet I've sat here a good hour — 'n' you know I ain't over-give to sittin', Mrs. Lathrop — tryin' to decide whether after all I would tell you or not. You see this subjeck is n't nowise new to me, but it'll be new to you, 'n' bein' new to you I can't see how anythin' 's goin' to be got out o' askin' you f'r advice. It ain't likely 't any one first go-off c'n think of things 't I ain't thought of already, 'n' you know yourself, Mrs. Lathrop, how little you ever have to say to me compared to what I say to you. Besides, 's far 's my observation 's extended no one don't ask f'r advice 'nless they've pretty well made up their mind not to take it, if so be 's it suits 'em better untook, 'n' when I make up my mind I'm goin' to do a thing anyhow so there ain't much use in me askin' you 'r anybody else what they think about it. A woman 's rich 's I be don't need to take no one else's say-so nohow — not 'nless she feels so inclined, 'n' the older I get the less I incline."

Mrs. Lathrop sighed slightly, but did not alter her position by a hair. Susan whirled her stocking, took a fresh breath, and went on:

"It's a subjeck 't I've been lookin' straight in the face, 's well 's upside down 'n' hind end to, f'r a good long time. I 'xpeck 't it'll mebbe come in the nature of a surprise to the c'mmunity in general, 'n' yet, to tell you the truth, Mrs. Lathrop, I was thinkin' o' this very thing away back las' spring when Mrs. Shores eloped.

.   .   .   .

"'F the minister's wife had n't come that day 'n' had n't talked as she did, I might 'a' been left less wore out and, as a consequence, have told you that night what I ain't never told you yet, for it was strong in my mind then 'n' it's strong in my mind now, 'n' bein' one o' them's wastes no words, I'll state to you at once, Mrs. Lathrop, 't before Mrs. Shores run away — 'n' after she run away too, f'r that matter — I was thinkin' very seriously o' adoptin' a baby."

"A—" said Mrs. Lathrop, opening her eyes somewhat.

"A baby," repeated Susan. "I feel you ought to be the first one to know it because, 's much 's I'm out, you'll naturally have the care of it the most of the time."

Mrs. Lathrop clawed feebly among her pieces and seemed somewhat bewildered as she clawed.

"Mrs. Shores' ba—" she queried.

Susan screamed.

"*Mrs. Lathrop!*" — she stopped knitting so that she might concentrate her entire strength into the extreme astonishment which she desired to render manifest in those two words — "Mrs. Lathrop! — Me! — adopt Mrs. Shores' baby! Adopt the baby of a woman as 'd gone off 'n' left it!"

Mrs. Lathrop looked deeply apologetic.

"I did n't know —" she ventured.

"Well, you'd ought to of," cried Susan, "'n' if you did n't I'd never own to it. Such a idea never entered my head, 'n' I can't conceive when nor how it entered yours. Only I'm free to confess to one thing, Mrs. Lathrop, 'n' that is 't 'f *I* was give to havin' ideas 's senseless 's yours often are, I'd certainly keep my mouth shut 'n' let people 's knows more do the talkin'."

Mrs. Lathrop swallowed the rebuke and remained passively overcome by the afterclap of her astonishment.

Susan began to knit again.

"I wasn't thinkin' o' Mrs. Shores' baby 'n' I wasn't thinkin' o' no baby in particular. I never said I was thinkin' of any baby — I said I was thinkin' of *a* baby. I sh'd think you could 'a' seen the difference, but even if you can't see it there is a difference just the same. My sakes alive! it's a serious enough matter decidin' to adopt some one for good 'n' all without hurryin' the doin' of it any. If you was 's rich 's I be, Mrs. Lathrop, you'd understand that better. 'N' if you was 's rich 's I be, you might not be in no more of a hurry 'n I am. I ain't in a hurry a *tall*. I ain't in a hurry 'n' I don't mean to be in a hurry. I'm only jus' a-gettin' on towards makin' up my mind."

Mrs. Lathrop slowly and meditatively drew a piece of sky-blue farmer's satin from her bag and looked at it absent-mindedly. Susan twirled her stocking and went on.

"'S long 's I've begun I may 's well make a clean breast of the whole now. O' course you don't know nothin', Mrs. Lathrop, but, to put the whole thing in a shell, this adoptin' of a child 's a good deal to consider. When a woman 's married, it's the Lord's will 'n' out o' the Bible 'n' to be took without no murmurin' 's to your own feelin's in the matter. Every one 's sorry for married people, no matter how their children turn out, because, good or bad, like enough they done their best, 'n' if they didn't it was always the other one's fault; but there ain't no one goin' to lay themselves out to try 'n' smooth my child's thorns into a bed o' roses for me. Every one 's jus' goin' to up 'n' blame me right 'n' left 'n' if it has a pug-nose or turns out bad I can't shoulder none of it onto the Lord, I'll jus' have the whole c'mmunity sayin' I've got myself 'n' no one else to thank. Now, when you know f'r sure 't you can't blame nobody else but jus' yourself, you go pretty slow, 'n' for that very reason I'm thinkin' this subjeck well over afore I decide. There's a good many questions to consider, —

my mind 's got to be made up whether boy or girl 'n' age 'n' so forth afore I shall open my lips to a livin' soul."

Mrs. Lathrop appeared to be slowly recovering from the effects of her surprise.

"Would you take a small —" she asked, perhaps with some mental reference to the remark that dowered her with the occasional charge of the future adopted Clegg.

"Well, I d'n' know. That's a very hard thing that comes up first of all every time 't I begin thinkin'. When most folks set out to adopt a baby, the main idea seems to be to try 'n' get 'em so young 't they can't never say for sure 's you ain't their mother."

Mrs. Lathrop nodded approval, mute but emphatic, of the wisdom of her friend's views.

"But I ain't got none o' that foolish sort o' notions in me. I would n't be its mother, 'n' 'f there was n't no one else to tell it so Mr. Kimball 'd rejoice to the first time I sent it down town alone. It's nigh to impossible to keep nothin' in the town with Mr. Kimball. A man f'rever talkin' like that's bound to tell everythin' sooner or later, 'n' I never was one to set any great store o' faith on a talker. When I don't want the whole town to know 't I'm layin' in rat-poison I buy of Shores, 'n' when I get a new dress I buy o' Kimball. I don't want my rats talked about 'n' I don't mind my dress. For which same reason I sh'll make no try 't foolin' my baby. I'll be content if it cooes. I remember Mrs. Macy's sayin' once 't a baby was sweetest when it cooes, 'n' I don't want to miss nothin', 'n' we ain't never kep' doves for me to be dead-sick o' the noise, so I want the cooin' age. I think it'll be pleasant comin' home days to hear the baby cooin', 'n' 'f it cooes too loud when I'm away you c'n always come over 'n' see if it's rolled anywhere. I c'n see that, generally speaking, it's a wise thing that folks jus' have to take 'em as they come, because when it's all for you to choose you want so much 't like 's not I can't be suited after all. It's goin' to be pretty hard decidin', 'n' when I've done decidin' it's goin' to be pretty hard findin'

a baby that's all 't I've decided; 'n' then, *if* I find it,—
then comes the raisin' of it, 'n' I espect that 'll be suthin'
jus' awful."

"How was you goin' to find—" Mrs. Lathrop asked.

"Well, I've got to go to town to look at winter coats,
'n' I thought 't when I'd found what I wanted I'd jus'
glance through two or three orphan asylums afore comin'
home."

Mrs. Lathrop pinned the purple to the yellow and shut
one eye so as to judge of the combination from the single
standpoint of the other. She seemed to be gradually re-
gaining her normal state of abnormal calmness.

"I thought 't your coat was pretty good," she said mildly,
as Susan altered her needles. The stocking started violently.

"Pretty good! It's most new. My heavens alive, Mrs.
Lathrop, don't you know 's well 's I do 't I ain't had my
new coat but four years 'n' then only to church!"

"You *said* 't you was goin' to get—" Mrs. Lathrop remarked, unpinning the purple as she spoke and replacing it
in the bag.

"*Mrs. Lathrop!* 'f you don't beat anythin' 't I ever saw
for puttin' words 't I never even dreamed of into other
folks's mouths! 'S if I should ever think o' buyin' a new coat
'n' the price-tag not even dirty on the inside o' mine yet! I
never said 't I was goin' to buy a coat,— I never thought
o' goin' to buy a coat,— what I did say was 't I was goin'
to *look at* coats, an' the reason 't I'm goin' to look at coats
is because I'm goin' to cut over the sleeves o' mine. I
thought all last winter 't it was pretty queer for a woman
's rich 's I be to wear old-fashioned sleeves — more particularly so where I c'n easy cut a new sleeve crossways out
o' the puffs o' the old ones. 'N' *that*'s why I want to look
at coats, Mrs. Lathrop, for I ain't in the habit o' settin' my
shears in where I can't see my way out."

Mrs. Lathrop fingered a piece of rusty black silk and
made no comment.

"When I get done lookin' at coats, lookin' 't orphans 'll

be jus' a nice change. If I see any 't I think might suit I 'll take their numbers 'n' come home 'n' see about decidin', 'n' if I don't see any 't I like I 'll come home jus' the same."

The clock struck nine. Mrs. Lathrop rose and gathered up her bag of pieces.

"I mus' be goin' home," she said.

"I was thinkin' that very same thing," said Susan, rising also. "It's our thinkin' so much the same 't keeps us friends, I guess."

Mrs. Lathrop sought her shawl and departed.

It was about a week later that the trip to town took place. The day was chosen to suit the opening of a most unprecedented Fire-Sale. Miss Clegg thought that the latest styles in coat-sleeves were likely to bloom broadcast on so auspicious an occasion, and Mrs. Lathrop herself was sufficiently infected by the advertising in the papers to dare to intrust her friend with the whole of a two-dollar bill to be judiciously invested if bargains should really run as wildly rife as was predicted.

Susan departed very early and did not get back till very late — so late in fact that her next-door neighbor had the time to become more than a little anxious as to the possibilities of some mischance having befallen her two-dollar bill.

But towards eight o'clock signs of life next door appeared to the anxious watcher in the Lathrop kitchen window, and one minute later she was on her way across. She found the front door, which was commonly open, to be uncommonly shut, and was forced to rap loudly and wait lengthily ere the survivor of the Fire-Sale came to let her in.

Then when the door did open the figure which appeared in the opening was such as to startle even the phlegmatically disposed chewer of clover.

"My heavens alive, Susan, whatever is the matter with—"

Susan backed faintly into the hall so as to allow the other to enter.

"I'm worn to a frazzle — that's all!" she said weakly and wearily.

They turned into the parlor, where the lamp was burning, and Mrs. Lathrop gave a little frightened scream:

"Susan! why, you look half —"

Miss Clegg collapsed at once heavily upon the haircloth-covered sofa.

"I guess you'd better make me some tea," she suggested, and shut her eyes.

Mrs. Lathrop had no doubt whatever on the subject. Hurrying out to the kitchen, she brewed a cup of the strongest possible tea in the fewest possible moments, and brought it in to the traveller. The latter drank with satisfaction, then leaned back with a sigh.

"It was a auction!" she said in tones that gasped.

Mrs. Lathrop could restrain her anxiety no longer.

"Did you get anything with my —" she asked.

"Yes; it's out in the hall with my shawl."

"What did —"

"It's a parrot," said Susan.

"A parrot!" cried Mrs. Lathrop, betraying as much feeling as it was in her to feel.

"Without any head," Susan added wearily.

"Without any head!"

Then Miss Clegg straightened up in her seat and opened her eyes.

"There ain't no need o' bein' so surprised," she said in that peculiar tone with which one who has spent another's money always defends his purchase, — "it's a stuffed parrot without any head."

"A stuffed parrot without any head!" Mrs. Lathrop repeated limply, and her tone was numb and indescribable.

"How much did it —" she asked after a minute.

"I bid it in for one dollar 'n' ninety-seven cents, — I was awful scared f'r fear it would go over your two dollars, an' it wasn't nothin' that I'd ever want, so I couldn't 'a' taken it off your hands if it *had* gone over your money."

"I wonder what I can do with it," her neighbor said feebly.

"You must hang it in the window so high 't the head don't show."

"I thought you said it did n't have no head."

Miss Clegg quitted the sofa abruptly and came over to her own chair; the tea appeared to be beginning to take effect.

"It *has n't* got no head! If it had a head, where would be the sense in hangin' it high a *tall?* It's your good luck, Mrs. Lathrop, 't it has n't got no head, for the man said 't if it had a head it would 'a' brought four or five dollars easy."

Mrs. Lathrop got up and went out into the hall to seek her parrot. When she brought it in and examined it by the light of the lamp, her expression became more than dubious.

"What did *you* get for your —" she asked at last.

"I did n't get nothin'. I did n't see nothin' 't I wanted, 'n' I learned long ago 't an auction's generally a good place f'r buyin' things 't you don't want after you 've bought 'em. Now take that parrot o' yours! — I would n't have him 'f you was to offer him to me for a gift; not to speak o' his not havin' no head, he looks to me like he had moths in him, — you look at him by daylight to-morrow 'n' see if it don't strike you so too."

Mrs. Lathrop was silent for a long time. Finally she said:

"Did you go to the Orphan Asylum?"

"Well — no — I did n't. I would 'a' gone only I got on the wrong car 'n' ended in a cemetery instead. I had a nice time there, though, walkin' roun' 'n' readin' ages, an' jus' as I was goin' out I met a monument man 't had a place right outside the gate, 'n' he took me to look at his things, 'n' then I remembered father — two years dead 'n' not a stone on him yet!"

Mrs. Lathrop laid the parrot aside with a heavy sigh and concentrated all her attention upon her friend's recital.

"The man was about 's pleasant a man 's ever I met. When I told him about father, he told me he took a interest in every word, whether I bought a monument of him or not. He said he'd show me all he had 'n' welcome 'n' it was no trouble but a joy. Then he took me all through his shop 'n' the shed behind, 'n' really I never had a nicer time. I see a lamb lyin' down first, 'n' I thought 't that would be nice f'r a little, but the further back we went the finer they got. The man wanted me to take a eagle grippin' a pen 'n' writin' father's name on a book 't he 's sittin' on to hold open while he writes. I told him 'f I bought any such monument I cert'nly would want the name somewhere else than up where no one but the eagle could read it. He said 't I could have the name below 'n' let the eagle be writin' ' Repose in Peace,' but I told him 't father died of paralysis after bein' in bed for twenty years 'n' that his idea o' Heaven was n't reposin' in peace, — he always looked forward to walkin' about 'n' bein' pretty lively there. Then the man said 't maybe suthin' simple would be more to my taste, 'n' he took me to where there was a pillow with a wreath of roses on it, but — my gracious, I'd never be so mean 's to put a pillow anywhere near father after all them years in bed, 'n' as to the roses they'd be jus' 's bad or worse, for you know yourself how they give him hay fever so 's we had to dig up all the bushes years ago.

"But I'll tell you, Mrs. Lathrop, what I *did* see that nobody on the wide earth c'd help wishin' was on top o' their grave the minute they laid eyes on it. It's a lion — a weepin' lion — kind o' tryin' to wipe his eyes with one paw. I tell you I never saw nothin' one quarter so handsome over no one yet, 'n' if I was n't thinkin' o' adoptin' a child I'd never rest until I'd set that lion on top of father. But o' course, as it is, I can't even think how it might look there; the livin' has rights over the dead, 'n' my child can't go without the necessaries of life while my father gets a weepin' lion 't when you come right square down to it he ain't got no more use for 'n' a cat has for two tails. No, I'm a rich woman, but all incomes has their outside fence. 'F a man 's got a million a year, he can't spend two million, 'n' I can't start in child raisin' 'n' tombstone father all in the same year. Father 'll have to wait, 'n' he got so used to it while he was alive 't he ought not to mind it much now he 's dead. But I give the man my address, 'n' he give me one o' his cards, 'n' when I go to the Orphan Asylum I may go back 'n' see him, an' maybe if I tell him about the baby he 'll reduce the lion some. The lion is awful high — strikes me. He 's three hunderd dollars, but the man says that 's because his tail 's out o' the same block. I asked him if he could n't take the tail off, but he said 't that would hurt his reputation. He said 'f I 'd go up the ladder to his second floor 'n' look down on the lion I 'd never talk about sawin' off his tail, 'n' he said 't anyhow cuttin' it off would only make it cost more because it was cut on in the first place. I saw the sense o' that, 'n' I remembered, too, 't even 'f folks in the cemetery never can see the tail, father 'll have to look at it from higher up 'n the ladder to the monument man's shed, 'n' I don't want him to think 't I economized on the tail of his tombstone. I tell you what, Mrs. Lathrop, I cert'nly do want that lion, but I can't have it, so I 've decided not to think of it again. The man c'd see I wanted it, 'n' I c'd see 't he really wanted me to have it. He felt so kind o' sorry for me 't he said he 'd do me a weepin' fox for one hunderd 'n' fifty, if I wanted it, but I did n't want no fox. Father did n't have nothin' like a fox — his nose was broad 'n' kind o' flat. He had n't nothin' like a lion, neither, but I 'd like to have the only lion in the cemetery ours."

Mrs. Lathrop nodded her head sympathetically.

Miss Clegg sighed and looked pensive for a moment, but it was soon over.

"'N' I 've decided about my child too," she continued briskly, — "I 've decided to have a boy. I decided goin' in on the train to-day. I 'd been sorter thinkin' that I 'd leave it to chance, but ordinary folks can't do no more 'n' that, 'n' where 's the good o' me bein' so open 'n' above-board 'f I dunno whether it'll be a boy or girl, after all?"

.   .   .   .

"What made you decide on a b—" asked Mrs. Lathrop.

"I didn't decide. I c'u'd n't decide, 'n' so I shook a nickel for heads 'n' tails."

"'N' it came a boy."

"No, it came a girl, 'n' the minute 't I see 't it was a girl I knew 't I'd wanted a boy all along, so, 's the good o' me bein' free to act 's I please is 't I do act as I please, I decided then 'n' there on a boy."

Mrs. Lathrop turned the parrot over.

"'F you was so set on a boy, why did you—"

"What do folks ever toss up for? To decide. Tossin' up always shows you jus' how much you did n't want what you get. Only, as a general thing, there's some one else who does want it, an' they grab it 'n' you go empty-handed. The good o' me tossin' is I c'n always take either side o' the nickel after I've tossed. I ain't nobody's fool—'n' I never was—'n' I never will be. But I guess I've got to ask you to go home now, Mrs. Lathrop. I've had a hard day 'n' I'm 'most too tired to pay attention to what you say any longer. I want to get to bed 'n' to sleep, 'n' then to-morrow maybe I'll feel like talkin' myself."

The third morning after Miss Clegg's trip to town she astonished her neighbor by tapping on the latter's kitchen window at the early hour of seven in the morning. Mrs. Lathrop was getting breakfast, and her surprise caused her to jump unduly.

"Well, *Susan!*" she said, opening the door, "what ever is the—"

"Matter! Nothin' ain't the matter, only I've had a letter from the monument man. It come last night, 'n' the minister took it out o' the post-office 'n' sent it over by little 'Liza Em'ly when she come with the milk this mornin'. I dunno whether to thank the minister for bein' so kind or whether to ask him to mind his own business. It's got 'Important' on the corner, 'n' sometimes I don't go to the post-office for two days at a time, but jus' the same it strikes me 't I ain't altogether in favor o' the minister's carryin' my mail home with him any time he feels so inclined. If I'd 'a' married him, I never'd 'a' allowed him to interfere with my affairs, 'n' 's long 's I did n't marry him I don't see no good reason for his doin' so now."

Susan paused and looked at the letter which she held in her hand. Mrs. Lathrop slid one of the kitchen chairs up behind her, and she sat down, still looking at the letter.

"It's from the monument man," she said again, "'n' I don't know what ever I shall do about it, I'm sure."

Mrs. Lathrop was all attention.

"It's about the lion. He says 't he's been 'n' took some black chalk 'n' marked around under him 'Sacred to the memory of Blank Clegg,' 'n' he says 't it looks so noble 't he's had an offer for the monument 'n' he wants me to come in 'n' see it afore he sells it to — to some one else."

There was a short silence, broken at last by Mrs. Lathrop.

"Your father's name wa'n't 'Blank,'" she said; "it was 'Henry.'"

Susan knit her brows.

"I know, 'n' that's one thing 't's been troublin' me. It's written out in good plain letters — 'Blank Clegg' — 'n' I've been tryin' 'n' tryin' to think what I could 'a' said to 'a' made him suppose 't it could 'a' been 'Blank.' That'd be the last name in the wide world for anybody to name anybody else, I sh'd suppose, 'n' I can't see for the life o' me why that monument man sh'd 'a' hit on it for father. I'm cert'nly mighty glad that he's only marked it on in black chalk 'n' not chopped it out o' the bottom o' the lion. O' course 'f he'd chopped it out I'd 'a' had to 'a' taken it an' it'd jus' made me the laughin'-stock o' the whole community. I know lots o' folks 't are plenty mean enough 's to say 't that lion was weepin' because I did n't know my own father's name."

Mrs. Lathrop looked sober.

"So I guess I've got to go to town by to-day's ten o'clock. I ain't no intention o' takin' the lion, but I *shall* like to stand off a little ways 'n' look at the part o' the name 't 's spelt right. Later maybe I'll visit a few asylums — I ain't sure. But anyway I thought I'd jus' run over 'n' let you know 't I was goin', 'n' ask you if there's anythin' 't I can get f'r you while I'm in town."

"No, there is n't," said Mrs. Lathrop with great firmness. Susan rose to go.

"I'm thinkin' o' buyin' the Shores baby outfit," she said. "I guess Mr. Shores'll be glad to sell it cheap. They say 't he can't bear to be reminded o' the baby, 'n' I don't well see what else the crib 'n' the baby carriage can remind him of."

"I wonder if the sewing-machine reminds him o' Mrs. Shores," said Mrs. Lathrop. "I'd be glad to buy it if it did 'n' 'f he was wantin' to sell it cheap."

"I dunno why it sh'd remind him o' Mrs. Shores," said Susan; "she never sewed on it none. She never did nothin' 's far 's I c'd make out except to sit on the front porch 'n' talk to his clerk. My, but I sh'd think he'd hate the sight o' that front porch. If it c'd be got off, I'd like to buy that of him too. My front porch 's awful old 'n' shaky 'n' I'll need a good porch to wheel baby on. He c'd take my porch in part payment. It's bein' so old 'n' shaky would n't matter to him I don't suppose, for I'll bet a dollar he'll never let no other wife o' his sit out on no porch o' his, not 'ntil after he's dead 'n' buried anyway; 'n' as for sittin' on a porch himself, well, all is I know 't if it was me it'd scorch my rockers."

"What time do you think 't you'll get back?" asked Mrs. Lathrop.

"I ain't sure. 'F I should get real interested huntin' orphans, I might stay until it was too dark to see 'em good. I can't tell nothin' about it, though. You'd better watch for the light in the kitchen, 'n' when you see it burnin' I wish 't you'd come right over."

Mrs. Lathrop agreed to this arrangement, and Miss Clegg went home to get ready for town.

She returned about five o'clock, and the mere general aspect of her approaching figure betokened some doing or doings so well worthy of neighborly interest that Mrs. Lathrop left her bread in the oven and flew to satisfy her curiosity.

She found her friend warming her feet by the kitchen stove, and one look at her radiant countenance sufficed.

"You found a baby!"

Susan upraised supremely joyful eyes.

"No," she replied, "but I've bought the weepin' lion!"

Mrs. Lathrop sat suddenly down.

"You never saw anythin' so grand in all your life! He rubbed the 'Blank' off with a wet cloth 'n' wrote in the 'Henry' with me standin' right there. I never see anythin' that went right through me that way before. Puttin' on 'Henry' seemed to bring the lion right into the family, an'—well, you can believe me or not jus' as you please, Mrs. Lathrop, but I up 'n' begin to cry right then 'n' there. The monument man made me sit down on a uncut block 'n' lean my back up against a 'No-Cross-no-Crown', 'n' while I sat there he chalked in father's birth 'n' death 'n' 'Erected by his devoted daughter Susan,' 'n' at that I stood right up 'n' said 't I'd take it, 'n' it wasn't no hasty decision, neither, f'r after I'd made up my mind I couldn't see no good reason for continuin' to sit there 'n' draw frost out o' granite 'n' into my shoulder-blades jus' for the looks o' the thing."

"But about the ba—" said Mrs. Lathrop.

"Oh, the baby'll have to go. I told you all along 't it had to be one or t' other an' in the end it's the lion as has come out on top. I guess I wasn't cut out to be a mother like I was a daughter. I know 't I never wanted a baby for myself half like I've wanted that lion for my dead 'n' gone father. Do you know, Mrs. Lathrop, I do believe 't I had a presentiment the first time I ever see that lion. Suthin' sort o' crep' right up my back, 'n' I'm jus' sure 't folks'll come

from miles roun' to see it. I guess it's the Finger o' Fate.
When you come to think o' it, it's all for the best jus' the
way 't it's come out. The baby'd 'a' grown up an' gone
off somewhere, an' the lion 'll stay right where you put him,
for he's so heavy that the monument man says we'll have
to drive piles all down aroun' father. Then, too, maybe I
could n't 'a' managed a boy an' I can scour that lion all I
want to. 'N' I will scour him too, — nobody need n't suppose 't I've paid three hunderd dollars f'r anythin' to let
it get mossy. I've invited the monument man 'n' his wife
to come 'n' visit me while he's gettin' the lion in place, 'n'
he says he's so pleased over me 'n' nobody else gettin' it 't
he's goin' to give me a paper sayin' 't when I die he'll chop
my date in f'r nothin'. I tell you what, Mrs. Lathrop, I
certainly am glad 't I've got the sense to know when I'm
well off, 'n' I cert'nly do feel that in this particular case
I'm mighty lucky. So all's well 't ends well."

Mrs. Lathrop nodded.

TOM MASSON

Thomas L. Masson is in many respects worthy the title of dean of living American humorists; he has contributed so long — so much — and so well — and has made himself such a unique authority on the whole subject of American humor. He has published a dozen books, has for years been a power on *Life,* and more recently he has been added to the editorial staff of the *Saturday Evening Post.* He was born in Essex, Connecticut, July 21, 1866.

THE MAN WHO CAME BACK [1]

HENRY BILKINS, when he returned, had been dead exactly ten years. Under the new order, he was the first man to return. We don't know how many others came back later. The facts about one individual are all that should be crowded into a story like this.

In the same suit he had worn at his funeral ten years before — slightly mustier from having, during this period, reposed in the family vault — Henry Bilkins stood on the corner of F Street and Sunset Avenue. This was where his funeral had passed.

It was an ornate and magnificent funeral, as those functions go, but it had been sincere and widespread with a genuine grief that had slipped its dam and overflowed into the surrounding country. For Henry Bilkins was a man beloved. He had worked hard, he had raised a family, he had left a fortune and a successful business, and cut off as he had been, just beyond his prime, those who had become dependent upon his advice, his judgment, his way of shouldering their responsibilities, those who loved him for his

---

[1] From " A Corner in Women." Copyright, 1905, by Moffat, Yard and Company. Reprinted by permission of the author.

kindliness, his sympathies, his companionship — all these were prostrated by the shock of his sudden departure.

That was why Henry Bilkins came back, when, under the new method, first discovered by the distinguished president of a Society of Psychical Research he found that he could come back. It was a sense of duty to others. There was no reason to suppose that he was n't having a good time where he was — for he had been a model man — but, knowing how he had been missed, how badly they all felt about it, how dependent they were upon him, and all that, Henry Bilkins felt that he must go where duty called. So here he was.

He walked down the street to his office of the old sign, that had now been changed to a new one, with his son's name. He entered the lower door. He walked up the stairs. He entered the office. There had been changes, but he caught the word "Private," and entered that door before he could be stopped. He faced his eldest son.

"Arthur!"

"Father!"

There was for a moment considerable excitement. Not the sort which females invariably exhibit, but a real man-to-man excitement, brought out by such an unprecedented shock. Then they sat down calmly and talked it over.

"I have n't a cent," said Henry Bilkins. "We never used it where I was."

Arthur was now married, and the business — well, business was n't quite so good as it had been, and there were certain babies — still, his was a generous, a filial nature.

"Of course," he replied, opening the cash drawer. "Here, father, is a hundred dollars. That will last you until —— "

Henry Bilkins took the bills and folded them up carefully. Certain things were beginning to reveal themselves.

"I left you most of my money, Arthur."

Then, the truth coming to him, he got up smiling and said:

"Don't let me disturb you, my boy. I'm going around now to renew some of the old ties. By the way, how's your mother?"

Arthur's face changed.

"Mother's all right, sir," he said, with something of the old-time deference. "Perhaps you'd better not see her until — well, I'll go with you. We'll make an appointment. I want to think it over."

Henry Bilkins began the rounds of his old friends. First he called on Gadsby. Gadsby and he had played golf once a week for the last five years of Bilkins' life. There were the usual startling preliminaries.

"I'd dearly love to play with you this afternoon," said Gadsby, "but — well, I have an engagement with Perkins. To-morrow? One with Hopkins. Perhaps some day next week."

Bilkins left Gadsby and called on Whittler and Dimpleton, and the president of his old bank, who was still alive, and he even went so far as to hire an auto and make a journey to the suburbs to visit his old secretary, who had married the assistant bookkeeper the year after his death, and had now a little brood of her own.

At five o'clock in the afternoon he went back to his son's office. Arthur was waiting for him — looking slightly paler and more anxious even than in the morning. They sat down silently.

"Arthur," said Henry Bilkins, at last, "I have made a singular discovery. Nobody wants me back. My old friends have all forgotten me, and while they expressed a certain degree of pleasure in seeing me, it was mostly perfunctory. I couldn't take up the threads again. I left you my money. It would be awkward, even if it were practicable, to give it back to me. The ties by which I was united to you were broken, and have all healed or been united to other interests. Now, Arthur, I'm going back — nay, don't protest. We might as well be honest. Besides, it's perfectly natural that I should be forgotten. Yes, Arthur,

I'm going to return. But there's just one thing, Arthur, before I go — just one thing. I know, of course, your mother's married. I saw it in your face. But I'd like to see her — to press her hand — to say good-day to her, just for old time's sake. Can you arrange this for me, my boy — over the phone?"

Henry Bilkins' voice actually shook. His son got up.

"Father," he said, "I, too, have been thinking this over. You are right. It isn't because I'm hard-hearted — but this is a practical world. And so, father, I'm ready to agree with you. Yes, you'd better go back. But it wouldn't be advisable for you to see mother."

"Why not? Isn't she happily married?"

"Oh, yes. But, you see, father, mother has married a man — well, he's a nice man, but he needs regulating. And the only way she can succeed in regulating him is to hold you up to him as a model. She keeps your picture on the wall as a constant example. We all help her more or less. Your memory, your virtues, keep him toeing the mark. He has to live up to you. Now, father, you see what would happen if —— "

Henry Bilkins got up. He held out his hand.

"I understand," he muttered, "those new cars that pass here go to the cemetery, don't they? Well, good-bye, Arthur, I'm glad to have seen you even for this short time. I'm going back, don't worry." He was gone.

The door closed behind him. There was a moment's pause.

Then Arthur got up and opened it.

"Father," he called.

The old gentleman turned on the landing.

"Excuse me, father." said Arthur, "but you might let me have what's left of that hundred — if you don't mind, father."

GEOGRAPHY [1]

"Pa, I've got something to own up to."

"All right — unburden yourself."

"Will you scold me?"

"Not if you are real penitent. What have you been doing, anyway?"

"Well, I haven't got my geography lesson right, and the teacher says I should study it more at home."

"Your teacher is right. You mustn't be an ignoramus, my boy, no matter what else you are."

"What is an ignoramus?"

"Oh, anyone who doesn't know his lesson. A doctor may be an ignoramus, or a member of the Senate, or even an expert in a popular murder case."

"Gracious! I don't want to be one, pa, and I want you to help me. Will you tell me about geography?"

"Of course, my dear boy. Just ask me what you want to know."

"Well, pa, where is New York?"

"It's situated on the first floor of the Waldorf-Astoria."

"What's that? A country?"

"No, it's a caravanserai."

"Oh, my, what a word! What is a caravanserai?"

"You wouldn't understand if I told you. It's a sort of a place of public irreverence where people go who are too rich to live in homes. Ask me something easier."

"All right. Tell me where Washington is."

"It's a small hamlet, located at the foot of Wall Street."

"Why, I thought it was a glorious capital."

"Yes, every four years — on inauguration day — it's the most glorious capital in the world. On other days it is what I have said."

"How nice to know that. Now, pa, what part of the world is the United States in?"

[1] From "A Corner in Women." Copyright, 1905, by Moffat, Yard and Company. Reprinted by permission of the author.

"It is in that part, my son, known as the Rockefeller belt, which extends from latitude 32 north to 32 south."

"Is it very far from Boston?"

"What? The United States?"

"Yes."

"Oh, no! It's just south of Boston. Boston people often visit the United States — when they come to New York."

"And how about Chicago, pa? That's a place I have heard of."

"Yes, my boy, everyone has heard of Chicago, except the people who live in St. Louis. Chicago occupies the rest of the country."

"How is that?"

"I will explain. Tammany Hall, the Waldorf, Wall Street and the Standard Oil, together with Mr. Carnegie's house, occupy one part of the Rockefeller belt, and Chicago occupies the rest."

"Oh, my! I hope I shall remember all those names. But isn't Philadelphia somewhere near Chicago?"

"Oh, no. Philadelphia is about two hundred years away from Chicago."

"But, pa, I thought every country had cities."

"It has, my boy. That is one of its complaints. The State of New York, which is a sort of half country, has been troubled with Albany for some time, and The Rockefeller Belt, which is really a country in a way, has long had Kansas on the knee. It's hard to explain all these distinctions to your young mind, but remember what I have said, and some day you will understand."

"But what is a city?"

"A city is a collection of individuals banded together for mutual discomfort."

"Is Brooklyn a city?"

"Well, hardly. Brooklyn is a polygamous trolley run, entirely surrounded by pressed brick."

"And what is a State?"

"A State is a large piece of wooded and cleared land,

almost entirely covered by mortgages and owned by politicians."

"And what is a country?"

"Oh, any place where an Irishman or a Jew hails from."

"Dear me, my head is so full! I guess I have learned enough. My, but you are a great man!"

"Thank you, my boy, I know something. If you digest all I've told you, you will be at the head of your class."

"That's so, pa. What a surprise I will be to my teacher."

ELLIS PARKER BUTLER

Ellis Parker Butler, one of our most talented humorists of Middle West extraction, was born in Muscatine, Iowa, December 5, 1869, a member of what he describes "as a mighty poorly financed family." As a youth working in a grocery store, he wrote at night with definitely formed ideals, and was successful in selling verses, sketches and stories to *Life*, *Puck*, *Judge* and *Truth* and finally even "made the *Century*", the great goal of those days, with a short story. Upon this he came East and with characteristic independence started in as a "free lance" which, except for a very short experience, he has always been. He now has some twenty-two book titles to his credit. "Pigs is Pigs", one of his short stories, has probably had the largest circulation in book form of any short story ever written in America. Mr. Butler lives in an old mansion at Flushing, Long Island, which has been his home for many years.

THE ADVENTURE OF THE CRIMSON CORD [1]

I

I HAD not seen Perkins for six months or so, and things were dull. I was beginning to tire of sitting indolently in my office, with nothing to do but clip coupons from my bonds. Money is good enough in its way, but it is not interesting unless it is doing something lively — doubling itself or getting lost. What I wanted was excitement, — an adventure, — and I knew that if I could find Perkins, I could have both. A scheme is a business adventure, and Perkins was the greatest schemer in or out of Chicago.

Just then Perkins walked into my office.

"Perkins," I said, as soon as he had arranged his feet comfortably on my desk, "I'm tired. I'm restless. I have been wishing for you for a month. I want to go into a big

---

[1] From "Perkins of Portland." Copyright, 1906, by Small, Maynard & Company. Reprinted by permission of the author and publishers.

scheme, and make a lot of new, up-to-date cash. I'm sick of this tame, old cash that I have. It isn't interesting. No cash is interesting except the coming cash."

"I'm with you," said Perkins; "what is your scheme?"

"I have none," I said sadly. "That is just my trouble. I have sat here for days trying to think of a good, practical scheme, but I can't. I don't believe there is an unworked scheme in the whole wide, wide world."

Perkins waved his hand.

"My boy," he exclaimed, "there are millions! You've thousands of 'em right here in your office! You're falling over them, sitting on them, walking on them! Schemes? Everything is a scheme. Everything has money in it!"

I shrugged my shoulders.

"Yes," I said, "for you. But you are a genius."

"Genius, yes," Perkins said, smiling cheerfully, "else why Perkins the Great? Why Perkins the Originator? Why the Great and Only Perkins of Portland?"

"All right," I said, "what I want is for your genius to get busy. I'll give you a week to work up a good scheme."

Perkins pushed back his hat, and brought his feet to the floor with a smack.

"Why the delay?" he queried. "Time is money. Hand me something from your desk."

I looked in my pigeonholes, and pulled from one a small ball of string. Perkins took it in his hand, and looked at it with great admiration.

"What is it?" he asked seriously.

"That," I said, humoring him, for I knew something great would be evolved from his wonderful brain, "is a ball of red twine I bought at the ten-cent store. I bought it last Saturday. It was sold to me by a freckled young lady in a white shirt-waist. I paid — "

"Stop!" Perkins cried, "what is it?"

I looked at the ball of twine curiously. I tried to see something remarkable in it. I couldn't. It remained a simple ball of red twine, and I told Perkins so.

"The difference," declared Perkins, "between mediocrity and genius! Mediocrity always sees red twine; genius
sees a ball of Crimson Cord!"

He leaned back in his chair, and looked at me triumph-
antly. He folded his arms as if he had settled the matter.
His attitude seemed to say that he had made a fortune for
us. Suddenly he reached forward, and, grasping my scis-
sors, began snipping off small lengths of the twine.

"The Crimson Cord!" he ejaculated. "What does it
suggest?"

I told him that it suggested a parcel from the druggist's.
I had often seen just such twine about a druggist's parcel.

Perkins sniffed disdainfully.

"Druggists?" he exclaimed with disgust. "Mystery!
Blood! 'The Crimson Cord.' Daggers! Murder! Stran-
gling! Clues! 'The Crimson Cord' — "

He motioned wildly with his hands, as if the possibilities
of the phrase were quite beyond his power of expression.

"It sounds like a book," I suggested.

"Great!" cried Perkins. "A novel! The novel! Think
of the words ' A Crimson Cord' in blood-red letters six feet
high on a white ground!" He pulled his hat over his eyes,
and spread out his hands; and I think he shuddered.

"Think of 'A Crimson Cord,'" he muttered, "in blood-
red letters on a ground of dead, sepulchral black, with a
crimson cord writhing through them like a serpent."

He sat up suddenly, and threw one hand in the air.

"Think," he cried, "of the words in black on white, with
a crimson cord drawn taut across the whole ad.!"

He beamed upon me.

"The cover of the book," he said quite calmly, "will be
white, — virgin, spotless white, — with black lettering, and
the cord in crimson. With each copy we will give a crimson
silk cord for a book-mark. Each copy will be done up in a
white box and tied with crimson cord."

He closed his eyes and tilted his head upward.

"A thick book," he said, "with deckel edges and pictures

by Christy. No, pictures by Pyle. Deep, mysterious pictures! Shadows and gloom! And wide, wide margins. And a gloomy foreword. One-fifty per copy, at all booksellers."

Perkins opened his eyes and set his hat straight with a quick motion of his hand. He arose and pulled on his gloves.

"Where are you going?" I asked.

"Contracts!" he said. "Contracts for advertising! We must boom 'The Crimson Cord!' We must boom her big!"

He went out and closed the door. Presently, when I supposed him well on the way down-town, he opened the door and inserted his head.

"Gilt tops," he announced. "One million copies the first impression!"

And then he was gone.

II

A week later Chicago and the greater part of the United States was placarded with "The Crimson Cord." Perkins did his work thoroughly and well, and great was the interest in the mysterious title. It was an old dodge, but a good one. Nothing appeared on the advertisements but the mere title. No word as to what "The Crimson Cord" was. Perkins merely announced the words, and left them to rankle in the reader's mind; and as a natural consequence each new advertisement served to excite new interest.

When we made our contracts for magazine advertising, —and we took a full page in every worthy magazine,— the publishers were at a loss to classify the advertisement; and it sometimes appeared among the breakfast foods, and sometimes sandwiched in between the automobiles and the hot-water heaters. Only one publication placed it among the books.

But it was all good advertising, and Perkins was a busy man. He racked his inventive brain for new methods of placing the title before the public. In fact, so busy was he at his labor of introducing the title, that he quite forgot the book itself.

One day he came to the office with a small rectangular package. He unwrapped it in his customary enthusiastic manner, and set on my desk a cigar-box bound in the style he had selected for the binding of "The Crimson Cord." It was then I spoke of the advisability of having something to the book besides the cover and a boom.

"Perkins," I said, "don't you think it is about time we got hold of the novel — the reading, the words?"

For a moment he seemed stunned. It was clear that he had quite forgotten that book-buyers like to have a little reading-matter in their books. But he was only dismayed for a moment.

"Tut!" he cried presently. "All in good time! The novel is easy. Anything will do. I'm no literary man. I don't read a book in a year. You get the novel."

"But I don't read a book in five years!" I exclaimed. "I don't know anything about books. I don't know where to get a novel."

"Advertise!" he exclaimed. "Advertise! You can get anything, from an apron to an ancestor, if you advertise for it. Offer a prize — offer a thousand dollars for the best novel. There must be thousands of novels not in use."

Perkins was right. I advertised as he suggested, and learned that there were thousands of novels not in use. They came to us by basketfuls and cartloads. We had novels of all kinds, — historical and hysterical, humorous and numerous, but particularly numerous. You would be surprised to learn how many ready-made novels can be had on short notice. It beats quick lunch. And most of them are equally indigestible. I read one or two, but I was no judge of novels. Perkins suggested that we draw lots to see which we should use.

It really made little difference what the story was about. "The Crimson Cord" fits almost any kind of a book. It is a nice, non-committal sort of title, and might mean the guilt that bound two sinners, or the tie of affection that binds lovers, or a blood relationship, or it might be a mystification title with nothing in the book about it.

But the choice settled itself. One morning a manuscript arrived that was tied with a piece of red twine, and we chose that one for good luck because of the twine. Perkins said that was a sufficient excuse for the title, too. We would publish the book anonymously, and let it be known that the only clue to the writer was the crimson cord with which the manuscript was tied when we received it. It would be a first-class advertisement.

Perkins, however, was not much interested in the story, and he left me to settle the details. I wrote to the author asking him to call, and he turned out to be a young woman.

Our interview was rather shy. I was a little doubtful about the proper way to talk to a real author, being purely a Chicagoan myself; and I had an idea that, while my usual vocabulary was good enough for business purposes, it might be too easy-going to impress a literary person properly, and in trying to talk up to her standard I had to be very careful in my choice of words. No publisher likes to have his authors think he is weak in the grammar line.

Miss Rosa Belle Vincent, however, was quite as flustered as I was. She seemed ill at ease and anxious to get away, which I supposed was because she had not often conversed with publishers who paid a thousand dollars cash in advance for a manuscript.

She was not at all what I had thought an author would look like. She didn't even wear glasses. If I had met her on the street I should have said, "There goes a pretty flip stenographer." She was that kind — big picture hat and high pompadour.

I was afraid she would try to run the talk into literary lines and Ibsen and Gorky, where I would have been swamped in a minute, but she didn't; and, although I had wondered how to break the subject of money when conversing with one who must be thinking of nobler things, I found she was less shy when on that subject than when talking about her book.

"Well, now," I said, as soon as I had got her seated, "we have decided to buy this novel of yours. Can you recommend it as a thoroughly respectable and intellectual production?"

She said she could.

"Haven't you read it?" she asked in some surprise.

"No," I stammered. "At least, not yet. I'm going to as soon as I can find the requisite leisure. You see, we are very busy just now — very busy. But if you can vouch for the story being a first-class article, — something, say, like 'The Vicar of Wakefield,' or 'David Harum,' — we'll take it."

"Now you're talking," she said. "And do I get the check now?"

"Wait," I said, "not so fast. I have forgotten one thing," and I saw her face fall. "We want the privilege of publishing the novel under a title of our own, and anonymously. If that is not satisfactory, the deal is off."

She brightened in a moment.

"It's a go, if that's all," she said. "Call it whatever you please; and the more anonymous it is, the better it will suit yours truly."

So we settled the matter then and there; and when I gave her our check for a thousand, she said I was all right.

III

Half an hour after Miss Vincent had left the office, Perkins came in with his arms full of bundles, which he opened, spreading their contents on my desk.

He had a pair of suspenders with nickel-silver mountings, a tie, a lady's belt, a pair of low shoes, a shirt, a box of cigars, a package of cookies, and a half a dozen other things of divers and miscellaneous character. I poked them over and examined them, while he leaned against the desk with his legs crossed. He was beaming upon me.

"Well," I said, "what is it — a bargain sale?"

Perkins leaned over and tapped the pile with his long forefinger.

"Aftermath!" he crowed. "Aftermath!"

"The dickens it is!" I exclaimed. "And what has aftermath got to do with this truck? It looks like the aftermath of a notion store."

He tipped his "Air-the-Hair" hat over one ear, and put his thumbs in the armholes of his "ready-tailored" vest.

"Genius!" he announced. "Brains! Foresight! Else why Perkins the Great? Why not Perkins the Nobody?"

He raised the suspenders tenderly from the pile, and fondled them in his hands.

"See this?" he asked, running his finger along the red corded edge of the elastic. He took up the tie, and ran his nail along the red stripe that formed the selvedge on the back, and said, "See this?" He pointed to the red laces of the low shoes and asked, "See this?" And so through the whole collection.

"What is it?" he asked. "It's genius! It's foresight!"

He waved his hand over the pile.

"The Aftermath!" he exclaimed.

"These suspenders are the Crimson Cord suspenders. These shoes are the Crimson Cord shoes. This tie is the Crimson Cord tie. These crackers are the Crimson Cord brand. Perkins & Co. get out a great book, 'The Crimson Cord'! Sell five million copies. Dramatized, it runs three hundred nights. Everybody talking Crimson Cord. Country goes Crimson Cord crazy. Result — up jump Crimson Cord this and Crimson Cord that. Who gets the benefit? Perkins & Co.? No! We pay the advertising bills, and the other man sells his Crimson Cord cigars. That is usual."

"Yes," I said, "I'm smoking a David Harum cigar this minute, and I am wearing a Carvel collar."

"How prevent it?" asked Perkins. "One way only, —

discovered by Perkins. Copyright the words 'Crimson Cord' as trade-mark for every possible thing. Sell the trade-mark on royalty. Ten per cent. of all receipts for 'Crimson Cord' brands comes to Perkins & Co. Get a cinch on the Aftermath!"

"Perkins!" I cried, "I admire you. You are a genius! And have you contracts with all these — notions?"

"Yes," said Perkins, "that's Perkins's method. Who originated the Crimson Cord? Perkins did. Who is entitled to the profits on the Crimson Cord? Perkins is. Perkins is wide-awake all the time. Perkins gets a profit on the aftermath and the math and the before the math."

And so he did. He made his new contracts with the magazines on the exchange plan. We gave a page of advertising in the "Crimson Cord" for a page of advertising in the magazine. We guaranteed five million circulation. We arranged with all the manufacturers of the Crimson Cord brands of goods to give coupons, one hundred of which entitled the holder to a copy of "The Crimson Cord." With a pair of Crimson Cord suspenders you get five coupons; with each Crimson Cord cigar, one coupon; and so on.

IV

On the first of October we announced in our advertisement that "The Crimson Cord" was a book; the greatest novel of the century; a thrilling, exciting tale of love. Miss Vincent had told me it was a love story. Just to make everything sure, however, I sent the manuscript to Professor Wiggins, who is the most erudite man I ever met. He knows eighteen languages, and reads Egyptian as easily as I read English. In fact, his specialty is old Egyptian ruins and so on. He has written several books on them.

Professor said the novel seemed to him very light and trashy, but grammatically O. K. He said he never read novels, not having time; but he thought that "The Crimson

Cord" was just about the sort of thing a silly public that refused to buy his "Some Light on the Dynastic Proclivities of the Hyksos" would scramble for. On the whole, I considered the report satisfactory.

We found we would be unable to have Pyle illustrate the book, he being too busy, so we turned it over to a young man at the Art Institute.

That was the fifteenth of October, and we had promised the book to the public for the first of November, but we had it already in type; and the young man, — his name was Gilkowsky, — promised to work night and day on the illustrations.

The next morning, almost as soon as I reached the office, Gilkowsky came in. He seemed a little hesitant, but I welcomed him warmly, and he spoke up.

"I have a girl I go with," he said; and I wondered what I had to do with Mr. Gilkowsky's girl, but he continued: —

"She's a nice girl and a good looker, but she's got bad taste in some things. She's too loud in hats and too trashy in literature. I don't like to say this about her, but it's true; and I'm trying to educate her in good hats and good literature. So I thought it would be a good thing to take around this 'Crimson Cord' and let her read it to me."

I nodded.

"Did she like it?" I asked.

Mr. Gilkowsky looked at me closely.

"She did," he said, but not so enthusiastically as I had expected. "It's her favorite book. Now I don't know what your scheme is, and I suppose you know what you are doing better than I do; but I thought perhaps I had better come around before I got to work on the illustrations and see if, perhaps, you hadn't given me the wrong manuscript."

"No, that was the right manuscript," I said. "Was there anything wrong about it?"

Mr. Gilkowsky laughed nervously.

"Oh, no!" he said. "But did you read it?"

I told him I had not, because I had been so rushed with details connected with advertising the book.

"Well," he said, "I'll tell you. This girl of mine reads pretty trashy stuff, and she knows about all the cheap novels there are. She dotes on 'The Duchess', and puts her last dime into Braddon. She knows them all by heart. Have you ever read 'Lady Audley's Secret'?"

"I see," I said. "One is a sequel to the other."

"No," said Mr. Gilkowsky, "one is the other. Some one has flimflammed you and sold you a typewritten copy of 'Lady Audley's Secret' as a new novel."

V

When I told Perkins, he merely remarked that he thought every publishing house ought to have some one in it who knew something about books, apart from the advertising end, although that was, of course, the most important. He said we might go ahead and publish "Lady Audley's Secret" under the title of "The Crimson Cord", as such things had been done before; but the best thing to do would be to charge Rosa Belle Vincent's thousand dollars to profit and loss, and hustle for another novel — something reliable, and not shop-worn.

Perkins had been studying the literature market a little, and he advised me to get something from Indiana this time; so I telegraphed an advertisement to the Indianapolis papers, and two days later we had ninety-eight historical novels by Indiana authors from which to choose. Several were of the right length; and we chose one, and sent it to Mr. Gilkowsky, with a request that he read it to his sweetheart. She had never read it before.

We sent a detective to Dillville, Ind., where the author lived; and the report we received was most satisfactory.

The author was a sober, industrious young man, just out of the high school, and bore a first-class reputation for honesty. He had never been in Virginia, where the scene of his story was laid, and they had no library in Dillville; and our detective assured us that the young man was in every way fitted to write a historical novel.

"The Crimson Cord" made an immense success. You can guess how it boomed when I say that, although it was published at a dollar and a half, it was sold by every department store for fifty-four cents, away below cost, just like sugar, or Vandeventer's Baby Food, or Q & Z Corsets, or any other staple. We sold our first edition of five million copies inside of three months, and got out another edition of two million, and a specially illustrated holiday edition, and an "edition de luxe"; and "The Crimson Cord" is still selling in paper-covered cheap edition.

With the royalties received from the aftermath and the profit on the book itself, we made — well, Perkins has a country place at Lakewood, and I have my cottage at Newport.

MONTAGUE GLASS

This rare portrayer of the Hebrew as an American business man — his prescriptive calling — a field which Mr. Glass alone has discovered and developed, comes by right of inheritance to his fame, as his ancestors were of an old well-known Jewish family in "the Minories" — London. Montague Glass was born in Manchester, England, July 23, 1877, and his parents brought him to this country when he was barely thirteen years old. He grew up among the types he has portrayed, receiving his education at the College of the City of New York, and New York University. His two principal characters, "Abe Potash" and "Morris Perlmutter", are classical additions to the gallery of American humorous portraits, and there are many subsidiary ones equally carefully drawn. He has achieved success as a playwright also. His fame, as the one man who has "dared and done", in portraying the American commercial Jew, is unique.

DIAMOND CUT DIAMOND [1]

I

'YES, Mawruss," Abe Potash commented as he glanced over the "Business Troubles" column of the Daily Cloak and Suit Record, "Hymie Kotzen is certainly playing in hard luck."

"Is he?" Morris Perlmutter replied. "Well, he don't look it when I seen him in the Harlem Winter Garden last night, Abe. Him and Mrs. Kotzen was eating a family porterhouse between 'em with tchampanyer wine yet."

"Well, Mawruss," Abe said, "he needs it tchampanyer wine, Mawruss. Last month I seen it he gets stung two thousand by Cohen & Schondorf, and today he's chief mourner by the Ready Pay Store, Barnet Fischman proprietor. Barney stuck him for fifteen hundred, Mawruss, so I guess he needs it tchampanyer wine to cheer him up."

[1] From the *Saturday Evening Post*. Copyright, 1909, by Curtis Publishing Company. Reprinted by permission of the author.

"Well, maybe he needs it diamonds to cheer him up, also, Abe," Morris added. "That feller got diamonds on him, Abe, like 'lectric lights on the front of a moving-picture show."

"Diamonds never harmed nobody's credit, Mawruss," Abe rejoined. "You can get your money out of diamonds most any time, Mawruss. I see by the papers diamonds increase in price thirty per cent in six months already. Yes, Mawruss, diamonds goes up every day."

"And so does the feller what wears 'em, Abe," Morris went on. "In fact, the way that Hymie Kotzen does business I shouldn't be surprised if he goes up any day, too. Andrew Carnegie couldn't stand it the failures what that feller gets into, Abe."

"That's just hard luck, Mawruss," Abe replied; "and if he wears it diamonds, Mawruss, he paid for 'em himself, Mawruss, and he's got a right to wear 'em. So far what I hear it, Mawruss, he never stuck nobody for a cent."

"Oh, Hymie ain't no crook, Abe," Morris admitted, "but I ain't got no use for a feller wearing diamonds. Diamonds looks good on women, Abe, and maybe also on a hotel-clerk or a feller what runs a restaurant, Abe, but a business man ain't got no right wearing diamonds."

"Of course, Mawruss, people's got their likes and dislikes," Abe said; "but all the same I seen it many a decent, respectable feller with a good business, Abe, what wants a little accommodation at his bank. But he gets turned down just because he goes around looking like a slob; while a feller what can't pay his own laundry bill, Mawruss, has no trouble getting a thousand dollars because the second vice-president is buffaloed already by a stovepipe hat, a Prince Albert coat and a four-carat stone with a flaw in it."

"Well, a four-carat stone wouldn't affect me none, Abe," Morris said, "and believe me, Abe, Hymie Kotzen's diamonds don't worry me none, neither. All I'm troubling about now is that I got an appetite like a horse, so I guess I'll go to lunch."

Abe jumped to his feet. "Give me a chance oncet in a while, Mawruss," he protested. "Every day comes half-past twelve you got to go to your lunch. Ain't I got no stomach, neither, Mawruss?"

"Oh, go ahead if you want to," Morris grumbled, "only don't stay all day, Abe. Remember there's other people wants to eat, too, Abe."

"I guess the shoe pinches on the other foot now, Mawruss," Abe retorted as he put on his hat. "When I get through eating I'll be back."

He walked across the street to Wasserbauer's café and restaurant and seated himself at his favorite table.

"Well, Mr. Potash," Louis, the waiter, cried, dusting off the tablecloth with a red-and-white towel, "some nice *Metzelsuppe* today, huh?"

"No, Louis," Abe replied as he took a dill pickle from a dishful on the table, "I guess I won't have no soup today. Give me some *gedämpftes Kalbfleisch mit Kartoffelklösse.*"

"Right away quick, Mr. Potash," said Louis, starting to hurry away.

"Ain't I nobody here, Louis?" cried a bass voice at the table behind Abe. "Do I sit here all day?"

"Ex-cuse me, Mr. Kotzen," Louis exclaimed. "Some nice roast chicken today, Mr. Kotzen?"

"I'll tell you what I want it, Louis, not you me," Mr. Kotzen grunted. "If I want to eat it roast chicken I'll say so. If I don't I won't."

"Sure, sure," Louis cried, rubbing his hands in a perfect frenzy of apology.

"Gimme a *Schweizerkäse* sandwich and a cup of coffee," Mr. Kotzen concluded, "and if you don't think you can bring it back here in half an hour, Louis, let me know, that's all and I'll ask Wasserbauer if he can help you out."

Abe had started on his second dill pickle, and he held it in his hand as he turned around in his chair. "Hallo, Hymie," he said; "ain't you feeling good today?"

"Oh, hallo, Abe," Kotzen cried, glancing over; "why don't you come over and sit at my table?"

"I guess I will," Abe replied. He rose to his feet with his napkin tucked into his collar and, carrying the dish of dill pickles with him, he moved over to Kotzen's table.

"What's the matter, Hymie?" Abe asked. "You ain't sick, are you?"

"That depends what you call it sick, Abe," Hymie replied. "I don't got to see no doctor exactly, Abe, if that's what you mean. But that Sam Feder by the Kosciusko Bank, I was over to see him just now, and I bet you he makes me sick."

"I thought you always got along pretty good with Sam, Hymie," Abe mumbled through a mouthful of dill pickle.

"So I do," said Hymie; "but he heard it something about this here Ready Pay Store and how I'm in it for fifteen hundred, and also this Cohen & Schondorf sticks me also, and he's getting anxious. So, either he wants me I should give him over a couple of accounts, or either I should take up some of my paper. Well, you know Feder, Abe. He don't want nothing but A Number One concerns, and then he got the bank's lawyer what is his son-in-law, De Witt C. Feinholz, that he should draw up the papers; and so it goes. I got it bills receivable due the first of the month, five thousand dollars from such people like Heller, Blumenkrohn & Co., of Cincinnati, and The Emporium, Duluth, all gilt-edge accounts, Abe, and why should I lose it twenty per cent on them, ain't it?"

"Sure," Abe murmured.

"Well, that's what I told Feder," Hymie went on. "If I got to take up a couple of thousand dollars I'll do it. But running a big plant like I got it, Abe, naturally it makes me a little short."

"Naturally," Abe agreed. He scented what was coming.

"But anyhow, I says to Feder, I got it lots of friends in the trade, and I ain't exactly broke yet, neither, Abe."

He lifted his Swiss-cheese sandwich in his left hand, holding out the third finger the better to display a five-carat stone, while Abe devoted himself to his veal.

"Of course, Abe," Hymie continued, "on the first of the month—that's only two weeks already—things will be running easy for me."

He looked at Abe for encouragement, but Abe's facial expression was completely hidden by veal stew, fragments of which were clinging to his eyebrows.

"But, naturally, I'm at present a little short," Hymie croaked, "and so I thought maybe you could help me out with, say, a thousand dollars till the first of the month, say."

Abe laid down his knife and fork and massaged his face with his napkin.

"For my part, Hymie," he said, "you should have it in a minute. I know it you are good as gold, and if you say that you will pay on the first of the month a U-nited States bond ain't no better."

He paused impressively and laid a hand on Hymie's knee.

"Only, Hymie," he concluded, "I got it a partner. Ain't it? And you know Mawruss Perlmutter, Hymie. He's a pretty hard customer, Hymie, and if I was to draw you the firm's check for a thousand, Hymie, that feller would have a receiver by the court tomorrow morning already. He's a holy terror, Hymie, believe me."

Hymie sipped gloomily at his coffee.

"But Mawruss Perlmutter was always a pretty good friend of mine, Abe," he said. "Why shouldn't he be willing to give it me if you are agreeable? Ain't it? And, anyhow, Abe, it can't do no harm to ask him."

"Well, Hymie, he's over at the store now," Abe replied. "Go ahead and ask him."

"I know it what he'd say if I ask him, Abe. He'd tell me I should see you; but you say I should see him, and then I'm up in the air. Ain't it?"

Abe treated himself to a final rubdown with the napkin and scrambled to his feet.

"All right, Hymie," he said. "If you want me I should ask him I'll ask him."

"Remember, Abe," Hymie said as Abe turned away, "only till the first, so sure what I'm sitting here. I'll ring you up in a quarter of an hour."

When Abe entered the firm's sample-room five minutes later he found Morris consuming the last of some crullers and coffee brought in from a near-by bakery by Jake, the shipping clerk.

"Well, Abe, maybe you think that's a joke you should keep me here a couple of hours already," Morris said.

"Many a time I got to say that to you already, Mawruss," Abe rejoined. "But, anyhow, I didn't eat it so much, Mawruss. It was Hymie Kotzen what keeps me."

"Hymie Kotzen!" Morris cried. "What for should he keep you, Abe? Blows you to some tchampanyer wine, maybe?"

"Tchampanyer he ain't drinking it today, Mawruss, I bet yer," Abe replied. "He wants to lend it from us a thousand dollars."

Morris laughed raucously.

"What a chance!" he said.

"Till the first of the month, Mawruss," Abe continued, "and I thought maybe we would let him have it."

Morris ceased laughing and glared at Abe.

"Tchampanyer you must have been drinking it, Abe," he commented.

"Why shouldn't we let him have it, Mawruss?" Abe demanded. "Hymie's a good feller, Mawruss, and a smart business man, too."

"Is he?" Morris yelled. "Well, he ain't smart enough to keep out of failures like Barney Fischman's and Cohen & Schondorf's, Abe, but he's too smart to lend it us a thousand dollars, supposing we was short for a couple of days. No, Abe, I heard it enough about Hymie Kotzen already. I wouldn't positively not lend him nothing, Abe, and that's flat."

To end the discussion effectually he went to the cutting-room upstairs and remained there when Hymie rang up.

"It ain't no use, Hymie," Abe said. "Mawruss wouldn't think of it. We're short ourselves. You've no idee what trouble we got it with some of our collections."

"But, Abe," Hymie protested, "I got to have the money. I promised Feder I would give it him this afternoon."

Abe remained silent.

"I tell you what I'll do, Abe," Hymie insisted; "I'll come around and see you."

"It won't be no use, Hymie," Abe said, but Central was his only auditor, for Hymie had hung up the receiver. Indeed, Abe had hardly returned to the sample-room before Hymie entered the store door.

"Where's Mawruss?" he asked.

"Up in the cutting-room," Abe replied.

"Good!" Hymie cried. "Now, looky' here, Abe, I got a proposition to make it to you."

He tugged at the diamond ring on the third finger of his left hand and laid it on a sample-table. Then from his shirt-bosom he unscrewed a miniature locomotive headlight, which he deposited beside the ring.

"See them stones, Abe?" he continued. "They costed it me one thousand three hundred dollars during the panic already, and today I wouldn't take two thousand for 'em. Now, Abe, you sit right down and write me out a check for a thousand dollars, and so help me I should never stir out of this here office, Abe, if I ain't on the spot with a thousand dollars in hand two weeks from today, Abe, you can keep them stones, settings and all."

Abe's eyes fairly bulged out of his head as he looked at the blazing diamonds.

"But, Hymie," he exclaimed, "I don't want your diamonds. If I had it the money myself, Hymie, believe me, you are welcome to it like you was my own brother."

"I know all about that, Abe," Hymie replied, "but you ain't Mawruss, and if you got such a regard for me what you claim you have, Abe, go upstairs and ask Mawruss Perlmutter will he do it me the favor and let me have that thousand dollars with the stones as security."

Without further parley Abe turned and left the sample-room.

"Mawruss," he called from the foot of the stairs, "come down here once. I want to show you something."

In the mean time Hymie pulled down the shades and turned on the electric lights. Then he took a swatch of black velveteen from his pocket and arranged it over the sample-table with the two gems in its folds.

"Hymie Kotzen is inside the sample-room," Abe explained when Morris appeared in answer to his summons.

"Well, what have I got to do with Hymie Kotzen?" Morris demanded.

"Come inside and speak to him, Mawruss," Abe rejoined. "He won't eat you."

"Maybe you think I'm scared to turn him down, Abe?" Morris concluded as he led the way to the sample-room. "Well, I'll show you different."

"Hallo, Mawruss," Hymie cried. "What's the good word?"

Morris grunted an inarticulate greeting.

"What you got all the shades down for, Abe?" he asked.

"Don't touch 'em," Hymie said. "Just you have a look at this sample-table first."

Hymie seized Morris by the arm and turned him around until he faced the velveteen.

"Ain't them peaches, Mawruss?" he asked.

Morris stared at the diamonds, almost hypnotized by their brilliancy.

"Them stones belong to you, Mawruss," Hymie went on, "if I don't pay you inside of two weeks the thousand dollars what you're going to lend me."

"We ain't going to lend you no thousand dollars, Hymie," Morris said at last, "because we ain't got it to lend. We need it in our own business, Hymie, and, besides, you got the wrong idee. We ain't no pawnbrokers, Hymie; we are in the cloak and suit business."

"Hymie knows it all about that, Mawruss," Abe broke in, "and he shows he ain't no creek, neither. If he's willing to trust you with them diamonds, Mawruss, we should be willing to trust him with a thousand dollars. Ain't it?"

"He could trust me with the diamonds, Abe, because I ain't got no use for diamonds," Morris replied. "If any one gives me diamonds that I should take care of it into the safe they go. I ain't a person what sticks diamonds all over myself, Abe, and I don't buy no tchampanyer wine one day and come around trying to lend it from people a thousand dollars the next day, Abe."

"It was my wife's birthday," Hymie explained; "and if I got to spend it my last cent, Mawruss, I always buy tchampanyer on my wife's birthday."

"All right, Hymie," Morris retorted; "if you think it so much of your wife, lend it from her a thousand dollars."

"Make an end, make an end," Abe cried; "I hear it enough already. Put them diamonds in the safe and we give Hymie a check for a thousand dollars."

Morris shrugged his shoulders.

"All right, Abe," he said. "Do what you please, but remember what I tell it you now. I don't know nothing about diamonds and I don't care nothing about diamonds, and if it should be that we got to keep it the diamonds I don't want nothing to do with them. All I want it is my share of the thousand dollars."

He turned on his heel and banged the sample-room door behind him, while Abe pulled up the shades and Hymie turned off the lights.

"That's a fine crank for you, Abe," Hymie exclaimed.

Abe said nothing, but sat down and wrote out a check for a thousand dollars.

"I hope them diamonds is worth it," he murmured, handing the check to Hymie.

"If they ain't," Hymie replied as he made for the door, "I'll eat 'em, Abe, and I ain't got too good a di-gestion, neither."

II

At intervals of fifteen minutes during the remainder of the afternoon Morris visited the safe and inspected the diamonds until Abe was moved to criticise his partner's behavior.

"Them diamonds ain't going to run away, Mawruss."

"Maybe they will, Abe," Morris replied, "if we leave the safe open and people comes in and out all the time."

"So far, nobody ain't taken nothing out of that safe, Mawruss," Abe retorted; "but if you want to lock the safe I'm agreeable."

"What for should we lock the safe?" Morris asked. "We are all the time getting things out of it what we need. Ain't it? A better idee I got it, Abe, is that you should put on the ring and I will wear the pin, or you wear the pin and I will put on the ring."

"No, siree, Mawruss," Abe replied. "If I put it on a big pin like that and I got to take it off again in a week's time might I would catch a cold on my chest, maybe. Besides, I ain't built for diamonds, Mawruss. So, you wear 'em both, Mawruss."

Morris forced a hollow laugh.

"Me wear 'em, Abe!" he exclaimed. "No, siree, Abe, I'm not the kind what wears diamonds. I leave that to sports like Hymie Kotzen."

Nevertheless he placed the ring on the third finger of his left hand, with the stone turned in, and carefully wrapping up the pin in tissue-paper he placed it in his waistcoat pocket. The next day was Wednesday, and he screwed the pin into his shirt-front underneath a four-in-hand scarf. On Thursday he wore the ring with the stone exposed, and on Friday he discarded the four-in-hand scarf for a bow tie and shamelessly flaunted both ring and pin.

"Mawruss," Abe commented on Saturday, "must you stick out your little finger when you smoke it a cigar?"

"Habits what I was born with, Abe," Morris replied. "I can't help it none."

"Maybe you was born with a diamond ring on your little finger. What?" Morris glared at his partner.

"If you think that I enjoy it wearing that ring, Abe," he declared, "you are much mistaken. You got us to take these here diamonds, Abe, and if they got stole on us, Abe, we are not only out the thousand dollars, but we would also got to pay it so much more as Hymie Kotzen would sue us for in the courts. I got to wear this here ring, Abe, and that's all there is to it."

He walked away to the rear of the store with the air of a martyr, while Abe gazed after him in silent admiration.

Two weeks sped quickly by, during which Morris safe-guarded the diamonds with the utmost zest and enjoyment, and at length the settling day arrived. Morris was superintending the unpacking of piece goods in the cutting-room when Abe darted upstairs.

"Mawruss," he hissed, "Hymie Kotzen is downstairs."

By a feat of legerdemain that a conjurer might have envied, Morris transferred the pin and ring to his waist-coat pocket and followed Abe to the sample-room.

"Well, Hymie," Morris cried, "we thought you would be prompt on the day. Ain't it?"

Hymie smiled a sickly smirk in which there was as little mirth as there was friendliness.

"You got another think coming," Hymie replied.

"What d'ye mean?" Morris exclaimed.

"I'm up against it, boys," Hymie explained. "I expected to get it a check for two thousand from Heller, Blumenkrohn this morning."

"And didn't it come?" Abe asked.

"Sure it come," Hymie replied, "but it was only sixteen hundred and twenty dollars. They claim it three hundred and eighty dollars for shortage in delivery, so I returned 'em the check."

"You returned 'em the check, Hymie?" Morris cried. "And we got to wait for our thousand dollars because you made it a shortage in delivery."

"I didn't make no shortage in delivery," Hymie declared.

"Well, Hymie," Abe broke in, "you say it yourself Heller, Blumenkrohn is gilt-edge, A Number One people. They ain't going to claim no shortage if there wasn't none, Hymie."

"I guess you don't know Louis Blumenkrohn, Abe," Hymie retorted. "He claims it shortage before he unpacks the goods already."

"Well, what has that got to do with us, Hymie?" Morris burst out.

"You see how it is, boys," Hymie explained; "so I got to ask it you a couple of weeks' extension."

"A couple of weeks' extension is nix, Hymie," Abe said, and Morris nodded his head in approval.

"Either you give it us the thousand, Hymie," was Morris' ultimatum, "or either we keep the diamonds, and that's all there is to it."

"Now, Mawruss," Hymie protested, "you ain't going to shut down on me like that! Make it two weeks more and I'll give you a hundred dollars bonus and interest at six per cent."

Abe shook his head. "No, Hymie," he said firmly, "we ain't no loan sharks. If you got to get that thousand dollars today you will manage it somehow. So that's the way it stands. We keep open here till six o'clock, Hymie, and the diamonds will be waiting for you so soon as you bring us the thousand dollars. That's all."

There was a note of finality in Abe's tones that made Hymie put on his hat and leave without another word.

"Yes, Abe," Morris commented as the door closed behind Hymie, "so liberal you must be with my money.

Ain't I told you from the very start that feller is a lowlife? Tchampanyer he must drink it on his wife's birthday, Abe, and also he got to wear it diamonds, Abe, when he ain't got enough money to pay his laundry bill yet."

"I ain't worrying, Mawruss," Abe replied. "He ain't going to let us keep them diamonds for a thousand dollars, Mawruss. They're worth a whole lot more as that, Mawruss."

"I don't know how much they're worth, Abe," Morris grunted, putting on his hat, "but one thing I do know: I'm going across the street to get a shave; and then I'm going right down to Sig Pollak on Maiden Lane, Abe, and I'll find out just how much they are worth."

A moment later he descended the basement steps into the barber-shop under Wasserbauer's café and restaurant.

"Hallo, Mawruss," a voice cried from the proprietor's chair. "Ain't it a hot weather?"

It was Sam Feder, vice-president of the Kosciusko Bank, who spoke. He was midway in the divided enjoyment of a shampoo and a large black cigar, while an electric fan oscillated over his head.

"I bet yer it's hot, Mr. Feder," Morris agreed, taking off his coat.

"Why don't you take your vest off, too, Mawruss?" Sam Feder suggested.

"That's a good idee," Morris replied, peeling off his waistcoat. He hung it next to his coat and relapsed with a sigh into the nearest vacant chair.

"Just once around, Phil," he said to the barber, and closed his eyes for a short nap.

When he woke up ten minutes later Phil was spraying him with witch-hazel while the proprietor stood idly in front of the mirror and curled his flowing black mustache.

"Don't take it so particular, Phil," Morris enjoined. "I ain't got it all day to sit here in this chair."

"All right, Mr. Perlmutter, all right," Phil cried, and in

less than three minutes, powdered, oiled and combed, Morris climbed out of the chair. His coat was in waiting, held by a diminutive Italian brushboy, but Morris waved his hand impatiently.

"My vest," he demanded. "I don't put my coat on under my vest."

The brushboy turned to the vacant row of hooks.

"No gotta da vest," he said.

"What!" Morris gasped.

"You didn't have no vest on, did you, Mr. Perlmutter?" the proprietor asked.

"Sure I had a vest," Morris cried. "Where is it?"

On the wall hung a sign which advised customers to check their clothing with the cashier or no responsibility would be assumed by the management, and it was to this notice that the proprietor pointed before answering.

"I guess somebody must have pinched it," he replied nonchalantly.

III

It was not until two hours after the disappearance of his waistcoat that Morris returned to the store. In the mean time he had been to police headquarters and had inserted an advertisement in three daily newspapers. Moreover he had consulted a lawyer, the eminent Henry D. Feldman, and had received no consolation either on the score of the barber's liability to Potash & Perlmutter or of his own liability to Kotzen.

"Well, Mawruss," Abe said, "how much are them diamonds worth?"

Then he looked up and for the first time saw his partner's haggard face.

"Holy smokes!" he cried. "They're winder-glass."

Morris shook his head. "I wish they was," he croaked.

"You wish they was!" Abe repeated in accents of amazement. "What d'ye mean?"

"Somebody pinched 'em on me," Morris replied.

"What!" Abe shouted.

"S-sh," Morris hissed as the door opened. It was Hymie Kotzen who entered.

"Well, boys," he cried, "every cloud is silverplated. Ain't it? No sooner did I get back to my store than I get a letter from Henry D. Feldman that Cohen & Schondorf want to settle for forty cents cash. On the head of that, mind you, in comes Rudolph Heller from Cincinnati, and when I tell him about the check what they sent it me he fixes it up on the spot."

He beamed at Abe and Morris.

"So, bring out them diamonds, boys," he concluded, "and we'll settle up C. O. D."

He pulled a roll of bills from his pocket and toyed with them, but neither Abe nor Morris stirred.

"What's the hurry, Hymie?" Abe asked feebly.

"What's the hurry, Abe!" Hymie repeated. "Well, ain't that a fine question for you to ask it of me! Don't sit there like a dummy, Abe. Get the diamonds and we'll fix it up."

"But wouldn't tomorrow do as well?" Morris asked.

Hymie sat back and eyed Morris suspiciously.

"What are you trying to do, Mawruss?" he asked. "Make jokes with me?"

"I ain't making no jokes, Hymie," Morris replied. "The fact is, Hymie, we got it the diamonds, now — in our — now — safety-deposit box, and it ain't convenient to get at it now."

"Oh, it ain't, ain't it?" Hymie cried. "Well, it's got to be convenient; so, Abe, you get a move on you and go down to them safety-deposit vaults and fetch them."

"Let Mawruss fetch 'em," Abe replied wearily. "The safety deposit is his idee, Hymie, not mine."

Hymie turned to Morris. "Go ahead, Mawruss," he said, "you fetch 'em."

"I was only stringing you, Hymie," Morris croaked. "We ain't got 'em in no safety-deposit vault at all."

"That settles it," Hymie cried, jumping to his feet and jamming his hat down with both hands.

"Where you going, Hymie?" Abe called after him.

"For a policeman," Hymie said. "I want them diamonds and I'm going to have 'em too."

Morris ran to the store door and grabbed Hymie by the coat tails.

"Wait a minute," he yelled. "Hymie, I'm surprised at you that you should act that way."

Hymie stopped short.

"I ain't acting, Mawruss," he said. "It's you what's acting. All I want it is you should give me my ring and pin, and I am satisfied to pay you the thousand dollars."

They returned to the sample-room and once more sat down.

"I'll tell you the truth, Hymie," Morris said at last. "I loaned them diamonds to somebody, and that's the way it is."

"You loaned 'em to somebody!" Hymie cried, jumping once more to his feet. "My diamonds you loaned it, Mawruss? Well, all I got to say is either you get them diamonds back right away, or either I will call a policeman and make you arrested."

"Make me arrested, then, Hymie," Morris replied resignedly, "because the feller what I loaned them diamonds to won't return 'em for two weeks anyhow."

Hymie sat down again.

"For two weeks, hey?" he said. He passed his handkerchief over his face and looked at Abe.

"That's a fine, nervy partner what you got it, Abe, I must say," he commented.

"Well, Hymie," Abe replied, "so long as you can't get them diamonds back for two weeks keep the thousand dollars for two weeks and we won't charge you no interest nor nothing."

"No, siree," Hymie said; "either I pay you the thousand

now, Abe, or I don't pay it you for three months, and no interest nor nothing."

Abe looked at Morris, who nodded his head slowly.

"What do we care, Abe," he said, "two weeks or three months is no difference now, ain't it?"

"I'm agreeable, then, Hymie," Abe declared.

"All right," Hymie said eagerly; "put it down in writing and sign it, and I am satisfied you should keep the diamonds three months."

Abe sat down at his desk and scratched away for five minutes.

"Here it is, Hymie," he said at last. "Hyman Kotzen and Potash & Perlmutter agrees it that one thousand dollars what he lent it off of them should not be returned for three months from date, no interest nor nothing. And also, that Potash & Perlmutter should not give up the diamonds, neither. POTASH & PERLMUTTER."

"That's all right," Hymie said. He folded the paper into his pocketbook and turned to Morris.

"Also it is understood, Mawruss, you should n't lend them diamonds to nobody else," he concluded, and a minute later the store door closed behind him.

After he had gone there was an ominous silence which Abe was the first to break.

"Well, Mawruss," he said, "ain't that a fine mess you got us into it? Must you wore it them diamonds, Mawruss? Why could n't you leave 'em in the safe?"

Morris made no answer.

"Or if you had to lose 'em, Mawruss," Abe went on, "why did n't you done it the day we loaned Hymie the money. Then we could of stopped our check by the bank. Now we can do it nothing."

"I did n't lose the diamonds, Abe," Morris protested. "I left 'em in my vest in the barber-shop and somebody took it the vest."

"Well, ain't you got no suspicions, Mawruss?" Abe asked. "Think, Mawruss, who was it took the vest?"

Morris raised his head and was about to reply when the store door opened and Sam Feder, vice-president of the Kosciusko Bank, entered bearing a brown paper parcel under his arm.

A personal visit from so well-known a financier covered Abe with embarrassment, and he jumped to his feet and rushed out of the sample-room with both arms outstretched.

"Mr. Feder," he exclaimed, "ain't this indeed a pleasure? Come inside, Mr. Feder. Come inside into our sample-room."

He brought out a seat for the vice-president and dusted it carefully.

"I ain't come to see you, Abe," Mr. Feder said; "I come to see that partner of yours."

He untied the string that bound the brown paper parcel and pulled out its contents.

"Why!" Morris gasped. "That's my vest."

"Sure it is," Mr. Feder replied, "and it just fits me, Mawruss. In fact, it fits me so good that when I went to the barber-shop in a two-piece suit this morning, Mawruss, I come away with a three-piece suit and a souvenir besides."

Mr. Feder put his hand in his trousers pocket and tumbled the missing ring and pin on to the baize-covered sample-room table.

"That was the souvenir, Abe," he said. "In fact, two souvenirs."

Morris and Abe stared at the diamonds, too stunned for utterance.

"You're a fine feller, Mawruss," Mr. Feder continued, "to be carrying around valuable stones like them in your vest pocket. Why, I showed them stones to a feller what was in my office an hour ago and he says they must be worth pretty near five hundred dollars."

He paused and looked at Morris.

"And he was a pretty good judge of diamonds, too," he continued.

"Who was the feller, Mr. Feder?" Abe asked.

"I guess you know, Abe," Mr. Feder replied. "His name is Hymie Kotzen."

GEORGE FITCH

The death of George Fitch in his thirties on August 9, 1915 — a newspaperman who was making his way into the front ranks of American humorists — was a distinct loss to a never overcrowded branch of our literature. Mr. Fitch was a mid-western man born in Galva, Illinois, on June 5, 1877, who gave us the flavor of his own environment steeped in a garb of humor that was national in feeling and scope. His "At Good Old Siwash" is unquestionably the best book of college humor thus far produced.

OLE SKJARSEN'S FIRST TOUCHDOWN [1]

AM I going to the game Saturday? Am I? Me? Am I going to eat some more food this year? Am I going to draw my pay this month? Am I going to leave my little old office at five P. M. or stay around and wait for opening time next morning? All foolish questions, pal. Very silly conversation. Pshaw!

Am I going to the game, you ask me? Is the sun going to get up tomorrow? You could n't keep me away from that game if you put a protective tariff of seventy-eight per cent ad valorem, whatever that means, on the front gate. I'm going to the game, and when the Siwash team comes out I'm going to get up and give as near a correct imitation of a Roman mob and a Polish riot as my throat will stand; and if we put a big crimp in those large-footed, moss-covered, humpy-shouldered behemoths from Muggledorfer, I'm going out tonight and burn the City Hall. Any Siwash man who is a gentleman would do it. I'll probably have to run like thunder to beat some of them to it.

You know how it is, old man. Or maybe you don't, be-

[1] From "At Good Old Siwash." Copyright, 1911, by Little, Brown, and Company.

cause you made all your end runs on the Glee Club. But I played football all through my college course and the microbe is still there. In the fall I think football, talk football, dream football, even though I have n't had a suit on for six years. And when I go out to the field and see little old Siwash lining up against a bunch of overgrown hippos from a college with a catalogue as thick as a city directory, the old mud-and-perspiration smell gets in my nostrils, and the desire to get under the bunch and feel the feet jabbing into my ribs boils up so strong that I have to hold on to myself with both hands. If you 've never sat on a hard board and wanted to be between two halfbacks with your hands on their shoulders, and the quarter ready to sock a ball into your solar plexus, and eleven men daring you to dodge 'em, and nine thousand friends and enemies raising Cain and keeping him well propped up in the grandstands — if you have n't had that want you would n't know a healthy, able-bodied want if you ran into it on the street.

Of course, I never got any further along than a scrub. But what 's the odds? A broken bone feels just as grand to a scrub as to a star. I sometimes think a scrub gets more real football knowledge than a varsity man, because he does n't have to addle his brain by worrying about holding his job and keeping his wind, and by dreaming that he has fumbled a punt and presented ninety-five yards to the hereditary enemies of his college. I played scrub football five years, four of 'em under Bost, the greatest coach who ever put wings on the heels of a two-hundred-pound hunk of meat; and while my ribs never lasted long enough to put me on the team, what I did n't learn about the game you could put in the other fellow's eye.

Say, but it 's great, learning football under a good coach. It 's the finest training a man can get anywhere on this Big Old Ball. Football is only the smallest thing you learn. You learn how to be patient when what you want to do is to chew somebody up and spit him into the gutter. You learn to control your temper when it is on the high speed, with

the throttle jerked wide open and buzzing like a hornet con-
vention. You learn, by having it told you, just how small
and foolish and insignificant you are, and how well this
earth could stagger along without you if some one were to
take a fly-killer and mash you with it. And you learn all
this at the time of life when your head is swelling up until
you mistake it for a planet, and regard whatever you say
as a volcanic disturbance.

I suppose you think, like the rest of the chaps who never
came out to practice but observed the game from the dollar-
and-a-half seats, that being coached in football is like being
instructed in German or calculus. You are told what to do
and how to do it, and then you recite. Far from it, my boy!
They don't bother telling you what to do and how to do it
on a big football field. Mostly they tell you what to do and
how you do it. And they do it artistically, too. Use plenty
of language. A football coach is picked out for his ready
tongue. He must be a conversationalist. He must be able
to talk to a greenhorn, with fine shoulders and a needle-
shaped head, until that greenhorn will pick up the ball and
take it through a Sioux war dance to get away from the
conversation. You can't reason with football men. They're
not logical, most of them. They are picked out for their
heels and shoulders and their leg muscles, and not for their
ability to look at you with luminous eyes and say: "Yes,
Professor, I think I understand." The way to make 'em
understand is to talk about them. Any man can understand
you while you are telling him that if he were just a little
bit slower he would have to be tied to the earth to keep up
with it. That hurts his pride. And when you hurt his
pride he takes it out on whatever is in front of him — which
is the other team. Never get in front of a football player
when you are coaching him.

But this brings me to the subject of Bost again. Bost is
still coaching Siwash. This makes his 'steenth year. I
guess he can stay there forever. He's coached all these
years and has never used the same adjectives to the same

man twice. There's a record for you! He's a little man, Bost is. He played end on some Western team when he only weighed one hundred and forty. Got his football knowledge there. But where he got his vocabulary is still a mystery. He has a way of convincing a man that a dill pickle would make a better guard than he is, and of making that man so jealous of the pickle that he will perform perfectly unreasonable feats for a week to beat it out for the place. He has a way of saying "Hurry up", with a few descriptive adjectives tacked on, that makes a man rub himself in the stung place for an hour; and oh, how mad he can make you while he is telling you pleasantly that while the little fellow playing against you is only a prep and has sloping shoulders and weighs one hundred and eleven stripped, he is making you look like a bale of hay that has been dumped by mistake on an athletic field. And say, when he gets a team in the gymnasium between halves, with the game going wrong, and stands up before them and sizes up their insect nerve and rubber backbone and hereditary awkwardness and incredible talent in doing the wrong thing, to say nothing of describing each individual blunder in that queer nasal clack of his — well, I'd rather be tied up in a great big frying-pan over a good hot stove for the same length of time, any day in the week. The reason Bost is a great coach is because his men don't dare play poorly. When they do he talks to them. If he would only hit them, or skin them by inches, or shoot at them, they wouldn't mind it so much; but when you get on the field with him and realize that if you miss a tackle he is going to get you out before the whole gang and tell you what a great mistake the Creator made when He put joints in your arms instead of letting them stick out stiff like any other signpost, you're not going to miss that tackle, that's all.

When Bost came to Siwash he succeeded a line of coaches who had been telling the fellows to get down low and hit the line hard, and had been showing them how to do it very patiently. Nice fellows, those coaches. Perfect gentlemen.

Make you proud to associate with them. They could take a herd of green farmer boys, with wrists like mules' ankles, and by Thanksgiving they would have them familiar with all the rudiments of the game. By that time the season would be over and all the schools in the vicinity would have beaten us by big scores. The next year the last year's crop of big farmer boys would stay at home to husk corn, and the coach would begin all over on a new crop. The result was, we were a dub school at football. Any school that could scare up a good rangy halfback and a line that could hold sheep could get up an adding festival at our expense any time. We lived in a perpetual state of fear. Some day we felt that the Normal School would come down and beat us. That would be the limit of disgrace. After that there would be nothing left to do but disband the college and take to drink to forget the past.

But Bost changed all that in one year. He didn't care to show any one how to play football. He was just interested in making the player afraid not to play it. When you went down the field on a punt you knew that if you missed your man he would tell you when you came back that two stone hitching-posts out of three could get past you in a six-foot alley. If you missed a punt you could expect to be told that you might catch a haystack by running with your arms wide open, but that was no way to catch a football. Maybe things like that don't sound jabby when two dozen men hear them! They kept us catching punts between classes, and tackling each other all the way to our rooms and back. We simply had to play football to keep from being bawled out. It's an awful thing to have a coach with a tongue like a cheese knife swinging away at you, and to know that if you get mad and quit, no one but the dear old coll. will suffer—but it gets the results. They use the same system in the East, but there they only swear at a man, I believe. Siwash is a mighty proper college and you can't swear on its campus, whatever else you do. Swearing is only a lazy man's substitute for thinking, anyway; and Bost wasn't lazy. He preferred the descriptive; he sat up nights thinking it out.

In Bost's second month he had the whole team so wrought up and anxious to please that they would have bucked brick walls and locomotives. Big, beefy men were running fifty yards, over and around determined opposition, in six seconds, and wondering nervously when they got up from under the pile if that was fast enough to keep Bost quiet. You never saw such abject and eager obedience. The pen may be mightier than the sword, but the tongue makes both of them look like feather ticklers.

We began to see the results before Bost had been tracing our pedigrees for two weeks. First game of the season was with that little old dinky Normal School which had been scaring us so for the past five years. We had been satisfied to push some awkward halfback over the line once, and then hold on to the enemy so tight he couldn't run; and we started out that year in the same old way. First half ended 0 to 0, with our boys pretty satisfied because they had kept the ball in Normal's territory. Bost led the team and the substitutes into the overgrown barn we used for a gymnasium, and while we were still patting ourselves approvingly in our minds he cut loose:

"You pasty-faced, overfed, white-livered beanbag experts, what do you mean by running a beauty show instead of a football game?" he yelled. "Do you suppose I came out here to be art director of a statuary exhibit? Does any one of you imagine for a holy minute that he knows the difference between a football game and ushering in a church? Don't fool yourselves. You don't; you don't know anything. All you ever knew about football I could carve on stone and put in my eye and never feel it. Nothing to nothing against a crowd of farmer boys who haven't known a football from a duck's egg for more than a week! Bah! If I ever turned the Old Folks' Home loose on you doll babies they'd run up a century while you were hunting for your handkerchiefs. Jackson, what do you suppose a halfback is for? I don't want cloak models. I want a man who can stick his head down and run. Don't be afraid of that bean of yours; it has n't got anything worth saving in it. When you get the ball you 're supposed to run with it and not sit around trying to hatch it. You, Saunders! You held that other guard just like a sweet-pea vine. Where did you ever learn that sweet, lovely way of falling down on your nose when a real man sneezes at you? Did you ever hear of sand? Eat it! Eat it! Fill yourself up with it. I want you to get in that line this half and stop something or I 'll make you play left end in a fancy-work club. Johnson, the only way to get you around the field is to put you on wheels and haul you. Next time you grow fast to the ground I 'm going to violate some forestry regulations and take an axe to you. Same to you, Briggs. You 'd make the All-America boundary posts, but that 's all. Vance, I picked you for a quarterback, but I made a mistake; you ought to be sorting eggs. That ball is n't red hot. You don't have to let go of it as soon as you get it. Don't be afraid, nobody will step on you. This is n't a rude game. It 's only a game of post-office. You need n't act so nervous about it. Maybe some of the big girls will kiss you, but it won't hurt."

Bost stopped for breath and eyed us. We were a sick-looking crowd. You could almost see the remarks sticking into us and quivering. We had come in feeling pretty virtuous, and what we were getting was a hideous surprise.

"Now I want to tell this tea-party something," continued Bost. "Either you 're going out on that field and score thirty points this last half or I 'm going to let the girls of Siwash play your football for you. I 'm tired of coaching men that are n't good at anything but falling down scientifically when they 're tackled. There is n't a broken nose among you. Every one of you will run back five yards to pick out a soft spot to fall. It 's got to stop. You 're going to hold on to that ball this half and take it places.

If some little fellow from Normal crosses his fingers and says 'naughty, naughty,' don't fall on the ball and yell 'down' until they can hear it downtown. Thirty points is what I want out of you this half, and if you don't get 'em — well, you just dare to come back here without them, that's all. Now get out on that field and jostle somebody. Git!"

Did we git? Well, rather. We were so mad our clothes smoked. We would have quit the game right there and resigned from the team, but we didn't dare to. Bost would have talked to us some more. And we didn't dare not to make those thirty points, either. It was an awful tough job, but we did it with a couple over. We raged like wild beasts. We scared those gentle Normalites out of their boots. I can't imagine how we ever got it into our heads that they could play football, anyway. When it was all over we went back to the gymnasium feeling righteously triumphant, and had another hour with Bost in which he took us all apart without anæsthetics, and showed us how Nature would have done a better job if she had used less wood and more brain tissue in our composition.

That day made the Siwash team. The school went wild over the score. Bost rounded up two or three more good players, and every afternoon he lashed us around the field with that wire-edged tongue of his. On Saturdays we played, and oh, how we worked! In the first half we were afraid of what Bost would say to us when we came off the field. In the second half we were mad at what he had said. And how he did drive us down the field in practice! I can remember whole cross sections of his talk yet:

"Faster, faster, you scows. Line up. Quick! Johnson, are you waiting for a stone-mason to set you? Snap the ball. Tear into them. Low! Low! Hi-i! You end, do you think you're the quarter pole in a horse race? Nine men went past you that time. If you can't touch 'em drop 'em a souvenir card. Line up. Faster, faster! Oh, thunder, hurry up! If you ran a funeral, center, the corpse would spoil on your hands. Wow. Fumble! Drop on that ball. Drop on it! Hogboom, you'd fumble a loving cup. Use your hand instead of your jaw to catch that ball. It isn't good to eat. That's four chances you've had. I could lose two games a day if I had you all the time. Now try that signal again — low, you linemen; there's no girls watching you. Snap it; snap it. Great Scott! Say, Hogboom, come here. When you get that ball, don't think we gave it to you to nurse. You're supposed to start the same day with the line. We give you that ball to take forward. Have you got to get an act of Congress to start those legs of yours? You'd make a good vault to store footballs in, but you're too stationary for a fullback. Now I'll give you one more chance———"

And maybe Hogboom wouldn't go some with that chance!

In a month we had a team that wouldn't have used past Siwash teams to hold its sweaters. It was mad all the time, and it played the game carnivorously. Siwash was delirious with joy. The whole school turned out for practice, and to see those eleven men snapping through signals up and down the field as fast as an ordinary man could run just congested us with happiness. You've no idea what a lovely time of the year autumn is when you can go out after classes and sit on a pine seat in the soft dusk and watch your college team pulling off end runs in as pretty formation as if they were chorus girls, while you discuss lazily with your friends just how many points it is going to run up on the neighboring schools. I never had the Presidency handed to me, but it couldn't make me feel any more contented or powerful or complacent than to be a busted-up scrub in Siwash, with a team like that to watch. I'm pretty sure of that.

But, happy as we were, Bost wasn't nearly content. He had ideals. I believe one of them must have been to run that team through a couple of brick flats without spoiling

the formation. Nothing satisfied him. He was particularly distressed about the fullback. Hogboom was a good
fellow and took signal practice perfectly, but he was no
fiend. He lacked the vivacity of a real, first-class Bengal
tiger. He would n't eat any one alive. He 'd run until he
was pulled down, but you never expected him to explode
in the midst of seven hostiles and ricochet down the field
for forty yards. He never jumped over two men and on
to another, and he never dodged two ways at once and
landed out three men with stiff arms on his way to the goal.
It was n't his style. He was good for two and a half yards
every time, but that did n't suit Bost. He was after
statistics, and what does a three-yard buck amount to when
you want 70 to 0 scores?

The result of this dissatisfaction was Ole Skjarsen. That
was the year when Bost disappeared for three days and
came back leading Ole by a rope — at least, he was towing
him by an old carpet bag when we sighted him. Bost found
him in a lumber camp, he afterward told us, and had to
explain to him what a college was before he would quit his
job. He thought it was something good to eat at first, I
believe. Ole was a timid young Norwegian giant, with a
rick of white hair and a reënforced-concrete physique. He
escaped from his clothes in all directions, and was so green
and bashful that you would have thought we were cannibals
from the way he shied at us — though, as that was the year
the bright hat-ribbons came in, I can't blame him. We
crowded around him as if he had been a T. R. capture
straight from Africa; and everybody helped him register
third prep, with business-college extras. Then we took him
out, harnessed him in football armour, and set to work to
teach him the game.

Bost went right to work on Ole in a businesslike manner.
He tossed him the football and said: " Catch it." Ole
watched it sail past and then tore after it like a pup retriev-
ing a stick. He got it in a few minutes and brought it back
to where Bost was raving.

"See here, you overgrown fox terrier," he shouted, "catch it on the fly. Here!" He hurled it at him.

"Aye ent seen no fly," said Ole, allowing the ball to pass on as he conversed.

"You cotton-headed Scandinavian cattleship ballast, catch that ball in your arms when I throw it to you, and don't let go of it," shrieked Bost, shooting it at him again.

"Oll right," said Ole patiently. He cornered the ball after a short struggle and stood hugging it faithfully.

"Toss it back, toss it back!" howled Bost, jumping up and down.

"Yu tal me to hold it," said Ole reproachfully, hugging it tighter than ever.

"Drop it, you Mammoth Cave of ignorance," yelled Bost. "If I had your head I'd sell it for cordwood. Drop it!"

Ole dropped the ball placidly. "Das ban fule game," he smiled dazedly. "Aye ent care for it. Eny faller got a Yewsharp?"

That was the opening chapter of Ole's instruction. The rest were just like it. You had to tell him to do a thing. You then had to show him how to do it. You then had to tell him how to stop doing it. After that you had to explain that he wasn't to refrain forever — just until he had to do it again. Then you had to persuade him to do it again. He was as good-natured as a lost puppy, and just as hard to reason with. In three nights Bost was so hoarse that he couldn't talk. He had called Ole everything in the dictionary that is fit to print; and the knowledge that Ole didn't understand more than a hundredth part of it, and didn't mind that, was wormwood to his soul.

For all that, we could see that if any one could teach Ole the game he would make a fine player. He was as hard as flint and so fast on his feet that we couldn't tackle him any more than we could have tackled a jack-rabbit. He learned to catch the ball in a night, and as for defense — his one-handed catches of flying players would have made a National League fielder envious. But with all of it he was perfectly useless. You had to start him, stop him, back him, speed him up, throttle him down and run him off the field just as if he had been a close-coupled, 1910 model scoot-cart. If we could have rigged up a driver's seat and run Ole by chauffeur it would have been all right. But every other method of trying to get him to understand what he was expected to do was a failure. He just grinned, took orders, executed them, and waited for more. When a two-hundred-and-twenty-pound man takes a football, wades through eleven frantic scrubs, shakes them all off, and then stops dead with a clear field to the goal before him — because his instructions ran out when he shook the last scrub — you can be pardoned for feeling hopeless about him.

That was what happened the day before the Muggle-dorfer game. Bost had been working Ole at fullback all evening. He and the captain had steered him up and down the field as carefully as if he had been a sea-going yacht. It was a wonderful sight. Ole was under perfect control. He advanced the ball five yards, ten yards, or twenty at command. Nothing could stop him. The scrubs represented only so many doormats to him. Every time he made a play he stopped at the latter end of it for instructions.

When he stopped the last time, with nothing before him but the goal, and asked placidly, " Vere skoll I take das ball now, Master Bost?" I thought the coach would expire of the heat. He positively steamed with suppressed emotion. He swelled and got purple about the face. We were alarmed and were getting ready to hoop him like a barrel when he found his tongue at last.

"You pale-eyed, prehistoric mudhead," he spluttered, "I've spent a week trying to get through that skull lining of yours. It's no use, you field boulder. Where do you keep your brains? Give me a chance at them. I just want to get into them one minute and stir them up with my finger. To think that I have to use you to play football when they are paying five dollars and a half for ox meat in Kansas City. Skjarsen, do you know anything at all?"

"Aye ban getting gude eddication," said Ole serenely. "Aye tank I ban college faller purty sune, I don't know. I like I skoll understand all das har big vorts yu make."

"You'll understand them, I don't think," moaned Bost. "You couldn't understand a swift kick in the ribs. You are a fool. Understand that, muttonhead?"

Ole understood. "Vy for yu call me fule?" he said indignantly. "Aye du yust vat you say."

"Ar-r-r-r!" bubbled Bost, walking around himself three or four times. "You do just what I say! Of course you do. Did I tell you to stop in the middle of the field? What would Muggledorfer do to you if you stopped there?"

"Yu ent tal me to go on," said Ole sullenly. "Aye go on, Aye gass, pooty qveek den."

"You bet you'll go on," said Bost. "Now, look here, you sausage material, tomorrow you play fullback. You stop everything that comes at you from the other side. Hear? You catch the ball when it comes to you. Hear? And when they give you the ball you take it, and don't you dare to stop with it. Get that? Can I get that into your head without a drill and a blast? If you dare to stop with that ball I'll ship you back to the lumber camp in a cattle car. Stop in the middle of the field—— Ow!"

But at this point we took Bost away.

The next afternoon we dressed Ole up in his armour — he invariably got it on wrong side out if we didn't help him — and took him out to the field. We confidently expected to promenade all over Muggledorfer — their coach was an innocent child beside Bost — and that was the reason why Ole was going to play. It didn't matter much what he did.

Ole was just coming to a boil when we got him into his clothes. Bost's remarks had gotten through his hide at last. He was pretty slow, Ole was, but he had begun getting mad the night before and had kept at the job all night and all morning. By afternoon he was seething, mostly in Norwegian. The injustice of being called a muttonhead all week for not obeying orders, and then being called a mudhead for stopping for orders, churned his soul, to say nothing of his language. He only averaged one English word in three, as he told us on the way out that today he was going to do exactly as he had been told or fill a martyr's grave — only that wasn't the way he put it.

The Muggledorfers were a pruny-looking lot. We had the game won when our team came out and glared at them. Bost had filled most of the positions with regular young mammoths, and when you dressed them up in football armor they were enough to make a Dreadnought a little nervous. The Muggleses kicked off to our team, and for a few plays we plowed along five or ten yards at a time. Then Ole was given the ball. He went twenty-five yards. Any other man would have been crushed to earth in five. He just waded through the middle of the line and went down the field, a moving mass of wriggling men. It was a wonderful play. They disinterred him at last and he started straight across the field for Bost.

"Aye ent mean to stop, Master Bost," he shouted. "Dese fallers har, dey squash me down ——"

We hauled him into line and went to work again. Ole had performed so well that the captain called his signal again. This time I hope I may be roasted in a subway in July if Ole didn't run twenty-five yards with four Muggledorfer men hanging on his legs. We stood up and yelled until our teeth ached. It took about five minutes to get Ole dug out, and then he started for Bost again.

"Honest, Master Bost, Aye ent mean to stop," he said imploringly. "Aye yust tal you, dese fallers ban devils. Aye fule dem naxt time ——"

"Line up and shut up," the captain shouted. The ball wasn't over twenty yards from the line, and as a matter of course the quarter shot it back to Ole. He put his head down, gave one mad-bull plunge, laid a windrow of Muggledorfer players out on either side, and shot over the goal line like a locomotive.

We rose up to cheer a few lines, but stopped to rubber.

Ole didn't stop at the goal line. He didn't stop at the fence. He put up one hand, hurdled it, and disappeared across the campus like a young whirlwind.

"He doesn't know enough to stop!" yelled Bost, rushing up to the fence. "Hustle up, you fellows, and bring him back!"

Three or four of us jumped the fence, but it was a hopeless game. Ole was disappearing up the campus and across the street. The Muggledorfer team was nonplussed and sort of indignant. To be bowled over by a cyclone, and then to have said cyclone break up the game by running away with the ball was to them a new idea in football. It wasn't to those of us who knew Ole, however. One of us telephoned down to the Leader office where Hinckley, an old team man, worked, and asked him to head off Ole and send him back. Muggledorfer kindly consented to call time, and we started after the fugitive ourselves.

Ten minutes later we met Hinckley downtown. He looked as if he had had a slight argument with a thirteen-inch shell. He was also mad.

"What was that you asked me to stop?" he snorted, pinning himself together. "Was it a gorilla or a high explosive? When did you fellows begin importing steam rollers for the team? I asked him to stop. I ordered him to stop. Then I went around in front of him to stop him—and he ran right over me. I held on for thirty yards, but that's no way to travel. I could have gone to the next town just as well, though. What sort of a game is this, and where is that tow-headed holy terror bound for?"

We gave the answer up, but we couldn't give up Ole. He was too valuable to lose. How to catch him was the sticker. An awful uproar in the street gave us an idea. It was Ted Harris in the only auto in town—one of the earliest brands of sneeze vehicles. In a minute more four of us were in, and Ted was chiveying the thing up the street.

If you've never chased an escaping fullback in one of those pioneer automobiles you've got something coming. Take it all around, a good, swift man, running all the time, could almost keep ahead of one. We pumped up a tire, fixed a wire or two, and cranked up a few times; and the upshot of it was we were five miles out on the state road before we caught sight of Ole.

He was trotting briskly when we caught up with him, the ball under his arm, and that patient, resigned expression on his face that he always had when Bost cussed him. "Stop, Ole," I yelled; "this is no Marathon. Come back. Climb in here with us."

Ole shook his head and let out a notch of speed.

"Stop, you mullethead," yelled Simpson above the roar of the auto—those old machines could roar some, too. "What do you mean by running off with our ball? You're not supposed to do hare-and-hounds in football."

Ole kept on running. We drove the car on ahead, stopped it across the road, and jumped out to stop him. When the attempt was over three of us picked up the fourth and put him aboard. Ole had tramped on us and had climbed over the auto.

Force wouldn't do, that was plain. "Where are you going, Ole?" we pleaded as we tore along beside him.

"Aye ent know," he panted, laboring up a hill; "das ban fule game, Aye tenk."

"Come on back and play some more," we urged. "Bost won't like it, your running all over the country this way."

"Das ban my orders," panted Ole. "Aye ent no fule, yentlemen; Aye know ven Aye ban doing right teng. Master Bost he say 'Keep on running!' Aye gass I run till hal freeze on top. Aye ent know why. Master Bost he know, I tenk."

"This is awful," said Lambert, the manager of the team. "He's taken Bost literally again—the chump. He'll run till he lands up in those pine woods again. And that ball cost the association five dollars. Besides, we want him. What are we going to do?"

" I know," I said. " We're going back to get Bost. I
guess the man who started him can stop him."

We left Ole still plugging north and ran back to town.
The game was still hanging fire. Bost was tearing his hair.
Of course, the Muggledorfer fellows could have insisted on
playing, but they weren't anxious. Ole or no Ole, we could
have walked all over them, and they knew it. Besides, they
were having too much fun with Bost. They were sitting
around, Indian-like, in their blankets, and every three
minutes their captain would go and ask Bost with perfect
politeness whether he thought they had better continue the
game there or move it on to the next town in time to catch
his fullback as he came through.

" Of course, we are in no hurry," he would explain pleasantly; "we're just here for amusement, anyway; and it's
as much fun watching you try to catch your players as it
is to get scored on. Why don't you hobble them, Mr. Bost?
A fifty-yard rope wouldn't interfere much with that gay
young Percheron of yours, and it would save you lots of
time rounding him up. Do you have to use a lariat when
you put his harness on?"

Fancy Bost having to take all that conversation, with no
adequate reply to make. When I got there he was blue in
the face. It didn't take him half a second to decide what
to do. Telling the captain of the Siwash team to go ahead
and play if Muggledorfer insisted, and on no account to
use that 32 double-X play except on first downs, he jumped
into the machine and we started for Ole.

There were no speed records in those days. Wouldn't
have made any difference if there were. Harris just turned on
all the juice his old double-opposed motor could soak up, and
when we hit the wooden crossings on the outskirts of town we
fellows in the tonneau went up so high that we changed sides
coming down. It wasn't over twenty minutes till we sighted
a little cloud of dust just beyond a little town to the north.
Pretty soon we saw it was Ole. He was still doing his nine
miles per. We caught up and Bost hopped out, still mad.

"Where in Billy-be-blamed are you going, you human trolley car?" he spluttered, sprinting along beside Skjarsen. "What do you mean by breaking up a game in the middle and vamoosing with the ball? Do you think we're going to win this game on mileage? Turn around, you chump, and climb into this car."

Ole looked around at him sadly. He kept on running as he did. "Aye ent care to stop," he said. "Aye kent suit you, Master Bost. You tal me aye skoll du a teng, den you cuss me for duing et. You tal me not to du a teng and you cuss me some more den. Aye tenk I yust keep on a-running, lak yu tal me tu last night. Et ent so hard bein' cussed ven yu ban running."

"I tell you to stop, you potato-top," gasped Bost. By this time he was fifteen yards behind and losing at every step. He had wasted too much breath on oratory. We picked him up in the car and set him alongside of Ole again.

"See here, Ole, I'm tired of this," he said, sprinting up by him again. "The game's waiting. Come on back. You're making a fool of yourself."

"Eny teng Aye du Aye ban beeg fule," said Ole gloomily. "Aye yust keep on runnin'. Fallers ent got breath to call me fule ven Aye run. Aye tenk das best vay."

We picked Bost up again thirty yards behind. Maybe he would have run better if he hadn't choked so in his conversation. In another minute we landed him abreast of Ole again. He got out and sprinted for the third time. He wabbled as he did it.

"Ole," he panted, "I've been mistaken in you. You are all right, Ole. I never saw a more intelligent fellow. I won't cuss you any more, Ole. If you'll stop now we'll take you back in an automobile — hold on there a minute; can't you see I'm all out of breath?"

"Aye ban gude faller, den?" asked Ole, letting out another link of speed.

"You are a" — puff-puff — "peach, Ole," gasped Bost. "I'll" — puff-puff — "never cuss you again. Please" —

puff-puff — "stop! Oh, hang it, I'm all in." And Bost sat down in the road.

A hundred yards on we noticed Ole slacken speed. "It's sinking through his skull," said Harris eagerly. In another minute he had stopped. We picked up Bost again and ran up to him. He surveyed us long and critically.

"Das ban qveer masheen," he said finally. "Aye tenk Aye lak Aye skoll be riding back in it. Aye ent care for das fullback game, Aye gass. It ban tu much running in it."

We took Ole back to town in twenty-two minutes, three chickens, a dog and a back spring. It was close to five o'clock when he ran out on the field again. The Muggle-dorfer team was still waiting. Time was no object to them. They would only play ten minutes, but in that ten minutes Ole made three scores. Five substitutes stood back of either goal and asked him with great politeness to stop as he tore over the line. And he did it. If any one else had run nine miles between halves he would have stopped a good deal short of the line. But as far as we could see, it hadn't winded Ole.

Bost went home by himself that night after the game, not stopping even to assure us that as a team we were beneath his contempt. The next afternoon he was, if anything, a little more vitriolic than ever — but not with Ole. Toward the middle of the signal practice he pulled himself together and touched Ole gently.

"My dear Mr. Skjarsen," he said apologetically, "if it will not annoy you too much, would you mind running the same way the rest of the team does? I don't insist on it, mind you, but it looks so much better to the audience, you know."

"Jas," said Ole; "Aye ban fule, Aye gass, but yu ban tu polite to say it."

STEPHEN LEACOCK

Stephen Leacock has so identified himself with American humorous literature that it is difficult to conceive that he is not a native American — indeed, most people believe that he is. Certainly his chief audience is American, but he is loved and honored and widely read in his own Canada, and is very popular in England. In fact, Stephen Leacock has more claims than most American humorists to being considered an international figure. He was born in England, December 30, 1869, but he was brought out to Canada as a child and has grown up a thorough Canadian — perhaps the most popular writer in the Dominion to-day. He is Professor of Political Economy in McGill University, Montreal, and people have often wondered where he finds time to write his amazing books. But here they are, a dozen titles and a new one every year or so, and this great nation the chief consumer; all of which is greatly to our credit (though "he *is* an Englishman") and constitutes him an inevitable factor in our literary tradition.

SPOOF. A THOUSAND–GUINEA NOVEL. NEW! FASCINATING! PERPLEXING![1]

CHAPTER I

R EADERS are requested to note that this novel has taken our special prize of a cheque for a thousand guineas. This alone guarantees for all intelligent readers a palpitating interest in every line of it. Among the thousands of MSS. which reached us — many of them coming in carts early in the morning, and moving in a dense phalanx, indistinguishable from the Covent Garden Market waggons; others pouring down our coal-chute during the working hours of the day; and others again being slipped

[1] From "Moonbeams from the Larger Lunacy." Copyright, 1915, by Dodd, Mead and Company. Reprinted by permission of author and publisher.

surreptitiously into our letter-box by pale, timid girls, scarcely more than children, after nightfall (in fact many of them came in their nightgowns), — this manuscript alone was the sole one — in fact the only one — to receive the prize of a cheque of a thousand guineas. To other competitors we may have given, inadvertently perhaps, a bag of sovereigns or a string of pearls, but to this story alone is awarded the first prize by the unanimous decision of our judges.

When we say that the latter body included two members of the Cabinet, two Lords of the Admiralty, and two bishops, with power in case of dispute to send all the MSS. to the Czar of Russia, our readers will breathe a sigh of relief to learn that the decision was instant and unanimous. Each one of them, in reply to our telegram, answered immediately SPOOF.

This novel represents the last word in up-to-date fiction. It is well known that the modern novel has got far beyond the point of mere story-telling. The childish attempt to *interest* the reader has long since been abandoned by all the best writers. They refuse to do it. The modern novel must convey a message, or else it must paint a picture, or remove a veil, or open a new chapter in human psychology. Otherwise it is no good. SPOOF does all of these things. The reader rises from its perusal perplexed, troubled, and yet so filled with information that rising itself is a difficulty.

We cannot, for obvious reasons, insert the whole of the first chapter. But the portion here presented was praised by *The Saturday Afternoon Review* as giving one of the most graphic and at the same time realistic pictures of America ever written in fiction.

Of the characters whom our readers are to imagine seated on the deck — on one of the many decks (all connected by elevators) — of the *Gloritania,* one word may be said. Vere de Lancy is (as the reviewers have under oath declared) a typical young Englishman of the upper class.

He is nephew to the Duke of —— , but of this fact no one on the ship, except the captain, the purser, the steward, and the passengers are, or is, aware.

In order entirely to conceal his identity, Vere de Lancy is travelling under the assumed name of Lancy de Vere. In order the better to hide the object of his journey, Lancy de Vere (as we shall now call him, though our readers will be able at any moment to turn his name backwards) has given it to be understood that he is travelling merely as a gentleman anxious to see America. This naturally baffles all those in contact with him.

The girl at his side — but perhaps we may best let her speak for herself.

.   .   .   .

Somehow as they sat together on the deck of the great steamer in the afterglow of the sunken sun, listening to the throbbing of the propeller (a rare sound which neither of them of course had ever heard before), de Vere felt that he must speak to her. Something of the mystery of the girl fascinated him. What was she doing here alone with no one but her mother and her maid, on the bosom of the Atlantic? Why was she here? Why was she not somewhere else? The thing puzzled, perplexed him. It would not let him alone. It fastened upon his brain. Somehow he felt that if he tried to drive it away, it might nip him in the ankle.

In the end he spoke.

'And you, too," he said, leaning over her deck-chair, "are going to America?"

He had suspected this ever since the boat left Liverpool. Now at length he framed his growing conviction into words.

"Yes," she assented, and then timidly, "it is 3,213 miles wide, is it not?"

"Yes," he said, "and 1,781 miles deep! It reaches from the forty-ninth parallel to the Gulf of Mexico."

"Oh," cried the girl, "what a vivid picture! I seem to see it."

"Its major axis," he went on, his voice sinking almost to a caress, "is formed by the Rocky Mountains, which are practically a prolongation of the Cordilleran Range. It is drained," he continued——

"How splendid!" said the girl.

"Yes, is it not? It is drained by the Mississippi, by the St. Lawrence, and — dare I say it? — by the Upper Colorado."

Somehow his hand had found hers in the half gloaming, but she did not check him.

"Go on," she said very simply; "I think I ought to hear it."

"The great central plain of the interior," he continued, "is formed by a vast alluvial deposit carried down as silt by the Mississippi. East of this the range of the Alleghanies, nowhere more than eight thousand feet in height, forms a secondary or subordinate axis from which the watershed falls to the Atlantic."

He was speaking very quietly but earnestly. No man had ever spoken to her like this before.

"What a wonderful picture!" she murmured half to herself, half aloud, and half not aloud and half not to herself.

"Through the whole of it," de Vere went on, "there run railways, most of them from east to west, though a few run from west to east. The Pennsylvania system alone has twenty-one thousand miles of track."

"Twenty-one thousand miles," she repeated; already she felt her will strangely subordinate to his.

He was holding her hand firmly clasped in his and looking into her face.

"Dare I tell you," he whispered, "how many employees it has?"

"Yes," she gasped, unable to resist.

"A hundred and fourteen thousand," he said.

There was silence. They were both thinking. Presently she spoke, timidly.

"Are there any cities there?"

"Cities!" he said enthusiastically, "ah, yes! let me try to give you a word-picture of them. Vast cities — with tall buildings, reaching to the very sky. Why, for instance, the new Woolworth Building in New York ——"

"Yes, yes," she broke in quickly, "how high is it?"

"Seven hundred and fifty feet."

The girl turned and faced him.

"Don't," she said. "I can't bear it. Some other time, perhaps, but not now."

She had risen and was gathering up her wraps. "And you," she said, "why are you going to America?"

"Why?" he answered. "Because I want to see, to know, to learn. And when I have learned and seen and known, I want other people to see and to learn and to know. I want to write it all down, all the vast palpitating picture of it. Ah! if I only could — I want to see" (and here he passed his hand through his hair as if trying to remember) "something of the relations of labour and capital, of the extraordinary development of industrial machinery, of the new and intricate organization of corporation finance, and in particular I want to try to analyse — no one has ever done it yet — the men who guide and drive it all. I want to set down the psychology of the multimillionaire!"

He paused. The girl stood irresolute. She was thinking (apparently, for if not, why stand there?).

"Perhaps," she faltered, "I could help you."

"You!"

"Yes, I might." She hesitated. "I — I — come from America."

"You!" said de Vere in astonishment. "With a face and voice like yours! It is impossible!"

The boldness of the compliment held her speechless for a moment.

"I do," she said; "my people lived just outside of Cohoes."

"They couldn't have," he said passionately.

"I shouldn't speak to you like this," the girl went on, "but it's because I feel from what you have said that you know and love America. And I think I can help you."

"You mean," he said, divining her idea, "that you can help me to meet a multimillionaire?"

"Yes," she answered, still hesitating.

"You know one?"

"Yes," still hesitating, "I know one."

She seemed about to say more, her lips had already opened, when suddenly the dull raucous blast of the fog-horn (they used a raucous one on this ship on purpose) cut the night air. Wet fog rolled in about them, wetting everything.

The girl shivered.

"I must go," she said; "good night."

For a moment de Vere was about to detain her. The wild thought leaped to his mind to ask her her name or at least her mother's. With a powerful effort he checked himself.

"Good night," he said.

She was gone.

CHAPTER II

Limits of space forbid the insertion of the whole of this chapter. Its opening contains one of the most vivid word-pictures of the inside of an American customs house ever pictured in words. From the customs wharf de Vere is driven in a taxi to the Belmont. Here he engages a room; here, too, he sleeps; here also, though cautiously at first, he eats. All this is so admirably described that only those who have driven in a taxi to an hotel and slept there can hope to appreciate it.

Limits of space also forbid our describing in full de Vere's vain quest in New York of the beautiful creature whom he had met on the steamer and whom he had lost from sight in the aigrette department of the customs house. A thousand times he cursed his folly in not having asked her name.

Meanwhile no word comes from her, till suddenly, mysteriously, unexpectedly, on the fourth day a note is handed to de Vere by the Third Assistant Head Waiter of the Belmont. It is addressed in a lady's hand. He tears it open. It contains only the written words, "*Call on Mr. J. Superman Overgold. He is a multimillionaire. He expects you.*"

To leap into a taxi (from the third story of the Belmont) was the work of a moment. To drive to the office of Mr. Overgold was less. The portion of the novel which follows is perhaps the most notable part of it. It is this part of the chapter which the *Hibbert Journal* declares to be the best piece of psychological analysis that appears in any novel of the season. We reproduce it here.

. . . .

"Exactly, exactly," said de Vere, writing rapidly in his note-book as he sat in one of the deep leather armchairs of the luxurious office of Mr. Overgold. "So you sometimes feel as if the whole thing were not worth while."

"I do," said Mr. Overgold. "I can't help asking myself what it all means. Is life, after all, merely a series of immaterial phenomena, self-developing and based solely on sensation and reaction, or is it something else?"

He paused for a moment to sign a cheque for $10,000 and throw it out of the window, and then went on, speaking still with the terse brevity of a man of business.

"Is sensation everywhere or is there perception too? On what grounds, if any, may the hypothesis of a self-explanatory consciousness be rejected? In how far are we warranted in supposing that innate ideas are inconsistent with pure materialism?"

De Vere listened, fascinated. Fortunately for himself,

he was a University man, fresh from the examination halls of his Alma Mater. He was able to respond at once.

"I think," he said modestly, "I grasp your thought. You mean — to what extent are we prepared to endorse Hegel's dictum of immaterial evolution?"

"Exactly," said Mr. Overgold. "How far, if at all, do we substantiate the Kantian hypothesis of the transcendental?"

"Precisely," said de Vere eagerly. "And for what reasons [naming them] must we reject Spencer's theory of the unknowable?"

"Entirely so," continued Mr. Overgold. "And why, if at all, does Bergsonian illusionism differ from pure nothingness?"

They both paused.

Mr. Overgold had risen. There was great weariness in his manner.

"It saddens one, does it not?" he said.

He had picked up a bundle of Panama two per cent. gold bonds and was looking at them in contempt.

"The emptiness of it all!" he muttered. He extended the bonds to de Vere.

"Do you want them," he said, "or shall I throw them away?"

"Give them to me," said de Vere quietly; "they are not worth the throwing."

"No, no," said Mr. Overgold, speaking half to himself, as he replaced the bonds in his desk. "It is a burden that I must carry alone. I have no right to ask any one to share it. But come," he continued, "I fear I am sadly lacking in the duties of international hospitality. I am forgetting what I owe to Anglo-American courtesy. I am neglecting the new obligations of our common Indo-Chinese policy. My motor is at the door. Pray let me take you to my house to lunch."

De Vere assented readily, telephoned to the Belmont not to keep lunch waiting for him, and in a moment was speeding up the magnificent Riverside Drive towards Mr. Overgold's home. On the way Mr. Overgold pointed out various objects of interest, — Grant's tomb, Lincoln's tomb, Edgar Allan Poe's grave, the ticket office of the New York Subway, and various other points of historic importance.

On arriving at the house, de Vere was ushered up a flight of broad marble steps to a hall fitted on every side with almost priceless *objets d'art* and others, ushered to the cloak-room and out of it, butlered into the lunch-room and foot-manned to a chair.

As they entered, a lady already seated at the table turned to meet them.

One glance was enough — plenty.

It was she — the object of de Vere's impassioned quest. A rich lunch-gown was girdled about her with a twelve-o'clock band of pearls.

She reached out her hand, smiling.

"Dorothea," said the multimillionaire, "this is Mr. de Vere. Mr. de Vere — my wife."

CHAPTER III

Of this next chapter we need only say that the *Blue Review* (Adults Only) declares it to be the most daring and yet conscientious handling of the sex-problem ever attempted and done. The fact that the *Congregational Times* declares that this chapter will undermine the whole foundations of English Society and let it fall, we pass over: we hold certificates in writing from a great number of the Anglican clergy, to the effect that they have carefully read the entire novel and see nothing in it.

. . . .

They stood looking at one another.

"So you did n't know," she murmured.

In a flash de Vere realised that she had n't known that he did n't know, and knew now that he knew.

He found no words.

The situation was a tense one. Nothing but the woman's innate tact could save it.

Dorothea Overgold rose to it with the dignity of a queen. She turned to her husband.

"Take your soup over to the window," she said, "and eat it there."

The millionaire took his soup to the window and sat beneath a little palm tree, eating it.

"You didn't know," she repeated.

"No," said de Vere; "how could I?"

"And yet," she went on, "you loved me, although you didn't know that I was married?"

"Yes," answered de Vere simply. "I loved you, in spite of it."

"How splendid!" she said.

There was a moment's silence. Mr. Overgold had returned to the table, the empty plate in his hand. His wife turned to him again with the same unfailing tact.

"Take your asparagus to the billiard-room," she said, "and eat it there."

"Does he know too?" asked de Vere.

"Mr. Overgold?" she said carelessly. "I suppose he does. *Eh après, mon ami?*"

French? Another mystery! Where and how had she learned it? de Vere asked himself. Not in France, certainly.

"I fear that you are very young, *amico mio*," Dorothea went on carelessly. "After all, what is there wrong in it *piccolo pochito?* To a man's mind perhaps — but to a woman, love is love."

She beckoned to the butler.

"Take Mr. Overgold a cutlet to the music-room," she said, "and give him his gorgonzola on the inkstand in the library."

"And now," she went on in that caressing way which seemed so natural to her, "don't let us think about it any more! After all, what is is, isn't it?"

"I suppose it is," said de Vere, half convinced in spite of himself.

"Or, at any rate," said Dorothea, "nothing can at the same time both be and not be. But come," she broke off, gaily dipping a macaroon in a glass of *crème de menthe* and offering it to him with a pretty gesture of camaraderie, "don't let's be gloomy any more. I want to take you with me to the matinée."

"Is he coming?" asked de Vere, pointing at Mr. Overgold's empty chair.

"Silly boy," laughed Dorothea. "Of course John is coming. You surely don't want to buy the tickets yourself."

.   .   .   .

The days that followed brought a strange new life to de Vere.

Dorothea was ever at his side. At the theatre, at the polo ground, in the park, everywhere they were together. And with them was Mr. Overgold.

The three were always together. At times at the theatre Dorothea and de Vere would sit downstairs and Mr. Overgold in the gallery; at other times, de Vere and Mr. Overgold would sit in the gallery and Dorothea downstairs; at times one of them would sit in Row A, another in Row B and a third in Row C; at other times two would sit in Row B and one in Row C; at the opera, at times, one of the three would sit listening, the others talking, at others two listening and one talking, and at other times three talking, and none listening.

Thus the three formed together one of the most perplexing, maddening triangles that ever disturbed the society of the metropolis.

.   .   .   .

The *dénouement* was bound to come.
It came.
It was late at night.

De Vere was standing beside Dorothea in the brilliantly lighted hall of the Grand Palaver Hotel, where they had had supper. Mr. Overgold was busy for a moment at the cashiers desk.

"Dorothea," de Vere whispered passionately, "I want to take you away, away from all this. I want you."

She turned and looked him full in the face. Then she put her hand in his, smiling bravely.

"I will come," she said.

"Listen," he went on, "the *Gloritania* sails for England to-morrow at midnight. I have everything ready. Will you come?"

"Yes," she answered, "I will"; and then passionately, "Dearest, I will follow you to England, to Liverpool, to the end of the earth."

She paused in thought a moment and then added.

"Come to the house just before midnight. William, the second chauffeur (he is devoted to me), shall be at the door with the third car. The fourth footman will bring my things—I can rely on him; the fifth housemaid can have them all ready—she would never betray me. I will have the under-gardner—the sixth—waiting at the iron gate to let you in; he would die rather than fail me."

She paused again—then she went on.

"There is only one thing, dearest, that I want to ask. It is not much. I hardly think you would refuse it at such an hour. May I bring my husband with me?"

De Vere's face blanched.

"Must you?" he said.

"I think I must," said Dorothea. "You don't know how I've grown to value, to lean upon, him. At times I have felt as if I always wanted him to be near me; I like to feel wherever I am—at the play, at a restaurant, anywhere—that I can reach out and touch him. I know," she continued, "that it's only a wild fancy and that others would laugh at it, but you can understand, can you not—*carino caruso mio?* And think, darling, in our new life, how busy he, too, will be — making money for all of us — in a new money market. It's just wonderful how he does it."

A great light of renunciation lit up de Vere's face.

"Bring him," he said.

"I knew that you would say that," she murmured, "and listen, *pochito* pocket-edition, may I ask one thing more, one weeny thing? William, the second chauffeur — I think he would fade away if I were gone — may I bring him, too? Yes! O my darling, how can I repay you? And the second footman, and the third housemaid — if I were gone I fear that none of — "

"Bring them all," said de Vere half bitterly; "we will all elope together."

As he spoke Mr. Overgold sauntered over from the cashier's desk, his open purse still in his hand, and joined them. There was a dreamy look upon his face.

"I wonder," he murmured, "whether personality survives or whether it, too, when up against the irresistible, dissolves and resolves itself into a series of negative reactions?"

De Vere's empty heart echoed the words.

Then they passed out and the night swallowed them up.

CHAPTER IV

At a little before midnight on the next night, two motors filled with muffled human beings might have been perceived, or seen, moving noiselessly from Riverside Drive to the steamer wharf where lay the *Gloritania.*

A night of intense darkness enveloped the Hudson. Outside the inside of the dockside a dense fog wrapped the Statue of Liberty. Beside the steamer customs officers and deportation officials moved silently to and fro in long black cloaks, carrying little deportation lanterns in their hands.

To these Mr. Overgold presented in silence his deportation certificates, granting his party permission to leave the

United States under the imbecility clause of the Interstate Commerce Act.

No objection was raised.

A few moments later the huge steamer was slipping away in the darkness.

On its deck a little group of people, standing beside a pile of first-class cabin luggage, directed a last sad look through their heavy black disguise at the rapidly vanishing shore which they could not see.

De Vere, who stood in the midst of them, clasping their hands, thus stood and gazed his last at America.

"Spoof!" he said.

IRVIN S. COBB

It was "Speaking of Operations" that stamped Cobb as a humorist. Originally published in the *Saturday Evening Post*, it was afterwards brought out in book form and sold upwards of 300,000 copies in five years. Born in Paducah, Kentucky, in 1876, Cobb commenced local newspaper work at sixteen and from the ranks of cub reporter he rose to the position of managing editor, until he made the inevitable jump to New York. Once he found a job there he made good as a star reporter and eventually wrote humorous stuff as a side-line. Now a plutocratic writer of fiction for the magazines, Cobb claims that his humor still represents only a third of his output, but the proportion is so conspicuously amusing that Cobb can't escape his classification. Besides you have only to meet Cobb and listen to his stories to classify him as a "natural born" humorist.

"SPEAKING OF OPERATIONS—"[1]

FOR years I have noticed that persons who underwent pruning or remodeling at the hands of a duly qualified surgeon, and survived, like to talk about it afterward. In the event of their not surviving I have no doubt they still liked to talk about it, but in a different locality. Of all the readily available topics for use, whether among friends or among strangers, an operation seems to be the handiest and most dependable. It beats the Tariff, or Roosevelt, or Bryan, or when this war is going to end, if ever, if you are a man talking to other men; and it is more exciting even than the question of how Mrs. Vernon Castle will wear her hair this season, if you are a woman talking to other women.

For mixed companies a whale is one of the best and the easiest things to talk about that I know of. In regard to whales and their peculiarities you can make almost any assertion without fear of successful contradiction. Nobody ever knows any more about them than you do. You are not hampered by facts. If some one mentions the blubber of the whale and you chime in and say it may be noticed for miles on a still day when the large but emotional creature has been moved to tears by some great sorrow coming into its life, everybody is bound to accept the statement. For after all how few among us really know whether a distressed whale sobs aloud or does so under its breath? Who, with any certainty, can tell whether a mother whale hatches her own egg her own self or leaves it on the sheltered bosom of a fjord to be incubated by the gentle warmth of the midnight sun? The possibilities of the proposition for purposes of informal debate, pro and con, are apparent at a glance.

The weather, of course, helps out amazingly when you are meeting people for the first time, because there is nearly always more or less weather going on somewhere and practically everybody has ideas about it. The human breakfast is also a wonderfully good topic to start up during one of those lulls. Try it yourself the next time the conversation seems to drag. Just speak up in an offhand kind of way and say that you never care much about breakfast — a slice of toast and a cup of weak tea start you off properly for doing a hard day's work. You will be surprised to note how things liven up and how eagerly all present join in. The lady on your left feels that you should know she always takes two lumps of sugar and nearly half cream, because she simply cannot abide hot milk, no matter what the doctors say. The gentleman on your right will be moved to confess he likes his eggs boiled for exactly three minutes, no more and no less. Buckwheat cakes and sausage find a champion and oatmeal rarely lacks a warm defender.

But after all, when all is said and done, the king of all topics is operations. Sooner or later, wherever two or more are gathered together it is reasonably certain that somebody will bring up an operation.

Until I passed through the experience of being operated

on myself, I never really realized what a precious conversational boon the subject is, and how great a part it plays in our intercourse with our fellow beings on this planet. To the teller it is enormously interesting, for he is not only the hero of the tale but the rest of the cast and the stage setting as well — the whole show, as they say; and if the listener has had a similar experience — and who is there among us in these days that has not taken a nap 'neath the shade of the old ether cone?— it acquires a doubled value.

"Speaking of operations —" you say, just like that, even though nobody present has spoken of them; and then you are off, with your new acquaintance sitting on the edge of his chair, or hers as the case may be and so frequently is, with hands clutched in polite but painful restraint, gills working up and down with impatience, eyes brightened with desire, tongue hung in the middle, waiting for you to pause to catch your breath, so that he or she may break in with a few personal recollections along the same line. From a mere conversation it resolves itself into a symptom symposium, and a perfectly splendid time is had by all.

EATING IN TWO OR THREE LANGUAGES [1]

Dickens, as will be recalled, specialized in mouth-watering descriptions of good things and typically British things to eat — roast sucking pigs, with apples in their snouts; and baked goose; and suety plum puddings like speckled cannon balls; and cold game pies as big round as barrel tops — and all such. He would n't find these things prevailing to any noticeable extent in his native island now.[2] Even the kidney, the same being the thing for which an Englishman mainly raises a sheep and which he always did know how to serve up better than any one else on earth, somehow does n't seem to be the kidney it once

[1] From "Eating in Two or Three Languages." Copyright, 1919, by George H. Doran Company.
[2] This was written in war-time.

upon a time was when it had the proper sorts of trimmings and sauces to go with it.

At this time England is no place for the epicure. In peacetime English cooks, as a rule, were not what you would call versatile; their range, as it were, was limited. Once, seeking to be blithesome and light of heart, I wrote an article in which I said there were only three dependable vegetables on the average Englishman's everyday menu — boiled potatoes, boiled cabbage, and a second helping of the boiled potatoes.

That was an error on my part; I was unintentionally guilty of the crime of underestimation. I should have added a fourth to the list of stand-bys — to wit: the vegetable marrow. For some reason, possibly because they are a stubborn and tenacious race, the English persist in looking upon the vegetable marrow as an object designed for human consumption, which is altogether the wrong view to take of it. As a foodstuff this article hasn't even the merit that attaches to stringy celery. You do not derive much nourishment from stale celery, but eating at it polishes the teeth and provides a healthful form of exercise that gives you an appetite for the rest of the meal.

From the vegetable marrow you derive no nourishment and certainly you derive no exercise; for, being a soft, weak, spiritless thing, it offers no resistance whatever, and it looks a good deal like a streak of solidified fog and tastes like the place where an indisposed carrot spent the night. Next to our summer squash it is the feeblest imitation that ever masqueraded in a skin and called itself a vegetable. Yet its friends over there seem to set much store by it.

Likewise the English cook has always gone in rather extensively for boiling things. When in doubt she boiled. But it takes a lot of retouching to restore to a piece of boiled meat the juicy essences that have been simmered and drenched out of it. Since the English people, with such admirable English thoroughness, cut down on fats and oils and bacon garnishments, so that the greases might be conserved for the fighting forces; and since they have so largely had to do without imported spices and condiments, because the cargo spaces in the ships coming in were needed for military essentials, the boiled dishes of England appear to have lost most of their taste.

You can do a lot of browsing about at an English table these days and come away ostensibly filled; but inside you there will be a persistent unsatisfied feeling, all the same, which is partly due, no doubt, to the lack of sweetening and partly due to the lack of fats, but due most of all, I think, to a natural disappointment in the results. In the old times a man didn't feel that he had dined well in England unless for an hour or two afterward he had the comfortable gorged sensation of a python full of pigeons.

A PLEA FOR OLD CAP COLLIER [1]

In my youth I was spanked freely and frequently for doing many different things that were forbidden, and also for doing the same thing many different times and getting caught doing it. That, of course, was before the Boy Scout movement had come along to show how easily and how sanely a boy's natural restlessness and a boy's natural love for adventure may be directed into helpful channels; that was when nearly everything a normal, active boy craved to do was wrong and, therefore, held to be a spankable offense.

This was a general rule in our town. It did not especially apply to any particular household, but it applied practically to all the households with which I was in any way familiar. It was a community where an old-fashioned brand of applied theology was most strictly applied. Heaven was a place which went unanimously Democratic every fall, because all the Republicans had gone elsewhere. Hell was a place full

of red-hot coals and clinkered sinners and unbaptized babies
and a smell like somebody cooking ham, with a deputy devil
coming in of a morning with an asbestos napkin draped
over his arm and flicking a fireproof cockroach off the table
cloth and leaning across the back of Satan's chair and saying: "Good mornin', boss.   How're you goin' to have your
lost souls this mornin' — fried on one side or turned over?"

Sunday was three weeks long, and longer than that if it
rained.   About all a fellow could do after he'd come back
from Sunday school was to sit round with his feet cramped
into the shoes and stockings which he never wore on week
days and with the rest of him incased in starchy, uncom-
fortable dress-up clothes — just sit round and sit round and
itch.   You couldn't scratch hard either.   It was sinful to
scratch audibly and with good, broad, free strokes, which
is the only satisfactory way to scratch.   In our town they
didn't spend Sunday; they kept the Sabbath, which is a very
different thing.

Looking back on my juvenile years it seems to me that,
generally speaking, when spanked I deserved it.   But always there were two punishable things against which —
being disciplined — my youthful spirit revolted with a sort
of inarticulate sense of injustice.   One was for violation of
the Sunday code, which struck me as wrong — the code, I
mean, not the violation — without knowing exactly why it
was wrong; and the other, repeated times without number,
was when I had been caught reading *nickul libruries*, er-
roneously referred to by our elders as dime novels.

I read them at every chance; so did every normal boy of
my acquaintance.   We traded lesser treasures for them; we
swapped them on the basis of two old volumes for one new
one; we maintained a clandestine circulating-library system
which had its branch offices in every stable loft in our part
of town.   The more daring among us read them in school
behind the shelter of an open geography propped up on the
desk.

Shall you ever forget the horror of the moment when,

HARRY LEON WILSON

Harry Leon Wilson, born in Oregon, May 1, 1867, has given us already several strong, sharply defined and fully developed types — "Ma Pettengill", "Ruggles" and "Bunker Bean." He has set them in an environment so fully bodied that he has practically created a new type of western humor. For the great god of humor presides ever and always over every scene and pours largess over every page. Is the accompanying story impossible? That is the query that will occur to many readers, but knowing the West as we do, we have decided that it really does not matter so long as one cannot imagine a more highly humorous situation for a setting in the West of to-day.

THE RED SPLASH OF ROMANCE [1]

THE walls of the big living room in the Arrowhead ranch house are tastefully enlivened here and there with artistic spoils of the owner, Mrs. Lysander John Pettengill. There are family portraits in crayon, photo-engravings of noble beasts clipped from the Breeder's Gazette, an etched cathedral or two, a stuffed and varnished trout of such size that no one would otherwise have believed in it, a print in three colors of a St. Bernard dog with a marked facial resemblance to the late William E. Gladstone, and a triumph of architectural perspective revealing two sides of the Pettengill block, corner of Fourth and Main Streets, Red Gap, made vivacious by a bearded fop on horseback who doffs his silk hat to a couple of overdressed ladies with parasols in a passing victoria.

And there is the photograph of the fat man. He is very large — both high and wide. He has filled the lens and now compels the eye. His broad face beams a friendly interest. His mustache is a flourishing, uncurbed, riotous growth above his billowy chin.

The checked coat, held recklessly aside by a hand on each hip, reveals an incredible expanse of waistcoat the pattern of which raves horribly. From pocket to pocket of this gaudy shield curves a watch chain of massive links — nearly a yard of it, one guesses.

Often I had glanced at this noisy thing tacked to the wall, entranced by the simple width of the man. Now on a late afternoon I loitered before it while my hostess changed from riding breeches to the gown of lavender and lace in which she elects to drink tea after a day's hard work along the valleys of the Arrowhead. And for the first time I observed a line of writing beneath the portrait, the writing of my hostess, a rough, downright, plain fashion of script: "Reading from left to right — Mr. Ben Sutton, Popular Society Favorite of Nome, Alaska."

"Reading from left to right!" Here was the intent facetious. And Ma Pettengill is never idly facetious. Always, as the advertisements say, "There's a reason!" And now, also for the first time, I noticed some printed verses on a sheet of thickish yellow paper tacked to the wall close beside the photograph — so close that I somehow divined an intimate relationship between the two. With difficulty removing my gaze from the gentleman who should be read from left to right, I scanned these verses:

Song of the Open Road

A child of the road — a gypsy I —
  My path o'er the land and sea;
With the fire of youth I warm my nights
  And my days are wild and free.

Then ho! for the wild, the open road!
  Afar from the haunts of men.
The woods and the hills for my spirit untamed —
  I'm away to mountain and glen.

If ever I tried to leave my hills
  To abide in the cramped haunts of men,
The urge of the wild to her wayward child
  Would drag me to freedom again.

I'm slave to the call of the open road;
  In your cities I'd stifle and die.
I'm off to the hills in fancy I see—
  On the breast of old earth I'll lie.

Wilfred Lennox, the Hobo Poet.
On a Coast-to-Coast Walking Tour.
These cards for sale.

I briefly pondered the lyric. It told its own simple story and could at once have been dismissed but for its divined and puzzling relationship to the popular society favorite of Nome, Alaska. What could there be in this?

Mrs. Lysander John Pettengill bustled in upon my speculation, but as usual I was compelled to wait for the talk I wanted. For some moments she would be only the tired owner of the Arrowhead ranch — in the tea gown of a débutante and with too much powder on one side of her nose — and she must have at least one cup of tea so corrosive that the Scotch whisky she adds to it is but a merciful dilution. She now drank eagerly of the fearful brew, dulled the bite of it with smoke from a hurriedly built cigarette, and relaxed gratefully into one of those chairs which are all that most of us remember William Morris for. Even then she must first murmur of the day's annoyances, provided this time by officials of the United States Forest Reserve. In the beginning I must always allow her a little to have her own way.

"The annual spring rumpus with them rangers," she wearily boomed. "Every year they tell me just where to turn my cattle out on the Reserve, and every year I go ahead and turn 'em out where I want 'em turned out, which ain't the same place at all, and then I have to listen patiently to their kicks and politely answer all letters from the higher-ups and wait for the official permit, which always

comes — and it's wearing on a body. Darn it! They'd
ought to know by this time I always get my own way. If
they was n't such a decent bunch I'd have words with 'em
giving me the same trouble year after year, probably because I'm a weak, defenseless woman. However!"

The lady rested largely, inert save for the hand that
raised the cigarette automatically to her lips. My moment
had come.

"What did Wilfred Lennox, the hobo poet, have to do
with Mr. Ben Sutton, of Nome, Alaska?" I gently inquired.

"More than he wanted," replied the lady. Her glance
warmed with memories; she hovered musingly on the verge
of recital. But the cigarette was half done and at its best.
I allowed her another moment, a moment in which she
laughed confidentially to herself, a little dry, throaty laugh.
I knew that laugh. She would be marshaling certain events
in their just and diverting order. But they seemed to be
many and of confusing values.

"Some said he not only was n't a hobo but was n't even
a poet," she presently murmured, and smoked again. Then:
"That Ben Sutton, now, he's a case. Comes from Alaska
and don't like fresh eggs for breakfast because he says they
ain't got any kick to 'em like Alaska eggs have along in
March, and he's got to have canned milk for his coffee.
Say, I got a three-quarters Jersey down in Red Gap gives
milk so rich that the cream just naturally trembles into
butter if you speak sharply to it or even give it a cross look;
not for Ben though. Had to send out for canned milk that
morning. I drew the line at hunting up case eggs for him
though. He had to put up with insipid fresh ones. And
fat, that man! My lands! He travels a lot in the West
when he does leave home, and he tells me it's the fear of his
life he'll get wedged into one of them narrow-gauge Pull-
mans some time and have to be chopped out. Well, as I
was saying —— " She paused.

"But you have n't begun," I protested. I sharply tapped
the printed verses and the photograph reading from left to

right. Now she became animated, speaking as she expertly rolled a fresh cigarette.

"Say, did you ever think what aggravating minxes women are after they been married a few years — after the wedding ring gets worn a little bit thin?"

This was not only brutal; it seemed irrelevant.

"Wilfred Lennox——" I tried to insist, but she commandingly raised the new cigarette at me.

"Yes, sir! Ever know one of 'em married for as long as ten years that didn't in her secret heart have a sort of contempt for her life partner as being a stuffy, plodding truck horse? Of course they keep a certain dull respect for him as a provider, but they can't see him as dashing and romantic any more; he ain't daring and adventurous. All he ever does is go down and open up the store or push back the rolltop, and keep from getting run over on the street. One day's like another with him, never having any wild, lawless instincts or reckless moods that make a man fascinating — about the nearest he ever comes to adventure is when he opens the bills the first of the month. And she often seeing him without any collar on, and needing a shave mebbe, and cherishing her own secret romantic dreams, while like as not he's prosily figuring out how he's going to make the next payment on the endowment policy.

"It's a hard, tiresome life women lead, chained to these here plodders. That's why rich widows generally pick out the dashing young devils they do for their second, having buried the man that made it for 'em. Oh, they like him well enough, call him 'Father' real tenderly and see that he changes to the heavy flannels on time, but he don't ever thrill them, and when they order three hundred and fifty dollars' worth of duds from the Boston Cash Emporium and dress up like a foreign countess, they don't do it for Father, they do it for the romantic guy in the magazine serial they're reading, the handsome, cynical adventurer that has such an awful power over women. They know darned well they won't ever meet him; still it's just as well to be ready in case he ever should make Red Gap — or wherever they live — and it's easy with the charge account there, and Father never fussing more than a little about the bills.

"Not that I blame 'em. We're all alike — innocent enough, with freaks here and there that ain't. Why, I remember about a thousand years ago I was reading a book called 'Lillian's Honor', in which the rightful earl didn't act like an earl had ought to, but went traveling off over the moors with a passel of gypsies, with all the she-gypsies falling in love with him, and no wonder — he was that dashing. Well, I used to think what might happen if he should come along while Lysander John was out with the beef round-up or something. I was well-meaning, understand, but at that I'd ought to have been laid out with a pick-handle. Oh, the nicest of us got specks inside us — if ever we did cut loose the best one of us would make the worst man of you look like nothing worse than a naughty little boy cutting up in Sunday school. What holds us, of course — we always dream of being took off our feet; of being carried off by main force against our wills while we snuggle up to the romantic brute and plead with him to spare us — and the most reckless of 'em don't often get their nerve up to that. Well, as I was saying —— "

But she was not saying. The thing moved too slowly. And still the woman paltered with her poisoned tea and made cigarettes and muttered inconsequently, as when she now broke out after a glance at the photograph:

"That Ben Sutton certainly runs amuck when he buys his vests. He must have about fifty, and the quietest one in the lot would make a leopard skin look like a piker." Again her glance dreamed off to visions.

I seated myself before her with some emphasis and said firmly: "Now then!" It worked.

"Wilfred Lennox," she began, "calling himself the hobo poet, gets into Red Gap one day and makes the rounds with that there piece of his poetry you see; pushes into stores and offices and hands the piece out, and like as not they crowd a dime or two bits onto him and send him along. That's what I done. I was waiting in Dr. Percy Hailey Martingale's office for a little painless dentistry, and I took Wilfred's poem and passed him a two-bit piece, and Doc Martingale does the same, and Wilfred blew on to the next office. A dashing and romantic figure he was, though kind of fat and pasty for a man that was walking from coast to coast, but a smooth talker with beautiful features and about nine hundred dollars' worth of hair and a soft hat and one of these flowing neckties. Red it was.

"So I looked over his piece of poetry — about the open road for his untamed spirit, and him being stifled in the cramped haunts of men — and of course I get his number. All right about the urge of the wild to her wayward child, but here he was spending a lot of time in the cramped haunts of men taking their small change away from 'em and not seeming to stifle one bit.

"Ain't this new style of tramp funny? Now instead of coming round to the back door and asking for a hand-out like any self-respecting tramp had ought to, they march up to the front door, and they're somebody with two or three names that's walking round the world on a wager they made with one of the Vanderbilt boys or John D. Rockefeller. They've walked thirty-eight hundred miles already and got the papers to prove it — a letter from the mayor of Scranton, Pennsylvania, and the mayor of Davenport, Iowa, and a picture post card of themselves on the courthouse steps at Denver, and they've bet forty thousand dollars they could start out without a cent and come back in twenty-two months with money in their pocket — and ain't it a good joke? — with everybody along the way entering into the spirit of it and passing them quarters and such, and thank you very much for your two bits for the picture post card — and they got another showing 'em in front of the Mormon Tabernacle at Salt Lake City, if you'd like that too — and thank you again — and now they'll be off once more to the open road and the wild free life. Not! Yes, two or three good firm Nots. Having milked the town they'll be right down to the dee-po with their silver changed to bills, waiting for No. 6 to come along, and ho! for the open railroad and another town that will skin pretty. I guess I've seen eight or ten of them boys in the last five years, with their letters from mayors.

"But this here Wilfred Lennox had a new graft. He was the first I'd give up to for mere poetry. He didn't have a single letter from a mayor, nor even a picture card of himself standing with his hat off in front of Pike's Peak — nothing but poetry. But, as I said, he was there with the talk about pining for the open road and despising the cramped haunts of men, and he had appealing eyes and all this flowing hair and necktie. So I says to myself: 'All right, Wilfred, you win!' and put my purse back in my bag and thought no more of it.

"Yet not so was it to be. Wilfred, working the best he could to make a living doing nothing, pretty soon got to the office of Alonzo Price, Choice Improved Real Estate and Price's Addition. Lon was out for the moment, but who should be there waiting for him but his wife, Mrs. Henrietta Templeton Price, recognized leader of our literary and artistic set. Or I think they call it a 'group' or a 'coterie' or something. Setting at Lon's desk she was, toying petulantly with horrid old pens and blotters, and probably bestowing glances of disrelish from time to time round the grimy office where her scrubby little husband toiled his days away in unromantic squalor.

"I got to tell you about Henrietta. She's one of them like I just said the harsh things about, with the secret cry in her heart for romance and adventure and other forbidden things, with a kindly contempt for peaceful Alonzo. She admits to being thirty-six, so you can figure it out for yourself. Of course she gets her husband wrong at that, as women so often do. Alonzo has probably the last pair of side whiskers outside of a steel engraving and stands five feet two, weighing a hundred and twenty-six pounds at the ring side, but he's game as a swordfish, and as for being romantic in the true sense of the word — well, no one that ever heard him sell a lot in Price's Addition — three miles and a half up on the mesa, with only the smoke of the canning factory to tell a body they was still near the busy haunts of men, that and a mile of concrete sidewalk leading a life of complete idleness — I say no one that ever listened to Lon sell a lot up there, pointing out on a blue print the proposed site of the Carnegie Library, would accuse him of not being romantic.

"But of course Henrietta never sees Lon's romance and he ain't always had the greatest patience with hers — like the time she got up the Art Loan Exhibit to get new books for the M. E. Sabbath-school library and got Spud Mulkins of the El Adobe to lend 'em the big gold-framed oil painting that hangs over his bar. Some of the other ladies objected to this — the picture was a big pink hussy lying down beside the ocean — but Henrietta says art for art's sake is pure to them that are pure, or something, and they're doing such things constantly in the East; and I'm darned if Spud didn't have his oil painting down and the mosquito netting ripped off it before Alonzo heard about it and put the Not-at-All on it. He wouldn't reason with Henrietta either. He just said his objection was that every man that saw it would put one foot up groping for the brass railing, which would be undignified for a Sabbath-school scheme, and that she'd better hunt out something with clothes on like Whistler's portrait of his mother, or, if she wanted the nude in art, to get the Horse Fair or something with animals.

"I tell you that to show you how they don't hit it off sometimes. Then Henrietta sulks. Kind of pinched and hungry looking she is, drapes her black hair down over one side of her high forehead, wears daring gowns — that's what she calls 'em anyway — and reads the most outrageous kinds of poetry out loud to them that will listen. Likes this Omar Something stuff about your path being beset with pitfalls and gin fizzes and getting soused out under a tree with your girl.

"I'm just telling you so you'll get Henrietta when Wilfred Lennox drips gracefully in with his piece of poetry in one hand. Of course she must have looked long and nervously at Wilfred, then read his poetry, then looked again. There before her was Romance against a background of Alonzo Price, who never had an adventurous or evil thought in his life, and wore rubbers! Oh, sure! He must have palsied her at once, this wild, free creature of the woods who couldn't stand the cramped haunts of men. And I have said that Wilfred was there with the wild, free words about himself, and the hat and tie and the waving brown hair that give him so much trouble. Shucks! I don't blame the woman. It's only a few years since we been let out from under lock and key. Give us a little time to get our bearings, say I. Wilfred was just one big red splash before her yearning eyes; he blinded her. And he stood there telling how this here life in the marts of trade would sure twist and blacken some of the very finest chords in his being. Something like that it must have been.

"Anyway about a quarter to six a procession went up Fourth Street, consisting of Wilfred Lennox, Henrietta and Alonzo. The latter was tripping along about three steps back of the other two and every once in a while he would stop for a minute and simply look puzzled. I saw him. It's really a great pity Lon insists on wearing a derby hat with his side whiskers. To my mind the two never seem meant for each other.

"The procession went to the Price mansion up on Ophir Avenue. And that evening Henrietta had in a few friends to listen to the poet recite his verses and tell anecdotes about himself. About five or six ladies in the parlor and their menfolks smoking out on the front porch. The men didn't seem to fall for Wilfred's open-road stuff the way the ladies did. Wilfred was a good reciter and held the ladies with his voice and his melting blue eyes with the long lashes, and Henrietta was envied for having nailed him. That is, the women envied her. The men sort of slouched off down to the front gate and then went down to the Temperance Billiard Parlor, where several of 'em got stewed. Most of 'em, like old Judge Ballard, who come to the country in '62, and Jeff Tuttle, who's always had more than he wanted of the open road, were very cold indeed to Wilfred's main proposition. It is probable that low mutterings might have been heard among 'em, especially after a traveling man that was playing pool said that the hobo poet had come in on the Pullman of No. 6.

"But I must say that Alonzo didn't seem to mutter any, from all I could hear. Pathetic, the way that little man will believe right up to the bitter end. He said that for a hobo Wilfred wrote very good poetry, better than most hobos could write, he thought, and that Henrietta always knew what she was doing. So the evening come to a peaceful end, most of the men getting back for their wives and Alonzo showing up in fair shape and plumb eager for the comfort of his guest. It was Alonzo's notion that the guest would of course want to sleep out in the front yard on the breast of old earth where he could look up at the pretty stars and feel at home, and he was getting out a roll of blankets when the guest said he didn't want to make the least bit of trouble and for one night he'd manage to sleep inside four stifling walls in a regular bed, like common people do. So Lon bedded him down in the guest chamber, but opened up the four windows in it and propped the door wide open so the poor fellow could have a breeze and not smother. He told this downtown the next morning, and he was beginning to look right puzzled indeed. He said the wayward child of Nature had got up after about half an hour and shut all the windows and the door. Lon thought first he was intending to commit suicide, but he didn't like to interfere. He was telling Jeff Tuttle and me about it when we happened to pass his office.

"'And there's another funny thing,' he says. 'This

chap was telling us all the way up home last night that he never ate meat — simply fruits and nuts with a mug of spring water. He said eating the carcasses of murdered beasts was abhorrent to him. But when we got down to the table he consented to partake of the roast beef and he did so repeatedly. We usually have cold meat for lunch the day after a rib roast, but there will be something else to-day; and along with the meat he drank two bottles of beer, though with mutterings of disgust. He said spring water in the hills was pure, but that water out of pipes was full of typhoid germs. He admitted that there were times when the grosser appetites assailed him. And they assailed him this morning too. He said he might bring himself to eat some chops, and he did it without scarcely a struggle. He ate six. He said living the nauseous artificial life even for one night brought back the hateful meat craving. I don't know. He is undeniably peculiar. And of course you've heard about Pettikin's affair for this evening?'

"We had. Just before leaving the house I had received Henrietta's card inviting me to the country club that evening 'to meet Mr. Wilfred Lennox, Poet and Nature Lover, who will recite his original verses and give a brief talk on The World's Debt to Poetry.' And there you have the whole trouble. Henrietta should have known better. But I've let out what women really are. I told Alonzo I would sure be among those present. I said it sounded good. And then Alonzo pipes up about Ben Sutton coming to town on the eleven forty-two from the West. Ben makes a trip out of Alaska every summer and never fails to stop off a day or two with Lon, they having been partners up North in '98.

"'Good old Ben will enjoy it too,' says Alonzo; 'and, furthermore, Ben will straighten out one or two little things that have puzzled me about this poet. He will understand his complex nature in a way that I confess I have been unequal to. What I mean is,' he says, 'there was talk when I left this morning of the poet consenting to take a class in poetry for several weeks in our thriving little city, and

Henrietta was urging him to make our house his home. I have a sort of feeling that Ben will be able to make several suggestions of prime value. I have never known him to fail at making suggestions.'

"Funny, the way the little man tried to put it over on us, letting on he was just puzzled — not really bothered, as he plainly was. You knew Henrietta was still seeing the big red splash of Romance, behind which the figure of her husband was totally obscured. Jeff Tuttle saw the facts, and he up and spoke in a very common way about what would quickly happen to any tramp that tried to camp in his house, poet or no poet, but that's neither here nor there. We left Alonzo looking cheerily forward to Ben Sutton on the eleven forty-two, and I went on to do some errands.

"In the course of these I discovered that others besides Henrietta had fell hard for the poet of Nature. I met Mrs. Dr. Percy Hailey Martingale and she just bubbles about him, she having been at the Prices' the night before.

"'Isn't he a glorious thing!' she says; 'and how grateful we should be for the dazzling bit of color he brings into our drab existence!' She is a good deal like that herself at times. And I met Beryl Mae Macomber, a well-known young society girl of seventeen, and Beryl Mae says: 'He's awfully good looking, but do you think he's sincere?' And even Mrs. Judge Ballard comes along and says: 'What a stimulus he should be to us in our dull lives! How he shows us the big, vital bits!' and her at that very minute going into Bullitt & Fleishacker's to buy shoes for her nine-year-old twin grandsons! And the Reverend Mrs. Wiley Knapp in at the Racquet Store wanting to know if the poet didn't make me think of some wild free creature of the woods — a deer or an antelope poised for instant flight while for one moment he timidly overlooked man in his hideous commercialism. But, of course, she was a minister's wife. I said he made me feel just like that. I said so to all of 'em. What else could I say? If I'd said what I thought there on the street I'd of been pinched. So I beat it home in self-protection. I was sympathizing good and hearty with Lon Price by that time and looking forward to Ben Sutton myself. I had a notion Ben would see the right of it where these poor dubs of husbands wouldn't — or wouldn't dast say it if they did.

"About five o'clock I took another run downtown for some things I'd forgot, with an eye out to see how Alonzo and Ben might be coming on. The fact is, seeing each other only once a year that way they're apt to kind of loosen up — if you know what I mean.

"No sign of 'em at first. Nothing but ladies young and old — even some of us older ranching set — making final purchases of ribbons and such for the sole benefit of Wilfred Lennox, and talking in a flushed manner about him whenever they met. Almost every darned one of 'em had made it a point to stroll past the Price mansion that afternoon where Wilfred was setting out on the lawn in a wicker chair with some bottles of beer, surveying Nature with a look of lofty approval and chatting with Henrietta about the real things of life.

"Beryl Mae Macomber had traipsed past four times, changing her clothes twice with a different shade of ribbon across her forehead and all her college pins on, and at last she'd simply walked right in and asked if she hadn't left her tennis racquet there last Tuesday. She says to Mrs. Judge Ballard and Mrs. Martingale and me in the Cut-Rate Pharmacy, she says: 'Oh, he's just awfully magnetic — but do you really think he's sincere?' Then she bought an ounce of Breath of Orient perfume and kind of two-stepped out. These other ladies spoke very sharply about the freedom Beryl Mae's aunt allowed her. Mrs. Martingale said the poet, it was true, had a compelling personality, but what was our young girls coming to? And if that child was hers ——

"So I left these two lady highbinders and went on into the retail side of the Family Liquor Store to order up some cooking sherry, and there over the partition from the bar side what do I hear but Alonzo Price and Ben Sutton! Right off I could tell they'd been pinning a few on. In fact, Alonzo was calling the bartender Mister. You don't know about Lon, but when he calls the bartender Mister the ship has sailed. Ten minutes after that he'll be crying over his operation. So I thought quick, remembering that we had now established a grillroom at the country club, consisting of a bar and three tables with bells on them, and a Chinaman, and that if Alonzo and Ben Sutton come there at all they had better come right — at least to start with. When I'd given my order I sent Louis Meyer in to tell the two gentlemen a lady wished to speak to them outside.

"In a minute Ben comes out alone. He was awful glad to see me and I said how well he looked, and he did look well, sort of cordial and bulging — his forehead bulges and his eyes bulge and his mustache and his chin, and he has cushions on his face. He beamed on me in a wide and hearty manner and explained that Alonzo refused to come out to meet a lady until he knew who she was, because you got to be careful in a small town like this where everyone talks. 'And besides,' says Ben, 'he's just broke down and begun to cry about his appendicitis that was three years ago. He's leaning his head on his arms down by the end of the bar and sobbing bitterly over it. He seems to grieve about it as a personal loss. I've tried to cheer him up and told him it was probably all for the best, but he says when it comes over him this way he simply can't stand it. And what shall I do?'

"Well, of course I seen the worst had happened with Alonzo. So I says to Ben: 'You know there's a party tonight and if that man ain't seen to he will certainly sink the ship. Now you get him out of that swamp and I'll think of something.' 'I'll do it,' says Ben, turning sideways so he could go through the doorway again. 'I'll do it,' he says, 'if I have to use force on the little scoundrel.'

"And sure enough, in a minute he edged out again with

Alonzo firmly fastened to him in some way. Lon hadn't wanted to come and didn't want to stay now, but he simply couldn't move. Say, that Ben Sutton would make an awful grand anchor for a captive balloon. Alonzo wiped his eyes until he could see who I was. Then I rebuked him, reminding him of his sacred duties as a prominent citizen, a husband and the secretary of the Red Gap Chamber of Commerce. 'Of course it's all right to take a drink now and then,' I says.

"Alonzo brightened at this. 'Good!' says he; 'now it's now and pretty soon it will be then. Let's go into a saloon or something like that!'

"'You'll come with me,' I says firmly. And I marched 'em down to the United States Grill, where I ordered tea and toast for 'em. Ben was sensible enough, but Alonzo was horrified at the thought of tea. 'It's tea or nice cold water for yours,' I says. And that set him off again. 'Water!' he sobs. 'Water! Water! Maybe you don't know that some dear cousins of mine have just lost their all in the Dayton flood — twenty years' gathering went in a minute, just like that!' and he tried to snap his fingers. All the same I got some hot tea into him and sent for Eddie Pierce to be out in front with his hack. While we was waiting for Eddie it occurs to Alonzo to telephone his wife. He come back very solemn and says: 'I told her I wouldn't be home to dinner because I was hungry and there probably wouldn't be enough meat, what with a vegetarian poet in the house. I told her I should sink to the level of a brute in the night life of our gay little city. I said I was a wayward child of Nature myself if you come right down to it.'

"'Good for you,' I says, having got word that Eddie is outside with his hack. 'And now for the open road!' 'Fine!' says Alonzo. 'My spirit is certainly feeling very untamed, like some poet's!' So I hustled 'em out and into the four-wheeler. Then I give Eddie Pierce private instructions. 'Get 'em out into the hills about four miles,'

I says, 'out past the Catholic burying ground, then make an excuse that your hack has broke down, and as soon as they set foot to the ground have them skates of yours run away. Pay no attention whatever to their pleadings or their profane threats, only yelling to 'em that you'll be back as soon as possible. But don't go back. They'll wait an hour or so, then walk. And they need to walk.'

"'You said something there,' says Eddie, glancing back at 'em. Ben Sutton was trying to cheer Alonzo up by reminding him of the Christmas night they went to sleep in the steam room of the Turkish bath at Nome, and the man forgot 'em and shut off the steam and they froze to the benches and had to be chisled off. And Eddie trotted off with his load. You'd ought to seen the way the hack sagged down on Ben's side. And I felt that I had done a good work, so I hurried home to get a bite to eat and dress and make the party, which I still felt would be a good party even if the husband of our hostess was among the killed or missing.

"I reached the clubhouse at eight o'clock of that beautiful June evening, to find the party already well assembled on the piazza and the front steps or strolling about the lawn, about eight or ten of our prominent society matrons and near as many husbands. And mebbe those dames hadn't lingered before their mirrors for final touches! Mrs. Martingale had on all her rings and the jade bracelet and the art-craft necklace with amethysts, and Mrs. Judge Ballard had done her hair a new way, and Beryl Mae Macomber, there with her aunt, not only had a new scarf with silver stars over her frail young shoulders and a band of cherry-colored velvet across her forehead, but she was wearing the first ankle watch ever seen in Red Gap. I couldn't begin to tell you the fussy improvements them ladies had made in themselves — and all, mind you, for the passing child of Nature who had never paid a bill for 'em in his life.

"Oh, it was a gay, careless throng with the mad light of

pleasure in its eyes, and all of 'em milling round Wilfred
Lennox, who was eating it up. Some bantered him ro-
guishly and some spoke in chest tones of what was the
real inner meaning of life after all. Henrietta Templeton
Price hovered near with the glad light of capture in her
eyes. Silent but proud, Henrietta was, careless but superior, reminding me of the hunter that has his picture
taken over in Africa with one negligent foot on the head
of a two-horned rhinoceros he's just killed.

"But again the husbands was kind of lurking in the
background, bunched up together. They seemed abashed
by this strange frenzy of their womenfolks. How'd they
know, the poor dubs, that a poet wasn't something a business man had ought to be polite and groveling to? They
affected an easy manner, but it was poor work. Even Judge
Ballard, who seems nine feet tall in his Prince Albert, and
usually looks quite dignified and hostile with his long dark
face and his mustache and goatee — even the good old
judge was rattled after a brief and unhappy effort to hold
a bit of converse with the guest of honor. Him and Jeff
Tuttle went to the grillroom twice in ten minutes. The
judge always takes his with a dash of pepper sauce in it,
but now it only seemed to make him more gloomy.

"Well, I was listening along, feeling elated that I'd put
Alonzo and Ben Sutton out of the way and wondering
when the show would begin — Beryl Mae in her high, innocent voice had just said to the poet: 'But seriously now,
are you sincere?' and I was getting some plenty of that,
when up the road in the dusk I seen Bush Jones driving
a dray-load of furniture. I wondered where in time any
family could be moving out that way. I didn't know any
houses beyond the club and I was pondering about this,
idly as you might say, when Bush Jones pulls his team up
right in front of the clubhouse, and there on the load is the
two I had tried to lose. In a big arm-chair beside a varnished center table sits Ben Sutton reading something that
I recognized as the yellow card with Wilfred's verses on it.

And across the dray from him on a red-plush sofa is Alzono Price singing My Wild Irish Rose in a very noisy tenor.

"Well, sir, I could have basted that fool Bush Jones with one of his own dray stakes. That man's got an intellect just powerful enough to take furniture from one house to another if the new address ain't too hard for him to commit to memory. That's Bush Jones all right! He has the machinery for thinking, but it all glitters as new as the day it was put in. So he'd come a mile out of his way with these two riots — and people off somewhere wondering where that last load of things was!

"The ladies all affected to ignore this disgraceful spectacle, with Henrietta sinking her nails into her bloodless palms, but the men broke out and cheered a little in a half-scared manner and some of 'em went down to help the new-comers climb out. Then Ben had words with Bush Jones because he wanted him to wait there and take 'em back to town when the party was over and Bush refused to wait. After suffering about twenty seconds in the throes of mental effort I reckon he discovered that he had business to attend to or was hungry or something. Anyway Ben paid him some money finally and he drove off after calling out ' Good night, all!' just as if nothing had happened.

"Alonzo and Ben Sutton joined the party without further formality. They didn't look so bad, either, so I saw my crooked work had done some good. Lon quit singing almost at once and walked good and his eyes didn't wabble, and he looked kind of desperate and respectable, and Ben was first-class, except he was slightly oratorical and his collar had melted the way fat men's do. And it was funny to see how every husband there bucked up when Ben come forward, as if all they had wanted was someone to make medicine for 'em before they begun the war dance. They mooched right up round Ben when he trampled a way into the flushed group about Wilfred.

"'At last the well-known stranger!' says Ben cordially, seizing one of Wilfred's pale, beautiful hands. 'I've been hearing so much of you, wayward child of the open road that you are, and I've just been reading your wonderful verses as I sat in my library. The woods and the hills for your spirit untamed and the fire of youth to warm your nights — that's the talk.' He paused and waved Wilfred's verses in a fat, freckled hand. Then he looks at him hard and peculiar and says: 'When you going to pull some of it for us?'

"Wilfred had looked slightly rattled from the beginning. Now he smiled, but only with his lips — he made it seem like a mere Swedish exercise or something, and the next second his face looked as if it had been sewed up for the winter.

"'Little star-eyed gypsy, I say, when are you going to pull some of that open-road stuff?' says Ben again, all cordial and sinister.

"Wilfred gulped and tried to be jaunty. 'Oh, as to that, I'm here to-day and there to-morrow,' he murmurs, and nervously fixes his necktie.

"'Oh my, and isn't that nice!' says Ben heartily — '"the urge of the wild to her wayward child"' — 'I know you're slave to it. And now you're going to tell us all about the open road, and then you and I are going to have an intimate chat and I'll tell you about it — about some of the dearest little open roads you ever saw, right round in these parts. I've just counted nine, all leading out of town to the cunningest mountains and glens that would make you write poetry hours at a time, with Nature's glad fruits and nuts and a mug of spring water and some bottled beer and a ham and some rump steak——'

"The stillness of that group had become darned painful, I want to tell you. There was a horrid fear that Ben Sutton might go too far, even for a country club. Every woman was shuddering and smiling in a painful manner, and the men regarding Ben with glistening eyes. And Ben felt it himself all at once. So he says: 'But I fear I am detaining you,' and let go of the end of Wilfred's tie that he had been toying with in a somewhat firm manner. 'Let us be on with your part of the evening's entertainment,' he says, 'but don't forget, gypsy wilding that you are, that you and I must have a chat about open roads the moment you have finished. I know we are cramping you. By that time you will be feeling the old, restless urge and you might take a road that wasn't open if I didn't direct you.'

"He patted Wilfred loudly on the back a couple of times and Wilfred ducked the third pat and got out of the group, and the ladies all began to flurry their voices about the lovely June evening but wouldn't it be pleasanter inside, and Henrietta tragically called from the doorway to come at once for God's sake, so they all went at once, with the men only half trailing, and inside we could hear 'em fixing chairs round and putting out a table for the poet to stand by, and so forth.

"Alonzo, however, had not trailed. He was over on the steps, holding Beryl Mae Macomber by her new scarf and telling her how flowerlike her beauty was. And old Judge Ballard was holding about half the men, including Ben Sutton, while he made a speech. I hung back to listen. 'Sir,' he was saying to Ben, 'Secretary Seward some years since purchased your territory from Russia for seven million dollars despite the protests of a clamorous and purblind opposition. How niggardly seems that purchase price at this moment! For Alaska has perfected you, sir, if it did not produce you. Gentlemen, I feel that we dealt unfairly by Russia. But that is in the dead past. It is not too late, however, to tiptoe to the grillroom and offer a toast to our young sister of the snows.'

"There was subdued cheers and they tiptoed. Ben Sutton was telling the judge that he felt highly complimented, but it was a mistake to ring in that snow stuff on Alaska. She'd suffered from it too long. He was going on to paint Alaska as something like Alabama—cooler nights of course, but bracing. Alonzo still had Beryl Mae by the scarf, telling her how flowerlike her beauty was.

"I went into the big room, picking a chair over by the door so I could keep tabs on that grillroom. Only three or four of the meekest husbands had come with us. And Wilfred started. I'll do him the justice to say he was game. The ladies thought anything bordering on rough-ness was all over, but Wilfred didn't. When he'd try to get a far-away look in his eyes while he was reciting his poetry he couldn't get it any farther away than the grill-room door. He was nervous but determined, for there had been notice given of a silver offering for him. He recited the verses on the card and the ladies all thrilled up at once, including Beryl Mae, who'd come in without her scarf. They just clenched their hands and hung on Wilfred's wild, free words.

"And after the poetry he kind of lectured about how man had ought to break away from the vile cities and seek the solace of great Mother Nature, where his bruised spirit could be healed and the veneer of civilization cast aside and the soul come into its own, and things like that. And he went on to say that out in the open the perspective of life is broadened and one is a laughing philosopher as long as the blue sky is overhead and the green grass underfoot. 'To lie,' says he, 'with relaxed muscles on the carpet of pine needles and look up through the gently swaying branches of majestic trees at the fleecy white clouds, dream-ing away the hours far from the sordid activities of the market place, is one of the best nerve tonics in all the world.' It was an unfortunate phrase for Wilfred, because some of the husbands had tiptoed out of the grillroom to listen, and there was a hearty cheer at this, led by Jeff Tuttle. 'Sure! Some nerve tonic!' they called out, and laughed coarsely. Then they rushed back to the grillroom without tiptoeing.

"The disgraceful interruption was tactfully covered by Wilfred and his audience. He took a sip from the glass of water and went on to talk about the world's debt to poetry. Then I sneaked out to the grillroom myself. By this time the Chinaman had got all tangled up with the orders and was putting out drinks every which way. And they was being taken willingly. Judge Ballard and Ben Sutton was now planting cotton in Alaska and getting good crops every year, and Ben was also promising to send the judge a lovely spotted fawnskin vest that an Indian had made for him, but made too small — not having more than six or eight fawns, I judged. And Alonzo had got a second start. Still he wasn't so bad yet, with Beryl Mae's scarf over his arm, and talking of the unparalleled beauties of Price's Addition to Red Gap, which he said he wouldn't trade even for the whole of Alaska if it was offered to him to-morrow — not that Ben Sutton wasn't the whitest soul God ever made and he'd like to hear some one say different — and so on.

"I mixed in with 'em and took a friendly drink myself, with the aim of smoothing things down, but I saw it would be delicate work. About all I could do was keep 'em reminded there was ladies present and it wasn't a barroom where anything could be rightly started. Doc Martingale's feelings was running high too, account, I suppose, of certain full-hearted things his wife had blurted out to him about the hypnotic eyes of this here Nature lover. He was quiet enough, but vicious, acting like he'd love to do some dental work on the poet that might or might not be painless for all he cared a hoot. He was taking his own drinks all alone, like clockwork — moody but systematic.

"Then we hear chairs pushed round in the other room and the chink of silver to be offered to the poet, and Henrietta come out to give word for the refreshments to be served. She found Alonzo in the hallway telling Beryl Mae how flowerlike her beauty was and giving her the elk's tooth charm off his watch chain. Beryl Mae was giggling heartily until she caught Henrietta's eye — like a cobra's.

"The refreshments was handed round peaceful enough, with the ladies pressing sardine sandwiches and chocolate cake and cups of coffee on to Wilfred and asking him interesting questions about his adventurous life in the open.

And the plans was all made for his class in poetry to be held at Henrietta's house, where the lady subscribers for a few weeks could come into contact with the higher realities of life, at eight dollars for the course, and Wilfred was beginning to cheer up again, though still subject to dismay when one of the husbands would glare in at him from the hall, and especially when Ben Sutton would look in with his bulging and expressive eyes and kind of bark at him.

"Then Ben Sutton come and stood in the doorway till he caught Wilfred's eye and beckoned to him. Wilfred pretended not to notice the first time, but Ben beckoned a little harder, so Wilfred excused himself to the six or eight ladies and went out. It seemed to me he first looked quick round him to make sure there wasn't any other way out. I was standing in the hall when Ben led him tenderly into the grillroom with two fingers.

"'Here is our well-known poet and *bon vivant*,' says Ben to Alonzo, who had followed 'em in. So Alonzo bristles up to Wilfred and glares at him and says: 'All joking aside, is that one of my new shirts you're wearing or is it not?'

"Wilfred gasped a couple times and says: 'Why, as to that, you see, the madam insisted——'

"Alonzo shut him off. 'How dare you drag a lady's name into a barroom brawl?' says he.

"'Don't shoot in here,' says Ben. 'You'd scare the ladies.'

"Wilfred went pasty, indeed, thinking his host was going to gun him.

"'Oh, very well, I won't then,' says Alonzo. 'I guess I can be a gentleman when necessary. But all joking aside, I want to ask him this: Does he consider poetry to be an accomplishment or a vice?'

"'I was going to put something like that to him myself, only I couldn't think of it,' says Doc Martingale, edging up and looking quite restrained and nervous in the arms.

I was afraid of the doc. I was afraid he was going to blemish Wilfred a couple of times right there.

"'An accomplishment or a vice? Answer yes or no!' orders the judge in a hard voice.

"The poet looks round at 'em and attempts to laugh merrily, but he only does it from the teeth out.

"'Laugh on, my proud beauty!' says Ben Sutton. Then he turns to the bunch. 'What we really ought to do,' he says, 'we ought to make a believer of him right here and now.'

"Even then, mind you, the husbands would have lost their nerve if Ben hadn't took the lead. Ben didn't have to live with their wives, so what cared he? Wilfred Lennox sort of shuffled his feet and smiled a smile of pure anxiety. He knew some way that this was nothing to cheer about.

"'I got it,' says Jeff Tuttle with the air of a thinker. 'We're cramping the poor cuss here. What he wants is the open road.'

"'What he really wants,' says Alonzo, 'is about six bottles of my pure, sparkling beer, but maybe he'll take the open road if we show him a good one.'

"'He wants the open road — show him a good one!' yells the other husbands in chorus. It was kind of like a song.

"'I had meant to be on my way,' says Wilfred, very cold and lofty.

"'You're here to-day and there to-morrow,' says Ben; 'but how can you be there to-morrow if you don't start from here now? — for the way is long and lonely.'

"'I was about to start,' says Wilfred, getting in a couple of steps toward the door.

"''Tis better so,' says Ben. 'This is no place for a county recorder's son, and there's a bully road out here open at both ends.'

"They made way for the poet, and a sickening silence reigned. Even the women gathered about the door of the other room was silent. They knew the thing had got out of their hands. The men closed in after Wilfred as he reached the steps. He there took his soft hat out from under his coat where he'd cached it. He went cautiously down the steps. Beryl Mae broke the silence.

"'Oh, Mr. Price,' says she, catching Alonzo by the sleeve, 'do you think he's really sincere?'

"'He is at this moment,' says Alonzo. 'He's behaving as sincerely as ever I saw a man behave.' And just then at the foot of the steps Wilfred made a tactical error. He started to run. The husbands and Ben Sutton gave the long yell and went in pursuit. Wilfred would have left them all if he hadn't run into the tennis net. He come down like a sack of meal.

"'There!' says Ben Sutton. 'Now he's done it — broke his neck or something. That's the way with some men — they'll try anything to get a laugh.'

"They went and picked the poet up. He was all right, only dazed.

"'But that's one of the roads that ain't open,' says Ben. 'And besides, you was going right toward the nasty old railroad that runs into the cramped haunts of men. You must have got turned round. Here!' He pointed out over the golf links. 'It's off that way that Mother Nature awaits her wayward child. Miles and miles of her — all open. Doesn't your gypsy soul hear the call? This way for the hills and glens, thou star-eyed woodling!' and he gently led Wilfred off over the links, the rest of the men trailing after and making some word racket, believe me. They was all good conversationalists at the moment. Doc Martingale was wanting the poet to run into a tennis net again, just for fun, and Jeff Tuttle says make him climb a tree like the monkeys do in their native glades, but Ben says just keep him away from the railroad, that's all. Good Mother Nature will attend to the rest.

"The wives by now was huddled round the side of the clubhouse, too scared to talk much, just muttering incoherently and wringing their hands, and Beryl Mae pipes up and says: 'Oh, perhaps I wronged him after all; perhaps deep down in his heart he was sincere.'

"The moon had come up now and we could see the mob with its victim starting off toward the Canadian Rockies. Then all at once they began to run, and I knew Wilfred had made another dash for liberty. Pretty soon they scattered out and seemed to be beating up the shrubbery down by the creek. And after a bit some of 'em straggled back. They paid no attention to us ladies, but made for the grillroom.

"'We lost him in that brush beyond the fifth hole,' says Alonzo. 'None of us is any match for him on level ground, but we got some good trackers and we're guarding the line to keep him headed off from the railroad and into his beloved hills.'

"'We should hurry back with refreshment for the faithful watchers,' says Judge Ballard. 'The fellow will surely try to double back to the railroad.'

"'Got to keep him away from the cramped haunts of business men,' says Alonzo, brightly.

"'I wish Clay, my faithful old hound, were still alive,' says the judge wistfully.

"'Say, I got a peach of a terrier down to the house right now,' says Jeff Tuttle, 'but he's only trained for bear — I never tried him on poets.'

"'He might tree him at that,' says Doc Martingale.

"'Percy,' cries his wife, 'have you forgotten your manhood?'

"'Yes,' says Percy.

"'Darling,' calls Henrietta, 'will you listen to reason a moment?'

"'No,' says Alonzo.

"'It's that creature from Alaska leading them on,' says Mrs. Judge Ballard — 'that overdressed drunken rowdy!'

"Ben Sutton looked right hurt at this. He buttoned his coat over his checked vest and says: 'I take that unkindly, madam! — calling me overdressed. I selected this suiting with great care. It ain't nice to call me overdressed. I feel it deeply.'

"But they was off again before one thing could lead to another, taking bottles of hard liquor they had uncorked. 'The open road! The open road!' they yelled as they went.

"Well, that's about all. Some of the wives begun to straggle off home, mostly in tears, and some hung round till later. I was one of these, not wishing to miss anything of an absorbing character. Edgar Tomlinson went early too. Edgar writes The Lounger in the Lobby column for the *Recorder,* and he'd come out to report the entertainment; but at one o'clock he said it was a case for the sporting editor and he'd try to get him out before the kill.

"At different times one or two of the hunters would straggle back for more drink. They said the quarry was making a long detour round their left flank, trying his darndest to get to the railroad, but they had hopes. And they had scattered out. Ever and anon you would hear the long howl of some lone drunkard that had got lost from the pack.

"About sun-up they all found themselves at the railroad track about a mile beyond the clubhouse, just at the head of Stender's grade. There they was voting to picket the track for a mile each way when along come the four-thirty-two way freight. It had slowed up some making the grade, and while they watched it what should dart out from a bunch of scrub oak but the active figure of Wilfred Lennox. He made one of them iron ladders all right and was on top of a car when the train come by, but none of 'em dast jump it because it had picked up speed again.

"They said Wilfred stood up and shook both fists at 'em and called 'em every name he could lay his tongue to — using language so coarse you'd never think it could have come from a poet's lips. They could see his handsome face working violently long after they couldn't hear him. Just my luck! I'm always missing something.

"So they come grouching back to the clubhouse and I took 'em home to breakfast. When we got down to the table old Judge Ballard says: 'What might have been an evening of rare enjoyment was converted into a detestable failure by that cur. I saw from the very beginning that he was determined to spoil our fun.'

"'The joke is sure on us,' says Ben Sutton, 'but I bear him no grudge. In fact, I did him an injustice. I knew he wasn't a poet, but I didn't believe he was even a hobo till he jumped that freight.'

"Alonzo was out in the hall telephoning Henrietta. We could hear his cheerful voice: 'No, Pettikins, no! It doesn't ache a bit. What's that? Of course I still do! You are the only woman that ever meant anything to me. What? What's that? Oh, I may have had errant fancies now and again, like the best of men — you know yourself how sensitive I am to a certain type of flowerlike beauty — but it never touches my deeper nature. Yes, certainly, I shall be right up the very minute good old Ben leaves — to-morrow or next day. What's that? Now, now! Don't do that! Just the minute he leaves — G'-by.'

"And the little brute hung up on her!"

JOHN KENDRICK BANGS

Of all our American humorists John Kendrick Bangs, born May 29, 1862, undoubtedly had the closest individual following. He was a genius as a lecturer and traveled this country to its boundaries during the last fifteen years of his life, and wherever he went he left a memorable personal mark. He began his career on *Life* as associate editor the year after it was founded — 1883. Later on he became editor of *Harper's* "Drawer" and, in 1904, assumed the reins of *Puck* in an effort at its renascence. He was one of the few literary artists of his own — or any other — time, who delighted to express himself orally — and even oratorically — and he became the most popular and notable humorous lecturer and after-dinner speaker this country has ever known. The list of his publications was continuous during this period and "The Idiot" and "The House-Boat on the Styx" bid fair to remain American classics. He died January 21, 1922.

THE IDIOT GOES CHRISTMAS SHOPPING[1]

"MERCY, Mr. Idiot," cried Mrs. Pedagog, as the Idiot entered the breakfast room in a very much disheveled condition, "what on earth has happened to you? Your sleeve is almost entirely torn from your coat, and you really look as if you had been dropped out of an aëroplane."

"Yes, Mrs. Pedagog," said the Idiot, wearily, "I feel that way. I started in to do my Christmas Shopping early yesterday, and what you now behold is the dreadful result. I went into Jimson and Slithers' Department Store to clean up my Christmas list, and, seeing a rather attractive bargain table off at one end of the middle aisle, in the innocence of my young heart, I tried to get to it. It contained a lot of mighty nice, useful presents that one could give to his

[1] From "Half-Hours With The Idiot." Copyright, 1917, Little, Brown, and Company.

friends and relatives and at the same time look his creditors in the face — pretty little cakes of pink soap made of rose leaves for five cents for three; lacquered boxes of hairpins at seven cents apiece; silver-handled toothpicks at two for five; French-gilt hatpins, with plate-glass amethysts and real glue emeralds set in their heads for ten cents a pair, and so on. Seen from the floor above, from which I looked down upon that busy hive, that bargain table was quite the most attractive thing you ever saw. It fairly glittered with temptation, and I went to it; or at least I tried to go to it. I had been so attracted by the giddy lure of the objects upon that table that I failed to notice the maelstrom of humanity that was whirling about it — or perhaps I would better say the femaelstrom of humanity that was eddying about its boundaries, for it was made up wholly of women, as I discovered to my sorrow a moment later when, caught in the swirl, I was tossed to and fro, whirled, pirouetted, revolved, twisted, turned, and generally whizzed about, like a cork on the surface of the Niagara whirlpool. What with the women trying to get to the table, and the women trying to get away from the table, and the women trying to get around the table, I haven't seen anything to beat it since the day I started to take a stroll one afternoon out in Kansas, and was picked up by a cyclone and landed down by the Alamo in San Antonio ten minutes later."

"You ought to have known better than to try to get through such a crowd as that these days," said the Doctor. "How are your ribs —"

"Know better?" retorted the Idiot. "How was I to know any better? There the thing was ready to do business, and nothing but a lot of tired-looking women about it. It looked easy enough, but after I had managed to get in as far as the second layer from the outside I discovered that it wasn't; and then I struggled to get out, but you might as well struggle to get away from the tentacles of an octopus as to try to get out of a place like that without knowing how. I was caught just as surely as a fox with his foot in a trap, and the harder I struggled to get out the nearer I was carried in toward the table itself. It required all my strategy to navigate my face away from the multitude of hatpins that surged about me on all sides. Twice I thought my nose was going to be served *en brochette*. Thrice did the penetrating points of those deadly pins pierce my coat and puncture the face of my watch. Three cigars I carried in my vest pocket were shredded into food for moths, and I give you my word that to keep from being smothered to death by ostrich feathers I bit off the tops of at least fifteen hats that were from time to time thrust in my face by that writhing mass of feminine loveliness. How many aigrettes I inhaled, and the number of artificial roses I swallowed, in my efforts to breathe and bite my way to freedom I shall never know, but I can tell you right now, I never want to eat another aigrette so long as I shall live, and I wouldn't swallow one more canvas-backed tea rose if I were starving. At one time I counted eight ladies standing on my feet instead of on their own; and while I lost all eight buttons off my vest, and six from various parts of my coat, when I got home last night I found enough gilt buttons, crocheted buttons, bone buttons, filagree buttons, and other assorted feminine buttons, inside my pockets to fill an innovation trunk. And talk about massages! I was rubbed this way, and scourged that way, and jack-planed the other way, until I began to fear I was about to be erased altogether. The back breadth of my overcoat was worn completely through, and the tails of my cutaway thereupon coming to the surface were transformed into a flowing fringe that made me look like the walking advertisement of a tassel factory. My watch chain caught upon the belt buckle of an Amazon in front of me, and the last I saw of it was trailing along behind her over on the other side of that whirling mass far beyond my reach. My strength was oozing, and my breath was coming in pants short enough to be worn by a bow-legged four-year-old pickaninny, when, making a last final herculean effort to get myself out of that surging eruption,

I was suddenly ejected from it, like Jonah from the jaws of the whale, but alas, under the bargain table itself, instead of on the outside, toward which I had fondly hoped I was moving."

"Great Heavens!" said the Poet. "What an experience. And you had to go through it all over again to escape finally?"

"Not on your life," said the Idiot. "I'd had enough. I just folded my shredded overcoat up into a pillow, and lay down and went to sleep there until the time came to close the shop for the night, when I sneaked out, filled my pockets full of soap, clothespins, and other knickknacks, and left a dollar bill on the floor to pay for them. They didn't deserve the dollar, considering the damage I had sustained, but for the sake of my poor but honest parents I felt that I ought to leave something in the way of ready money behind me to pay for the loot."

"It's a wonder you weren't arrested for shoplifting," said Mr. Brief.

"They couldn't have proved anything on me," said the Idiot, "even if they had thought of it. I had a perfectly good defense, anyhow."

"What was that?" asked the Lawyer.

"Temporary insanity," said the Idiot. "After my experience yesterday afternoon I am convinced that no jury in the world would hold that a man was in his right mind who, with no compelling reasons save generosity to stir him to do so, plunged into a maelstrom of that sort. It would be a clear case of either attempted suicide or mental aberration. Of course, if I had been dressed for it in a suit of armor, and had been armed with a battle-axe, or a long, sharp-pointed spear, it might have looked like a case of highway robbery; but no male human being in his right mind is going to subject himself to the hazards to life, limb, eye, ear, and happiness, that I risked when I entered that crowd for the sole purpose of getting away unobserved with a package of nickel-plated hairpins, worth four cents and selling at seven, and a couple of hand-painted fly swatters worth ten cents a gross."

The Landlady laughed a long, loud, silvery laugh, with just a little touch of derision in it.

"O you men, you men!" she ejaculated. "You call yourselves the stronger sex, and plume yourselves on your superior physical endurance, and yet when it comes to a test, where are you?"

"Under the table, Madame, under the table," sighed the Idiot. "I for one frankly admit the soft impeachment."

"Yes," said the Landlady, "but I'll warrant you never found a woman under the table. We women, weak and defenseless though we be, go through that sort of thing day after day from youth to age, and we never even think of complaining, much less giving up the fight the way you did. Once a woman gets her eye on a bargain, my dear Mr. Idiot, and really wants it, it would take a hundred and fifty maelstroms such as you have described to keep her from getting it."

"I don't doubt it," said the Idiot, "but you see, my dear Mrs. Pedagog," he added, "you women are brought up to that sort of thing. You are trained from infancy to tackle just such problems, while we poor men have no such advantages. The only practice in domestic rough-housing that we men ever get in our youth is possibly a season on the football team, or in those pleasing little games of childhood like snap-the-whip, and mumbledypeg where we have to dig pegs out of the ground with our noses. Later in life, perhaps, there will come a war to teach us how to assault an entrenched enemy, and occasionally, perhaps around election time, we may find ourselves mixed up in some kind of a free fight on the streets, but all of these things are as child's play compared to an assault upon a bargain table by one who has never practiced the necessary maneuvers. To begin with we are absolutely unarmed."

"Unarmed?" echoed the Landlady. "What would you carry, a Gatling gun?"

"Well, I never thought of that," said the Idiot, "but if I ever tackle the proposition again, which, believe me, is very doubtful, I'll bear the suggestion in mind. It sounds good. If I'd had a forty-two centimeter machine-gun along with me yesterday afternoon I might have stood a better chance."

"O you know perfectly well what I mean," said Mrs. Pedagog. "You implied that women are armed when they go shopping, while men are not."

"Well, aren't they?" asked the Idiot. "Every blessed daughter of Eve in that mêlée yesterday was armed, one might almost say, to the teeth. There wasn't one in the whole ninety-seven thousand of them that didn't have at least two hatpins thrust through the middle of her head with their sharp-pointed ends sticking out an inch and a half beyond her dear little ears; and every time a head was turned in any direction blood was shed automatically. All I had was the stiff rim of my derby hat, and even that fell off inside of three minutes, and I haven't seen hide nor hair of it since. Then what the hatpins failed to move out of their path other pins variously and strategically placed would tackle; and as for auxiliary weapons, what with sharp-edged jet and metal buttons sprouting from one end of the feminine form to the other, up the front, down the back, across the shoulders, along the hips, executing flank movements right and left, and diagonally athwart every available inch of superficial area elsewhere, aided and abetted by silver and steel-beaded handbags and feather-weight umbrellas for purposes of assault, I tell you every blessed damozel of the lot was a walking arsenal of destruction. All one of those women had to do was to whizz around three times like a dervish, poke her head either to the right or to the left, and gain three yards, while I might twist around like a pinwheel, or an electric fan, and get nothing for my pains save a skewered nose, or a poke in the back that suggested the presence of a member of the Black Hand Society. In addition to all this I fear I have sustained internal injuries of serious import. My teeth are intact, save for two feathers that are so deeply imbedded at the back of my wisdom teeth that I fear I shall have to have them pulled, but every time I breathe one of my ribs behaves as if in some way it had got itself tangled up with my left shoulder blade. Why, the pressure upon me at one time was so great that I began to feel like a rosebud placed inside the family Bible by an old maid whose lover has evaporated, to be pressed and preserved there until his return. This little pancake that is about to fulfill its destiny as a messenger from a cold and heartless outside world to my inner man, is a rotund, bulgent, balloon-shaped bit of puffed-up convex protuberance compared to the way I felt after that whirl of femininity had put me through the clothes-wringer. I was as flat as a joke of Caesar's after its four thousandth semiannual appearance in London Punch, and in respect to thickness I was pressed so thin that you could have rolled me around your umbrella, and still been able to get the cover on."

"You never were very deep, anyhow," suggested the Bibliomaniac.

"Whence the wonder of it grows," said the Idiot. "Normally I am fathomless compared to the thin, wafer-like quality of my improfundity as I flickered to the floor after that dreadful pressure was removed."

"How about women getting crushed?" demanded the Landlady defiantly. "If a poor miserable little wisp of a woman can go through that sort of thing, I don't see why a big, brawny man like you can't."

"Because, as I have already said," said the Idiot, "I wasn't dressed for it. My clothes aren't divided up into airtight compartments, rendering me practically unsinkable within, nor have I any steel-constructed garments covering my manly form to resist the pressure."

"And have women?" asked Mrs. Pedagog.

The Idiot blushed.

"How should I know, my dear Mrs. Pedagog?" replied

the Idiot. "I'm no authority on the subtle mysteries of feminine raiment, but from what I see in the shop windows, and in the advertising pages of the magazines, I should say that the modern woman could go through a courtship with a grizzly bear and come out absolutely undented. As I pass along the highways these days, and glance into the shop windows, mine eyes are constantly confronted by all sorts of feminine under-tackle, which in the days of our grandmothers were regarded as strictly confidential. I see steel-riveted contraptions, marked down from a dollar fifty-seven to ninety-eight cents, which have all the lithe, lissom grace of a Helen of Troy, the which I am led to infer the women of to-day purchase and insert themselves into, gaining thereby not only a marvelous symmetry of figure hitherto unknown to them, but that same security against the buffetings of a rude outside world as well, which a gilt-edged bond must feel when it finds itself locked up behind the armor-plated walls of a Safe Deposit Company. Except that these armorial undergarments are decorated with baby-blue ribbons, and sporadic, not to say spasmodic, doodads in filmy laces and chiffon, they differ in no respect from those wonderful combinations of slats, chest-protectors, and liver pads which our most accomplished football players wear at the emergent moments of their intellectual development at college. In point of fact, without really knowing anything about it, I venture the assertion that the woman of to-day wearing this steel-lined chiffon figure, and armed with seventy or eighty different kinds of pins from plain hat to safety, which protrude from various unexpected parts of her anatomy at the psychological moment, plus the devastating supply of buttons always available for moments of aggressive action, is the most powerfully and efficiently developed engine of war the world has yet produced. She is not only protected by her unyielding figure from the onslaughts of the enemy, but she fairly bristles as with unsuspected weapons of offense against which anything short of a herd of elephants on stampede would be powerless. Your modern Amazon is an absolutely irrefragable, irresistible creature, and it makes me shudder to think of what is going to happen when this war of the sexes, now in its infancy, really gets going, and we defenseless men have nothing but a few regiments of artillery, and a division or two of infantry and cavalry standing between us and an advancing column of super-insulated shoppers, using their handbags as clubs, their hatpins glistening wickedly in the morning light as they tango onward to the fray. When that day comes, frankly, I shall turn and run. I had my foretaste of that coming warfare in my pursuit of Christmas gifts yesterday afternoon, and my motto henceforth and forever is Never Again!"

"Then I suppose we need none of us expect to be remembered by you this Christmas," said the Doctor. "Alas, and alas! I shall miss the generous bounty which led you last year to present me with a cold waffle on Christmas morn."

"On the contrary, Doctor," said the Idiot. "Profiting from my experience of yesterday I am going to start in on an entirely new system of Christmas giving. No more boughten articles for me — my presents will be fashioned by loving hands without thought of dross. You and all the rest of my friends at this board are to be remembered as usual. For the Bibliomaniac I have a little surprise in store in the shape of a copy of the *Congressional Record* for December 7th which I picked up on a street car last Friday morning. It is an absolutely first edition, in the original wrappers, and will make a fine addition to his collection of Americana. For Mr. Brief I have a copy of the New York Telephone Book for 1906, which he will find full of most excellent addresses. For my dear friend, the Poet, I have set aside a charming collection of rejection slips from his friends the editors; and for you, Doctor, as an affectionate memento of my regard, I have prepared a little mixture of all the various medicines you have prescribed for me during the past five years, none of which I have ever taken, to the vast betterment of my health. These, consisting of squills, cod-liver oil, ipecac, quinine, iron tonic, soothing syrup, spirits of ammonia, horse liniment, himalaya bitters, and calomel, I have mixed together in one glorious concoction, which I shall bottle with my own hands in an old carboy I found up in the attic, on the side of which I have etched the words, When You Drink It Think of Me!"

"Thanks, awfully," said the Doctor. "I am sure a mixture of that sort could remind me of no one else."

"And, finally, for our dear Landlady," said the Idiot, smiling gallantly on Mrs. Pedagog, "I have the greatest surprise of all."

"I'll bet you a dollar I know what it is," said the Doctor.

"I'll take you," said the Idiot.

"You're going to pay your bill!" roared the Doctor.

"There's your dollar," said the Idiot, tossing a silver cartwheel across the table. "Better hand it right over to Mrs. Pedagog on account, yourself."

DON MARQUIS

Don Marquis (Donald Robert Perry Marquis) born in Walnut, Illinois, July 29, 1878, one of our most brilliant and versatile columnists, is a humorist of solid national repute by virtue of his original books, which now number a dozen or more, in prose and verse. He is the creator of that national character "The Old Soak."

PREFACE TO A BOOK OF FISHHOOKS [1]

THIS little book of flies and hooks and guts and hackles, which was presented to us by a friend who heard us say we liked to go fishing — we may as well admit at once that it is full of riddles we cannot rede. We know nothing about trout, and have no great ambition to learn. Fishing for trout has too much exertion and bodily effort about it to be attractive. One tramps about over rough country and gets one's self wet in cold water, and tangles one's hook in one's hair and ears, and all that sort of thing.

Our idea of fishing is to put all the exertion up to the fish. If they are ambitious we will catch them. If they are not, let them go about their business. If a fish expects to be caught by us he has to look alive. We give him his opportunity, and he must make the most of it.

Most of our fishing, and the only fishing we ever really enjoyed, was done with a worm, a hook, a leaden sinker, a line and a willow pole. We wouldn't know what to do with a reel. We expect a fish to eat the hook very thoroughly, to persist until he gets it well down and then to signal us that all is well by pulling the float under water;

[1] From "Prefaces." Copyright, 1919, by D. Appleton and Company. Reprinted by permission of the author.

a reel is superfluous; one flips the pole over one's head and the fish lands somewhere in the bushes behind.

A little quiet river or a creek, with low banks and plenty of big trees along the banks, is the only place to fish; and the fish should be mostly bullheads. Bullheads know their business; they hook themselves more completely and competently than any other fish. A bullhead will swallow the worm, the hook, and the lead sinker, a part of the line, and then grumble because he has n't been able to eat the float and the pole. And you can leave it all up to him. You can sit in the shade and watch the float bobbing and jerking about in the serene consciousness that he will do a good job. When he pulls the pole itself out of the socket of earth into which you have jabbed the butt end of it, then is the time to interfere and bring him to land. Don't hold the pole yourself; it is too much trouble.

Being out of the water does n't make much difference to the average bullhead. We don't suppose he could stand it more than two or three days, unless there was a damp wind blowing, but a few hours more or less are nothing to him. After having eaten as much of your fishing tackle as you will permit him to have before interfering, you might think that he would be a little dejected. But not so. You go to take the hook out of him, and he rushes at you and horns you, with a queer purring noise, and shows every disposition to fight it out on land.

And he seldom knows when he is dead. Often in the course of a day we have caught a bushel or so of bullheads and thrown them into the back of the buggy and driven home with them, five or six miles, maybe. Arrived at home we would find them stiff and caked with dried mud and dust, and to all appearances dead, having been out of the water and jogging along in the hot afternoon sun for a couple of hours. But throw them into a barrel of water, and in a few minutes they were swimming around as if nothing had happened, grinning over the top of the barrel and begging for more worms and hooks and lead sinkers.

Refreshed by his cool plunge, the beast was ready for another romp. The bullhead is not a beautiful fish, and has no claims to aristocracy, but he is enduring.

We never liked to fish from a boat. You have to row the thing about, and that is a lot of trouble. Select a big, shady tree that bends over a pool in some little inland stream and lie down under the tree, and lie there all day and fish and eat and smoke and chew tobacco and watch the dragonflies and spit into the water. If you feel like swimming a little, all right — it doesn't particularly bother the bullheads. But it is a mistake to go to sleep.

If you go to sleep while you are loafing, how are you going to know you are loafing? And if you don't know it, what satisfaction is there in it? And it is also a mistake to think too deeply. If you do that, about the time you begin to get on the track of the secret of the universe some fool fish will hook himself, and you will have to attend to him.

Lie with your hat over your face and watch thoughts carefully from under the brim of it as they come toward you out of the woods or up the creek. And if a thought that seems as if it were going to be too profound or troublesome tries to crawl up on you shoo it away and wait for an easy thought. And when you get an easy thought hold on to it and think it for a long time and enjoy it.

The best thoughts to have when you are fishing are the thoughts about what you would do if you had a million dollars. After a while you get sort of lenient toward the world, and unambitious, and think it's a little selfish of you to want a whole million, and say "Shucks! I'd be willing to take a hundred thousand!" And you think maybe if you roused up a little and looked over the edge of the bank you would see a streak of gold in the soil, and then you would go and buy that land of the farmer that owns it and get rich off of the gold. And then you remember that you don't know who owns the land and it would be considerable trouble to have to ask questions

around and find out. So it doesn't seem worth while to
look over the edge of the bank and see whether the gold is
there after all. And, anyhow, would it be fair, to whatever farmer owns the land, to buy it knowing there was
gold on it and never tell him? And what would you buy
it with? If you borrowed money to buy it with the fellow
you borrowed the money from would likely get the biggest
part of it, and you would have all your work and worry for
nothing, and so you don't look to see if the gold is there.
And then you get to thinking that probably there aren't
many people honest enough to pass up a fortune like that
just simply because somebody else owns it and you admire
yourself for being that honest.

You can find more things to admire yourself for, lying
around fishing like that, if you pick your thoughts properly.
Everybody ought to do it all the time and not work at anything else.

.   .   .   .

Several friends and literary advisers to whom we have
shown the foregoing preface have taken the trouble to intimate that they do not believe what we have said concerning the fish known as the bullhead; namely, that he can live
out of water for several hours. This only shows how little
some people know about bullheads. We might have told
a story of a particular bullhead far more incredible, and
equally true, but that we are aware of this general lack of
exact information concerning bullheads and did not care
to have our statements questioned by the ignorant.

This particular bullhead we caught and tamed when we
were about twelve years old, and named him Mr. Hoskins
because of his facial resemblance to a neighbor. Mr. Hoskins — not the fish, but the fish's godfather — had fallen
from a windmill in youth, upon his head, and his head had
been getting larger ever since, until he seemed all head,
with a few wiry spikes of beard and mustache around his
mouth. His intellect had not grown as his head grew; the

poor man used to go about calling attention to his large head, saying: "I fell off a windmill and the hogs ate me, all but my head — see my head!" He was pathetically proud of it. The fish looked like him, and with the heedless cruelty of boyhood we named the bullhead Mr. Hoskins.

Mr. Hoskins (the fish) dwelt in an old wash boiler under a maple tree. And it was beneath this maple tree that we used to feed all our other animals every morning — a black dog, a crow, a black and orange cat, a brown dog called Gustavus Adolphus after the Terrible Swede of that name, and an owl known (for we had been reading Dumas) as the Duchess de Montpensier. At that time, and in that place, the village butcher would give one a whole basketful of scraps and bones for a dime; the dogs, the cat, the crow and the Duchess would range themselves, solemnly expectant, in a row under the maple tree and catch the bits of meat we tossed to them in their mouths or beaks, no animal stepping out of his or her place in line and no animal offering to bite or peck its neighbor.

Mr. Hoskins, the bullhead, would come to the surface of the water and peer with one eye over the rim of the boiler, watching these proceedings closely. At first he watched them grouchily, we thought. A bullhead, however, is somewhat handicapped in the expression of the lighter and gayer emotions; his face is so constructed that even if he feels otherwise than gloomy and ill-humored he cannot show it. But as the spring wore into summer it seemed to us that Mr. Hoskins was getting friendlier, somehow. One day we tossed him a piece of meat and he snapped at it. After that we ranged the other beasts in a circle around the wash boiler, and if Gustavus Adolphus or the Duchess de Montpensier missed a piece of meat it fell to Mr. Hoskins. In ten days Mr. Hoskins could catch as well as any of them.

One morning we were alarmed to see that Mr. Hoskins's boiler had been overturned during the night, no doubt by some thirsty cow. He seemed dead when we picked him up and we dug a hole in the ground and threw him into it.

But before we had him covered a sudden summer rain came up and we sought shelter. It was a drenching rain; when it was over, a couple of hours later, we returned to Mr. Hoskins to find the hole filled with water and him flopping around in it. He was evidently feeling quite chipper, and was contentedly eating an angleworm.

We put him back in his boiler.* And then we began to experiment with Mr. Hoskins. If he could live out of water for two or three hours, why not for a whole day? Every morning we took him from his boiler at a certain time, and each day we kept him from the water ten minutes or so longer than the day preceding. By September he was able to go from seven in the morning until eight in the evening entirely out of water without suffering any apparent ill effects except a slight loss in weight. At first during the hours when he was out of water he would seem rather torpid, in fact almost comatose. But by giving him frequent cool drinks from a bottle with a quill in it we found that he became livelier. By autumn he could go until sunset on not more than two drinks of water.

He became a jollier companion, joining, so far as he was able, ourself and the other animals in all our sports. One of the most pleasant recollections of our boyhood is the memory of Mr. Hoskins flopping genially about the garden while Gustavus Adolphus and the other dog dug angleworms for Mr. Hoskins and the crow.

. When the chilly weather came in November we moved his wash boiler into the house and set it behind the kitchen range, as we did not care to run the risk of having him frozen. But with the cold weather his need for water grew less and less; he began to manifest something like pride in his ability to do without it; it was in January that he began to experience, or at least to affect, a repugnance toward being in water at all. Then we substituted for the boiler a box full of sawdust. Still, however, even during January

---

* The star marks the exact spot at which the more skeptical sort of person will likely cease to believe.

he would sometimes awake during the night and cry for a drink, and we insisted on a weekly bath.

At seven o'clock on the morning of St. Valentine's Day, 1890, we went into the kitchen and found that Mr. Hoskins had leaped from the floor to the hearth of the kitchen range, and had succeeded in working himself in among the warm ashes. He had felt cold during the night. After that we always put him to bed with a hot water bottle, and we remember well his cries of peevishness and discomfort on the night when the stopper came out of the bottle and drenched him.

We linger over these last days of February, hesitating to go on, because they were the last days in Mr. Hoskins's life. It was on February 28 that he went out of doors for the first time that year. Some one had left the cistern uncovered and he fell in. We heard his cries. We put a ladder down and plucked him from the black water. But it was too late. If he had only remembered how to swim, if we had only had the presence of mind to fling down a plank to him he might have kept himself afloat until we reached him with the ladder. But it was too late. We suppose that when he felt himself in the water a panic struck him. Those were days before every family had a pulmotor. We worked over him, but it was no use. It is silly perhaps to feel so badly over a little animal like that, but from that day to this we have never eaten a bullhead.

PREFACE TO A VOLUME OF POETRY [1]

We have often been asked to read the poems in the following collection at teas and similar soul and culture fights. We have always refused. It is not, as some of our friends believe, because of any excess of timidity that we consistently refuse.

It is because no one wants to pay us what it is worth to

[1] From "Prefaces." Copyright, 1919, by D. Appleton and Company. Reprinted by permission of the author.

us. We are perfectly willing, if we get enough money for it, to read poems at Teas, Dinners, Pugilistic Contests, Clam-bakes, Football Games, Prayer Meetings of Any Denomination, Clinics, Divorce Trials, Balls, Dedications, Lynchings, Launchings, Luncheons, Weddings, Jail Deliveries, Tonsil Removals, Ice Cream Socials, Legal Executions, Wrestling Matches, Tooth Pullings, Commencement Exercises, Operations for Appendicitis, Coming Out Parties, Taffy Pulls, Better Baby Contests, Dog Shows, Gambling House Raids, Sunday School Picnics, Pool Tournaments, Spelling Bees, Adenoid Unveilings, Murders, Church Suppers and Cremations. But money we must have.

For while reading one's own poems to a gang of strangers need not, of course, be absolutely degrading, yet it is bound to be a silly sort of performance.

And it is worth money. Poetry, with us, is a business; it takes time, muscular effort, nervous energy and, sometimes, thought, to produce a poem.

People do not ask painters to go to places and paint pictures for nothing, but they are forever trying to graft entertainment off of poets.

Our rates, henceforth, are as follows:

For reading small, blond, romantic poems, thirty-five dollars per poem. Blond, dove-colored or pink lyrics prominently featuring the Soul, thirty-five dollars each.

Humorous poems, not really very funny, twenty-five dollars each.

Humorous poems, with slightly sentimental flavor, forty dollars each.

Humorous poems, really quite funny, seventy-five dollars each.

Dialect poems mentioning persons called " Bill," " Jim," " Si," etc., Southern dialect, fifty dollars each; middle Western, fifty-five dollars.

Pathetic dialect verse charged for according to the quantity and quality of pathos desired. (See rates on Mother and Old Sweetheart poems.)

Sonnets, ten dollars each. Not less than five sonnets served with any one order.

Pash poems, one hundred dollars each. Pash poems, however, will only be read from the interior of a heavy wire cage.

Free verse, any kind, one dollar a line.

No matter how long or how short the lines actually are, for business purposes a line of free verse is to be considered as containing seven words.

Serious poems, melancholy tone, fifty dollars each.

For ten dollars additional, persons not to exceed twelve in number will be permitted to file by and feel the poet's heart beat after reading sad poems; persons in excess of twelve in number charged for at the rate of two dollars each.

Serious poems, optimistic in nature, fifty dollars each.

Old Sweetheart poems, in which she dies, one hundred dollars each. Old Folks at Home poems, sad, fifty dollars each; each reference to angels five dollars additional; father killed, mother left living, sixty-five dollars; both parents killed, seventy-five dollars; with dialect, one hundred dollars. Both parents killed during Christmas holidays, any dialect wanted, angels, toys, etc., two hundred dollars. Auditors' tears guaranteed, and for thirty-five dollars additional, poet also will cry while reading this old reliable line of family poetry.

Religious poems, not more than five stanzas, one hundred dollars each.

Agnostic poems, latest cut, one hundred thirty-five to one hundred seventy-five dollars each.

These agnostic goods are for very exclusive circles, as are our radical and anarchistic poems, which come at two hundred dollars each.

Tame revolutionary poems, usual Greenwich Village sort of thing, fifty dollars each; if read in Flatbush, sixty-five dollars each.

Really quite shocking revolutionary poems, two hundred dollars each. A very modern line of goods.

Write for special combination offers and rates on limericks. We have limericks listed in three categories:

Limericks Where Ladies Are Present.

Limericks Where Ladies Are Absent but Clergymen Are Present.

Limericks.

In the event that we are expected to Be Nice and Meet People, 20 per cent. added to above rates.

If expected to Meet People, and Being Nice is left optional with us, only 5 per cent. added to above rates.

Conversation on poetry or related topics charged for at rate of $75 an hour in addition to reading charges.

Conversation on Rabindranath Tagore: Listened To, $750 an hour. Participated In, $1,000 the first hour and $350 for every additional ten minutes thereafter.

Limericks composed on spot (discreet) twenty-five dollars each. Impromptu couplets, good, twenty dollars each; medium, twelve dollars and fifty cents each; quite bad impromptu couplets, five dollars each.

Poetry written by host, hostess or any guest, listened to at rate of one hundred dollars per quarter hour.

Compliments on same to author, ten dollars each, additional.

Compliments spoken so as to be overheard by more than eight persons, twenty dollars each.

Compliments dashed off in little informal notes, forty dollars each if notes are initialed, one hundred dollars each if notes are signed with full name.

For pretending to like Amy Lowell's work our rate is $1,000 an hour or any fraction thereof.

No orders filled amounting to less than two hundred dollars for ninety minutes' work. Certified check must be mailed with orders.

Prices quoted are f. o. b. Pennsylvania Station, N. Y. City.

Patrons will always confer a favor by reporting any inattention on the part of the audience.

GEORGE ADE

A writer who, looking out on this great new seething civilization saw that slang was its most highly cherished linguistic product, and proceeded to build an enduring literary monument therewith, must certainly be accounted among the most original of American geniuses. George Ade has elevated slang into a brilliant and worshipful medium of expression, from a humorous standpoint. His "Fables In Slang" are sheer works of art. He has also been and continues to be very successful in both the spoken and the silent drama. He was born in Kentland, Indiana, February 9, 1866. He is a bachelor and his home is his farm in his native State.

THE FABLE OF THE SPOTLIGHTERS AND THE SPOTTER [1]

ONCE a Traveller arrived at a Cure where the Water of the Healing Springs smelled so awful that the Management felt justified in asking $10 a Day.

This Traveller was a City Yap, which is worse than being a Begosher, because the R. F. D. Boob usually knows that he is below Par.

The City Yap is a Vertebrate with Shiny Hair, living under the dominion of the Traffic Cops.

He will stand in front of a Window, with others of his Kind, for an Hour at a time, watching a powerful Blonde demonstrate a Fireless Cooker.

When $100,000,000 gets married to a Title, it is the City Yap who has to be clubbed back by the Police so that the Bride can get her Purchase into the Sanctuary.

When Jack Dempsey or Prince Blozotski arrives by Special Train, the City Yap is the poor Google-Eye that you see standing in the Rain.

[1] From "Hand-made Fables." Copyright, 1920, by Doubleday, Page and Company. Reprinted by permission of author and publishers.

He believes that Greatness means having one's Name on the Front Page; consequently it is better to jump off the Williamsburg Bridge than to be an Emeritus Professor at Johns Hopkins.

Perhaps the Reader will ask: "Could a City Yap afford to put up at one of these Ten-a-Day Resorts?"

Listen!

Some of the City Yaps have been to Harvard. They have tailor-made Underwear, Gold Service for Company, De Luxe Editions, Divorce Papers — Everything.

This particular Species of Metropolitan Mokus used to Boast that he could walk into any Hotel and the Clerks would hoist the Flag.

Such a Claim might not seem Portentous to one residing in Grand Island or Waupaca, but there are Favoured Spots within the Republic at which being known by the Boys behind the Desk is the very Essence of Fame.

Sure enough, the Lad who gives out the Keys recognized the Traveller and called him by Name and let on as though the Tavern had just opened and here was the first Customer.

After the newly arrived Delegate from the Asphalt Jungles had read a Telegram saying that Frazzingham Preferred had advanced from ¾ to ⅞ on a Report that the King of Rumania had received a Letter from the King of Greece, he brushed up a little and then sauntered back to the Bureau of Information and asked the Room Clerk if any one was stopping in the House.

Of course he knew that some 500 Transients of fair Business Standing and the usual Family connections were scattered about the Premises.

When he said "Any One," he meant did they have any one who would get Attention from the Head Waiter Himself.

A true Worshipper of the Exalted Few regards the common Run of Humanity as mere Whitebait. If you wish to hand him a Thrill, you must show him a Tarpon.

"We have so many Stars here that even the Manager is trembling," replied Cuthbert, the refined Room Clerk. "Do you see that Bunch out on the Piazza, taking the Sun? Leave me call them off to you. First, there is Jimmy Hooper, supposed to be the nerviest Plunger on the Exchange. He can lose or win a Million without disturbing the Ash on his Cigarette. He makes all the other High Rollers in the world look like Marble Players. He is King of the Gilt-Edge Gams."

"I have read all about him in the Papers," said the Roof-Garden Rufus.

"Then there is Mr. Hiram Cherrib, who has closed out all his big Interests and puts in his Time endowing Hospitals and slipping Coin to Presbyterian Colleges. He allows that he will shoot every Bean in the old Tin Box and die Poor if he can do good to those that he formerly Did so successfully."

"For years I have yearned to get a peek at Mr. Cherrib," said the Café Habitué.

"And lookie! There is Mrs. Beverly Margrave, often called the uncrowned Empress of the American Hote Mond. You 've heard of her!"

"HAVE I?" exclaimed the Bumpkin from the Boulevards.

His Nostrils were quivering.

"She was a Terwhilligus from Baltimore, you may recall. I know People who would give their Eye-Teeth just to have her Insult them. Then they could say they had Met her. Right next to her Nobs is the famous preacher, Rev. Ormsby Toncell. They say he pulls down the biggest Salary and has the swellest lot of Box-Holders of any Parson in this whole Country. Even the English think he 's English. He must be a talented Guy, all right!"

"Hardly a week passes but I see an Interview with him," said the Subway Simp.

"As I live and breathe, she 's out there, too!" ejaculated the highly intelligent Room Clerk.

"Who?" asked the eager Cosmopolite.

"Lottie Limmet, the big Hit in that new Piece called

'Oh, Lizzie!' You remember — the Police made them change it. She had a Song that caused a Strike in the Orchestra. Some of the Musicians said they had Families."

"I tried to buy Seats" — in a Choking Whisper — "but they were sold out Eight Weeks in advance, and the Speculators asked Ten for Two on the Aisle."

"She is Some Gal. It is reported that they are going to put up a Statue of her at Yale. The Female Party right near her is supposed to be the Richest Woman in the Western Hemisphere."

"You don't mean Jane Plummer, the Widow that gets a Full Page in the Sunday Issue every two or three weeks?" asked the City Chap, his Cup of Joy just about ready to slop over.

"None other. I remember reading how much her Income would weigh if she changed it into Nickels. By the way, there's another Big Gun out there. I didn't notice him at first. Probably you've read the Editorial Attacks on Steve Gurney, the Political Boss."

"You don't mean the head of the Venal State Machine, who sits in a Back Room and gives orders to the Legislature and dictates Appointments and pulls all that Coarse Stuff, do you?"

"That's the Bird! I can see that you're well read. They've been trying for Years to get something on him and take his Measure, but he is still riding the Tractor."

"Me to put myself next," said Mr. H. Polloi. "I don't often get a Close-Up of these Immortals, and I'm sure going to Periscope."

So he edged out into the Sunlight and stalked his Prey.

There was one empty Chair right in the thick of the Who's Who, and he nailed it.

Oh, Joy! Oh, Bliss! And a couple of Raptures!

He found himself within smelling-distance of Lottie Limmet, the Forty-Second Street Parisienne.

There was no mistaking the much talked-of Cutie.

If Colours could be converted into Sounds her Costume would have been a Siren Whistle.

She had her Limbs crossed in such a way as to prove that she spared no Expense, but, nevertheless, her Knee-Caps were modestly concealed.

He knew it was She or Her because alongside of the Gay Creature and very Chummy was the famous Wall Street Blokie, Jimmy Hooper, dressed up like a Horse.

Yes, indeed! Shepherd's Plaid, Stripes on the Shirt, and a Bow Tie that looked like a Clot of Blood.

He had "Gambler" placarded all over him.

Our Hero knew that every Soubrette has a Gentleman Broker Friend who gives her Tips on the Market, so that ofttimes she will clean up as much as $300,000 at a Crack and then send her Mother a Watch.

He knew, because that was the part of the Paper he devoured.

It is easy to get acquainted with an Actress, so in a few minutes George W. Fresh was carrying on with the Footlight Favourite and exchanging Hot Ones with Jimmy the Sport.

Presently the one who had been identified as Steve Gurney, Malefactor and Enemy of the People, edged over with his Rocking Chair and joined in the gay chatter of the Bohemians.

After giving Steve the Up-and-Down, it was easy to believe all that had been printed about him in the Righteous Press.

He was undershot and had Fuzz on the Back of his Hands.

He looked like a Vessel Unloader who had put on a Mail Order Suit in order to attend a Clam Bake.

The sort of Person you wouldn't care to meet in a Lonesome Street on a Rainy Night.

While the Investigator was letting himself go, in the company of these Abandoned Characters, and wondering what the Boys at the Lunch Club would say when he pulled it on them, he sized the other Notables close at hand.

Mrs. Beverly Margrave was perceptibly annoyed by the immediate presence of the *Canaille*, meaning Ordinary Skates.

Her prim but high-priced Suit of Quaker Gray, the chiselled suggestion of Patrician Reserve on her cold features, the wince of Pain and the lifted Eyebrow when Steve Gurney guffawed loudly, and the fact that she was reading George Moore — all these Items meant much to the Observant Traveller.

Why deny Class Distinction when even a Stranger can single out a True Genevieve with Pink Corpuscles?

Near the Queen of the Swagger Set, a pale Gentleman in somber Attire seemed quite lost in contemplation of the hazy Landscape.

He gave no heed to the gabby Groundlings only a few feet away.

He held daintily between the Forefinger and Thumb a White Rose with slender Stem.

At intervals he would lift the gorgeous Bloom to the Olfactory Orifices and inhale in a conservative manner, closing his Eyes and seeming to pass into a pleasant Trance.

It was a Cinch to place this Party as the Rev. Ormsby Toncell.

The absence of Jewellery, the Ascetic Pallor, the simple adoration of Purity's Emblem — all these bespoke a Nature more Spiritual than Broadway.

Out by the Veranda Rail, seemingly lost in Meditation as he propped his Chin with a Newspaper made into a Roll, sat Horace Cherrib, the foremost Benefactor of his Time.

The City Fellow knew him by the Side Whiskers.

In every Good Show, the Elderly Person with Money who is trying to save some one else from Ruin and bring Happiness to the Deserving carries quite a mess of Ivy in front of each Listener.

Even if there had been no Trade-Marks, it would have been a Pipe to make the eminent Philanthropist.

The Light of Goodness twinkled in his Baby Blue Eyes and a Smile of infinite Kindliness illumined his Handsome Diagram.

He seemed oblivious, detached, quite unaware that others were watching him.

He was planning, dreaming — what? Possibly new Hospitals for the Crippled Children, more Colleges for the Farm Hands.

It was worth a Day's Journey just to sit and look at the great Cherrib.

You may be sure that the Lynx also improved this Golden Opportunity to get a line on Jane Plummer, the good old Standby of the Sunday Editor.

He knew her by the Ear-Bobs, which were Pearls about the size of Ripe Olives.

He had put in a lot of time studying Price Tags and he judged the Pearls would fetch close to $50,000 apiece, or $100,000 for the Two.

But, of course, she could afford it, so it was none of his Business.

Mrs. Plummer, whose Vast Fortune if converted into $1 Bills and placed End to End would reach from Boston to Omaha, was engaged in some sort of Fancy Work on a Tambourine Frame.

She chatted in a care-free way as her jewelled Fingers plied the busy Needle.

Her remarks were addressed to a timid little Woman in rusty Black, who seemed more or less Cowed, which proved that she must be the hired Companion.

The Boy from the City had learned by a careful course of Reading, while lying in Bed, that every Woman of tremendous Wealth is trailed by a Female Friday who is addressed by her last Name.

He tried to pick out a Label for this Worm and decided that it might be Wiggins or Tubbs.

While he was wallowing in blissful Juxtaposition to the Prominent, some one touched him on the Shoulder.

It was the Room Clerk.

"I am off Watch," said the Employee, "and will take you on for Nine Holes."

Excusing himself from the Musical Comedy Star and the bold Speculator and the unprincipled Corrupter, he started for the Locker Room with Cuthbert, who had put him next to the King Pins.

"You are unquestionably the Child of Fortune," said the Room Clerk. "I take it that Mixer is your Middle Name. You work fast."

"One is always safe in flagging a theatrical Fairy," was the modest Reply. "I had no hesitancy about busting in as soon as I heard my friend Jimmy Hooper kidding her along."

"Why, you poor Fish! You have been getting gay for a Half Hour with Mrs. Beverly Margrave, acknowledged Leader of the Young Married Set."

"You must be mistaken. Mrs. Margrave was dressed in Gray and reading one of them High-Brow Books, and she got peeved because we made so much Racket."

"The Lady in Gray who won't speak to any one is Lottie Limmet. She won't even sign Autograph Albums."

"Back up! Do you mean to tell me that Mrs. Beverly Margrave, who comes of the most Aristocratic Family in Maryland, would stand for all that Joshing from a Rounder like Hooper?"

"Are you talking about that Buddie with the Loud Checks and the Crimson Cravat?"

"Sure."

"That was the Rev. Ormsby Toncell, and, take it from me, he's a regular Human Being."

"I think you're Twisted."

"No chance. Room Clerks know everything."

"I'm almost positive that the Reverend Toncell sat over to my right. He was dressed something like an Undertaker and kept smelling a Rose."

"You just got them reversed, that's all. The one

with the Rose was Jimmy Hooper. He's Nuts about
Flowers and keeps a fresh Bouquet on his Desk all the
time."

"Have you got the unblushing Face to tell me that the
Jolly Party with the Make-Up was the exclusive Matron
and that a celebrated Preacher wore any such Stripes on his
Shirt?"

"That's what I'm trying to Convey."

"Well, I'll prove that you're off. Do you think Mrs.
Beverly Margrave and the Rev. Ormsby Toncell would
hobnob with Steve Gurney after what all the newspapers
have printed about him?"

"They didn't hobnob with Steve. They couldn't. He
never goes near a Silk Stocking unless he wants to use him,
and then he sends for him."

"Didn't I see it with my own Eyes?"

"Oh, you mean the big, square-jawed Burly that never
buttons his Vest! That was Horace Cherrib, whom I told
you about — the one that's going to save the World by
feeding it $10 Bills."

"I don't think you took a good Look."

"Cert'nly I did. Steve wasn't near you Folks. He sat
over there by himself and never chirped. 'Silent Steve,'
his Friends call him."

"I refuse to believe that a kind-faced and gentle Soul like
that is really the Boss of a disreputable Machine."

"No other kind could be. He wins out by making
Friends."

"Well, anyway, I made no miscue on the Rich Widow.
I marked her by the Expensive Pearls."

"Where do you get that Noise? Her Bill for Jewellery
last year was 85 cents. She bought a jet Hat-Pin."

"Oh, come off! You don't mean to say ——"

"Yes; the scared little Dame in the Black Gown, purchased direct from one of our largest Department Stores,
has more Currency than you and I could shovel with two
Shovels in two Weeks."

"How about the one with the enormous Pearls and the seven Rings?"

"Oh, that's her French Maid — from Wisconsin."

Moral: The recognized Types never run true to Form during the Vacation Period.

THE FABLE OF THE WAIST–BAND THAT WAS TAUT UP TO THE MOMENT IT GAVE WAY [1]

Once there was a Family consisting of Mr. and Mrs. Stuffer and three little Stuffers.

Mrs. Stuffer had belonged to the Bolt Family back in Fodderville, where she put on Weight before being shipped up to the City.

Her Mother was a Gullep, and Lineal Descendant of a New England Pilgrim named Grubb.

Mr. Stuffer also was well connected, never fear.

His Mother had been one of the Gobbels and his Grandsire on the other Branch of the Tree was often referred to, for he was none other than Phillip Gormann-Deizer, with a Colonial Home near the Gorge at Eatonville.

Their Folks, as far back as Records carried, had regarded America as the Land of Plenty and Then Some.

Also one of the Traditions coming from the grand old Pioneer Stock seemed to be that the Main Tract of the Alimentary System is the Home of the Soul.

The Stuffers could say truly that not one of their previous Relatives ever permitted a Guest to go away Hungry.

Sometimes he was taking Bi-Carb when he departed, but, Thank Edna, he never was craving Nourishment.

So the Family Honour stood safe and intact.

Back in the Country, where the Stuffers received their early Schooling as two-handed Scoopers, no Man could hold up his Head unless he was a bountiful Provider, and

[1] From "Hand-made Fables." Copyright, 1920, by Doubleday, Page and Company. Reprinted by permission of author and publishers.

no Woman was respected unless she had Apple Butter and two kinds of Pie on the Table.

Those were the Blissful Days when the Deacon with the Throat-Warmers would close his Eyes and ask that this Food be Blessed and Sanctified to our Uses.

And take it from Hortense, when the Deacon made that reasonable Request, there was something piled in front of him waiting to be Sanctified.

No one ever heard of Luxuries during that oleaginous Period.

Anything that could be Et was a Necessity.

The family that wanted a Sunday Dinner away back Yonder did not have to hock the Morris Chairs.

The Barn Lot was swarming with Springers; the Garden had many rows of Sass; Berries could be had for the Picking.

Anything you might think of was Ten Cents.

For one measly Dime, the genial Grocer would let you have a Pound of Butter or a Dozen Eggs or a Peck of Murphys or a hunk of Bacon or an armful of Roasting Ears.

Beans were about as costly as Gravel.

Off in the Pantry, the solid loaves of Salt-Rising Bread were stacked, careless-like, the same as Cord-Wood.

The Humble Toiler who stowed away 14 to 16 Spare-Ribs smothered with Kraut, four or five helpings of Fresh Vegetables, a few light Biscuits inlaid with golden Butter, and possibly a quarter of a mile of Noodles, would trick out his Modest Snack with Spiced Peaches, frosty Dough-nuts, and a little quart Bowl of preserved Cherries, to say nothing of Coffee Curdled with heavy Cream, and never suspect that he was living somewhat Snooky.

He was simply getting regular every-day Chow of the Farm-Hand variety.

It was on Sunday, when the Minister and his Wife or Cousin Elam's Family came over, that Mother extended herself and showed Class.

The Family never had Flowers on the Table, because the Space was taken up with Jams and Jells.

At that time, Dinner did not open with *Canapé Scabouche* followed by *Potage à la Bohonque*.

It opened with a Breast and a Second Joint and a couple of Drumsticks and much Gravy, with here and there a Giblet, and enough Mashed Potatoes to plaster a Small Room, and a Million Green Peas that never had been to Market, and an awful mix-up of String Beans, while the Odd Corners were chinked in with Cottage Cheese and Pickled Watermelon Rind and Sweet Peppers.

Butter was not rolled into Marbles during the Seventies.

Well, we should say Not!

It was lifted in half-pound Gobs, and those who smeared it never felt Improvident.

What is now called Service consisted of cleaning up the Trough and going back for another Load.

The Conversation was wholly made up of:

(1) Urgent Appeals for every one to Pack in a little bit more;

(2) Weak Protests from the Packees;

(3) Contrite Apologies from the Cook as to the Quality and Amount of Eatables in sight;

(4) Stereotyped Assurances to perturbed Hostess that everything was Swell, Elegant, and Hunky.

If the Fig Cake was a Triumph and the Jelly Cake held its Shape but the Hickory-Nut Cake went Blah, that called for a lot of Explaining.

There was a Time when every Woman thought that a soggy Cake was a Reflection on her Character. Then, if the Visitors moved slowly from the Dining Room with their Eyes protruding slightly, the Meal was voted a Success.

Not every Parlour sported an upright Piano, and the Citizen who guided a team of Bays from the front Pad of a two-seated Carriage was some Rajah, but the humblest Family waded knee-deep in Vittles.

When Winter came on, each Cellar in the Township was

loaded to the Guards with Turnips, Punkins, Bell-Flower Apples, Pop-Corn, Vinegar, Walnuts, Cabbage, Potatoes, Lye Hominy, Side-Meat, Canned Stuff, Hard Cider, Sorghum Molasses, Lard, Honey in the Comb, Rutabagas, Fruit-Jars in Platoons, Jelly-Glasses in Brigades, Sage, Carrots, Navy Beans, Corn Meal, Buckwheat Flour, Onions, and other Medicinal Herbs, with possibly a few chilled Geese and Rabbits for immediate Consumption.

A barbed-wire Entanglement could have been strung around any Domicile in the Autumn, and the imprisoned Family would have come out on May 1st wearing Double Chins.

After the Stuffers landed in Town and had to use pleading Language to get a couple of fibrous Chops, they would become sentimental over Memories of Hog-Killing.

Oh, Elmer!

The Steaming Kettles of Water and the sound of scraping Knives.

Pallid Carcasses suspended in the frosty Air and the gleeful Eviscerators singing "Molly Darling" as they Rummaged.

If a close-figuring Landlady, who tries to set a Table for Seven Per, could have seen the Cans of Lard, the Platters of Tenderloin, the Hams waiting to be Cured, and the Sausage Meat ready to glide into the Links, she would have declared it was all a Mirage.

It is hard for some People to realize, along in this Stretch of Tribulation, that not long ago, out where Things are Grown, everyone who sat down to a Repast was urged to make a Grand Drive and go as far as he liked.

The mere Thought of any one going light on new-laid Eggs, or laying off on Butter, or messing around with Bran, Excelsior, Sawdust, Husks, Chop-Feed, and other Substitutes for Something to Eat would have been too Silly for Utterance.

The Practice of Economy was well-nigh Universal, but it did not involve playing a Joke on the Œsophagus.

The Woman of the House was Thrifty, for she fed her Cook-Stove a Splinter at a Time.

When Pa's red Unmentionables with the Glass Buttons became too Intimate and Itchy, they were chopped down for Ulysses or Grover.

Patches were made into Quilts and Rags worked over into Carpets.

A Peach-Basket, treated with a Nickel's Worth of Gold Paint and decked out with Bows of Ribbon, became a Hanging Basket for the Pet Geranium.

All the spare Coppers went into the little Tin Bank.

Only a favoured Few were permitted to walk on the Brussels Carpet.

Any good Citizen of Jasper Township would have assured you that Frugality was his Middle Name.

But Frugality did not mean getting up from the Table unsatiated.

For any one to back away before he felt himself Distended would have been regarded as Evidence of a cowardly Nature.

As soon as a Member of the Family began to fly at the Menu with a lack of wolfish Enthusiasm, he was subject to treatment as an Invalid.

The real Local Gazimbat was the Lad who held the Flapjack Record and was ready to meet all Comers during the Sweet-Corn Season.

A never-failing Appetite for anything that could be carried in and planked on the Table was classed as one of the Christian Virtues.

The Owner was held in Regard as one who had acquired Moral Grandeur and lifted himself above the Weaklings.

He went around blowing that he could Eat Anything, and all the Light Feeders slunk into the Background when he lifted his Bazoo.

Now that you have a Steer on the Pre-Natal Influences and Environment of the Stuffer Family, can you see the

Bunch dropped down in a Residence Thoroughfare of a congested Metropolis, three miles from a Cow and six miles from a Hen that could be relied upon to come across every Day?

Although badly separated from the Base of Supplies, they were still true to the honoured Customs of the Grubbs and the Gobbels and the Gulleps.

Mrs. Stuffer often said that she would rather cut off her Right Hand than have an Acquaintance drop in and find one Section of the Dining-Room Table unoccupied by tempting Viands.

She remarked time and again that, Come what Might, she never would Stint her Loved Ones or deny them such simple Essentials as Fresh Eggs, Sure-Enough Butter, Steak cut thick, Leg of Lamb, and submerged Short-Cake.

And there were a Hundred Thousand More like her.

If one is accustomed to the Best — and no real Daughter of a generous Mother ever compromised on Seconds or Culls — one must not Pike when telephoning the Orders.

This elaborate Overture will give you a Rough Idea of what Mr. Stuffer was up against.

He came to the City on a Guarantee.

His Salary looked like the Income of J. P. Morgan until he began to check up the Outgo.

Back in Fodderville, a neat frame Dwelling with a scroll-saw Veranda, a bed of Peonies, and Exposure on four Sides would set you back about $15 per Moon.

Up in the City, you couldn't get a Hat-Rack for any such Money.

It seemed to the Stuffers that everything in Town was sold by the Minute or the Ounce.

It was a grievous Shock to the Missus when they began to weigh the Vegetables on her.

She had got used to having them thrown at her with a Shovel.

The Neighbours no longer brought in Produce at Special

inside Prices — Eggs figured by the wear and tear on the Fowl and no Overhead Charge on Honey except the Time put in by the Bees.

The Stuffers suddenly discovered that when you go out to spend a Dollar in the City, you don't have to take a Wheelbarrow along.

But Mr. Stuffer and Mrs. Stuffer and each of the miniature Stuffers had it firmly fixed in the Coke that the Minute you begin letting down on That to which you have been Accustomed you lose Self-Respect and indirectly confess to being in Straitened Circumstances.

It was all right for those living in Huts and Hovels to cheapen the Standards of Living, but the Stuffers could not endure the Thought of giving up any of the old Stand-by Dishes.

Some Persons of a Poetical Turn mark the changing Seasons by the Trailing Arbutus, which precedes the bold Iris; then old-fashioned Roses, followed by a riotous show of Dahlias; Autumn Leaves tinged Red and Yellow, harbingers of snowy Fields and icy Boughs.

Every Sign of the Zodiac meant a new Item in the Bill of Fare for the practical Stuffers.

With the first warm days of Spring, did they go looking for Wood-Violets?

Not one Look.

They began to sit up and demand Green Onions, Asparagus, Head Lettuce, and Strawberries.

June is the Month of Roses. Also of Fried Chicken and a pleasant gateway to Corn on the Cob.

Autumn Days need not be Melancholy if one is surrounded by Turkey and Mincemeat.

Even Winter has a Charm of its own, if Sausage and Buckwheat Cakes are ever smiling in the Background.

When Prices began to Sizz-Boom-Ah, the old Pay Envelope failed to stand up under the Strain, but can you expect one reared on the Fat of the Land to accept Macaroni as a Compromise?

The Producer would let out a Howl every time the Meat Bill came in, but he would have howled in a higher Key if the Good Woman had failed to throw him his Roast Beef and Mutton Chops.

He wielded a very consistent Knife and Fork and his daily Demand was for something that Sticks to the Ribs.

Of course, both of them saw the Article in the Paper, entitled "How to feed a Family of Five on 80 Cents a Day."

Once, just after the 1st of the Month, while Mr. Stuffer was still Bleeding, his Companion tried out a Sample Menu recommended by Hazel McGinnis Updyke, a famous Tipster weighing between 80 and 90 Pounds.

He stirred the watery Soup as if moved by a dull Curiosity as to the grains of Barley hiding at the Bottom, and then he gave Friend Wife a Look — but, Ooey, such a Look!

It seemed to say, "And this is the Woman who promised to Love, Honour, and be of some Help!"

Then came Rice Croquettes, one of the most startling Specimens of Near-Food ever touted by a Lady writing Syndicate Come-Ons and boarding at an Italian Table d'Hôte.

You eat it, but after you get through you are not sure that anything has Happened.

After which, Bread Pudding, said to have broken up more Homes than High White Shoes.

As Mr. Stuffer left the House, his well-meaning Partner felt in her Heart of Hearts that he was going out to a Restaurant to get some Ham and Eggs.

She resolved that never again would she ask him to be Untrue to his Nobler Self.

So, at the next Meal, she jollied him up with Lamb Steak and Kidneys, Mushrooms in Cream, Succotash, Waffles and Maple Syrup, Endive Salad and Sharp Cheese, with a Finale of Blueberry Pie *à la Mode*.

Experts tell us that Blueberry Pie, showing its bold Colour between the slopes of Vanilla Ice Cream, is practically the Last Word with those who want something to hit the Spot.

It is the *Pièce de Résistance,* the *Dénouement,* the Dramatic Climax, the Grand Transformation, Little Eva ascending to Paradise.

Nothing comes after it except the Pepsin Tablet and the Hot-Water Bag.

Mrs. Stuffer watched her Husband as he lighted his Sublima.

He had a Sleepy Look, which is always a Good Sign.

Then he Groaned, and she knew that she had won back his Love.

Any time you get them to Groaning, you are a Jewel of a Housekeeper.

Having set out to defy the Increased Cost and indulge themselves within Reason, the little Family soon found itself riding a troublous Sea with the Breakers just ahead. Man's Chief Enemies, they had been told long ago, are Pride, Lust, Avarice, etc.

Now they learned Different. They came to know that the two principal Destroyers of Happiness are the Middleman and the Cold-Storage Warehouse.

Hemmed in by extortionate Retailers, Food Pirates, and Commission Sharks, they stood Resolute and vowed they would never Surrender.

As they were riding over the Hills to the Poor-House, Mr. Stuffer made the dismal Observation that it was a Blue Finish for a Life of Honest Endeavour.

"That may be true," said Mrs. Stuffer, "but I have this Satisfaction," as she lifted her Head proudly: "I set a scrumptious Table to the very last."

Moral: Cling to your Ideals, such as they are.

OCTAVUS ROY COHEN

This young man, born on June 26, 1891, at Charleston, South Carolina, has already won very great laurels. He is the acknowledged chief living delineator of the American Negro, and indeed has originated, so far as that race is concerned, an entirely new school of writing. He has reared his own structure as to style and treatment. His first book of negro studies was published less than five years ago and he has since written six others. Perhaps his production is too rapid, since there is always danger of overstraining the note, particularly in the treatment of so emotional and colorful a race as the Negro — who, by the way, devours his books as eagerly as the white man. Mr. Cohen is a member of the bar but after practicing law for two years, he has devoted his time exclusively to writing.

NOBLESSE OBLIGED [1]

FLORIAN SLAPPEY scrutinized the other negro approvingly. "Napolium," he remarked, "ev'y time I obse'ves you I has a new idea."

Mr. Beezly nodded his shiny head meekly. "Yassuh, Mistuh Slappey."

"In fac'," continued Florian, "when I looks at you it seems 'sif ideas is the on'y things I ain't got nothin' else but."

"Yeah. Ain't you tootin'?"

"I is. I is suttinly doin' that, Mistuh Beezly. I is speckilatin' reegahdin' yo' immedjit future."

"Ain't it the truth?"

"It sho'ly is. Now, lemme think by myse'f fo' a minnit."

Napolium Beezly nodded acquiescence and the dapper

[1] From "Assorted Chocolates." Copyright, 1920, 1921, by Octavus Roy Cohen. Published by Dodd, Mead and Company. Reprinted by permission of author and publishers.

little fashion plate from Birmingham walked to the window of the dingy little room, where he stood gazing thoughtfully upon the dark seethe of traffic in South Rampart Street.

Napolium Beezly watched rather apprehensively. He was considerably awed by Florian's magnificence; frankly dazzled by the silk shirt, the immaculately pressed gray suit, the sporty straw hat, the silken hosiery and aggressive patent-leather shoes. And though Napolium was enormously flattered that Florian Slappey should find in him food for thought, he was nevertheless more or less frightened for fear those thoughts might result in a disruption of his placid cosmic scheme.

Napolium was supremely negative in type. He didn't claim his soul as his own because he wasn't at all sure of it. For three years he had existed in New Orleans, scraping along on odd stevedoring jobs, aloof from colored society, friendless, timid, bashful, retiring.

Suddenly Florian whirled. He had come successfully through the process of having an idea and his chocolate-creamy face was wreathed in a smile of triumph.

"Napolium," he quizzed, "you ain't got no frien's down heah in N'Yawlins, is you?"

"Nossuh. Nary one."

"N'r neither no relytives?"

"No kin n'r nothin'."

"Good job?"

"Once ev'y so often."

"Not now?"

"Nossuh."

"Them what does know you — they don' give much of a darn 'bouten you, does they?"

"How you know that, Mistuh Slappey?"

"You looks it." Florian paused, then: "You know I is from Bummin'ham?"

"Yassuh. I is hearn tell 'bouten you."

"Well, what you is hearn tell 'bouten me ain't even half

of what I is. Mebbe so you don' know that I is a philan-
dererpist, an' ———"

"A — a — how much?"

"A feller which gits his happiness outen doin' other folks
good."

"No?"

"Yeh. An', Napolium, I is fixin' to do you good!"

Napolium ducked. "I ain't astin' nobody to do me no
good no time; a feller done that to me once an' I ain't gotten
over it till yet."

"I is gwine he'p you whether you wan's to or not."

"I don' need no he'p."

"Huh!" Florian surveyed the other contemptuously.
"As a man, you jes nachelly ain't! I is gwine do you a
favor."

"I ain't gotten no money, Brother Slappey. Hones' ———"

"I ain't ast you fo' no money, is I?"

"No-o. But you mos' likely was fixin' to."

"I wa'n't fixin' to do nothin' of the kin'. N'r neither I
ain't never gwine ast you fo' no money, on 'count I reckon
it woul'n't be no use. Ise gwine he'p you — an' he'pin'
wuthless fellers like'n to you is 'bout the fondes' thing I
is of."

"Nossuh! Please ———" Napolium extended a pleading hand. "I reckon I is too wuthless fo' you to he'p."

"You mos' is, fo' a fac'. But not quite. An' not on'y is
I gwine he'p you but I is gwine pay you fo' bein' he'ped
besides."

"Huh?"

"Tha's which." Florian lowered his voice discreetly:
"Napolium — how 'd you like to be a prince?"

"A which?"

"A prince!"

"Who's him?"

"Who's him? Listen at you. Ain't you even know what
a prince is?"

"No-o. Not prezac'ly. What he is?"

"He's a—a—a—well, he's a feller that w'en he marries a woman she gits to be a princess!"

Napolium fancied that Florian was attempting humor and it therefore devolved upon him as host to laugh. Wherefore he crinkled up the corners of his eyes, opened his lips and emitted a throaty roar.

"Haw-haw! You is the jokines' feller, Brother Slappey!"

Florian became a mite peeved. "Ain't jokin'."

"You talks thataway."

"Trouble with you, Napolium, you ain't know when a man is se'ious. Now I asts you, frank an' man to man, how you would like to be a prince?"

Napolium couldn't understand and remarked as much. "How come you to talk sech foolishment, Brother Slappey?"

"I is got a reason. You know"—he glanced at the other speculatively—"you woul'n't make sech a bad prince if'n you was dressed swell an' proper an' was to be teached sumthin' 'bout princin' befo' you tried the job."

"Huh. Never heard of no princes like'n to what I is."

"They is a heap of things you ain't never hearn of, Napolium. They ain't ary single thing that I know of to keep you from bein' a prince," Florian declared.

"'Ceptin' that I ain't one."

"Who says you ain't a prince?"

"Nobody says I ain't. But they ain't nobody says I is."

"What nobody says you is don' matter a-tall. It's on'y when they's sumthin' folks says you ain't that you hadn't oughter be it. If'n they ain't no one says you ain't a prince an' I says you is a prince—then you is a prince by a majo'ity of one vote. Ain't that right?"

"H'm!" Napolium scratched his head. Florian's logic was irrefutable. "You talks soht of conwincin'."

"You is wuthless-lookin' enough," pursued Florian, "an' I un'erstan's you talks French, ain't it?"

"We-e-ell," answered the dazed Napolium honestly, "not prezac'ly."

"What you mean—not prezac'ly?"

"I talks French, but I don' know what I says when I talks it."

"Huh?"

"Y'see, I useter wuk with a cullud man fum the inside of Louisianny an' he di'n't talk nothin' but French, so tha's how come me to pick up the langwidge. I c'n make the same soun's he useter make, but I don' know what Ise sayin' when I does same."

Florian considered this phase of the question carefully. "Well, seems to me tha's the same as bein' a prince. They ain't ary cullud pusson in Bummin'ham gwine know what you is talkin' ain't French, so it's plenty good French fo' them."

"Says Bummin'ham?"

"Yeh."

"What I is got to do with Bummin'ham?"

"You is goin' there with me."

"Whaffo'?"

"Tha's where you is gwine begin yo' principleness."

"Oh!" Napolium thought it over for a while. "How come you to pick on me, Brother Slappey?"

"'Cause," returned Florian in all honesty, "you looks 'sif you was jes nachelly bohn to be puck on. An' you looks like you had li'l' enough sense to do what I says to do."

"H'mph! That depen's upon which you says do."

"I ain't gwine say nothin' which ain't easy. All you is got to do is to dress good, eat plen'y, don' do no wuk an' tell folks which bothers you to go to hell."

In the eyes of Mr. Napolium Beezly was born the faint light of interest. "Soun's like that job was made fo' me, Brother Slappey."

"It were — an' don' you never fo'git that I made it."

"I ain't. But — but — I ain't never be'n no prince befo'."

"Well," answered Florian sententiously, "it's a long worm which ain't got no turnin' an' they ain't no time like pretty soon to begin."

Napolium said nothing. For several minutes he repeated himself and then finally stammered forth a question: "C'n I ast you sumthin', Brother Slappey?"

"You c'n."

"Why you want I should be a prince?"

Florian hesitated, but only for a second. Then he seated himself on the edge of the rickety contraption which served the to-be prince as a bed and easy-chair. He extracted from the pocket of his beflowered waistcoat an imitation-silver cigarette case, from which he drew forth a Turkish cigarette. This he tapped delicately on a well-manicured finger nail. He inserted it languidly between shiny teeth, ignited the end and inhaled a refreshing puff of the heavy smoke.

"They's a woman in it," he began.

"I knowed that," came the unexpectedly sage answer from Prince Napolium.

"H'mph! Tha's one thing you ain't got to do — know things. Anyway, they's a woman in it an' her name is Marshmallow Jeepers, an' what she ain't got in looks she is got in money. Funny, ain't it, Napolium, how kind the good Lawd is to folks. If'n he don' han' 'em one thing he han's 'em another.

"Now, Marshmallow was done dirt when it come to bein' pretty, but her pa up an' died on her an' lef' her eight cullud houses which brings in rents of mos' a hund'ed dollars a month, cash money.

"Co'se, havin' all that money, Marshmallow don' need no looks in order to have men wantin' to ma'y her. Now me, I ain't merchantnerry, but one time I was gwine git ma'ied fo' love an' it di'n't git me nothin', so this time I says to myse'f I should ma'y Marshmallow an' git her money an' I c'n stay away fum the house so much it don' noways matter how ugly she is."

"Ain't you tootin'?" interjected Napolium admiringly.

"I is. An' also they is another feller in Bummin'ham which wan's to ma'y Marshmallow. His name is Maximillion Anslum, an' Ise heah to tell you, Napolium, that when it comes to wuthless, no-'count shiftlessness, that Maximillion is 'bout the mos' shiftlessest thing what is. Fu'thermo' he is got money of his own. Now I is sayin' to you, Napolium, that it's bad enough a feller should ma'y a woman like Marshmallow when he ain't got any money of his own, but when he is got some an' is willin' to ma'y a woman like'n to what she is, then I says he's a plumb hawg.

"But bein' rich, Maximillion is soht of gotten the inside track over me fo' Marshmallow's han' on account he is got money to spen' on her an' I ain't. Co'se I is got enough to sen' her a few flowers an' a bag of candy oncet in a while, but him — he takes her ridin' in taxis an' sen's two dozen flowers ev'y couple of days an' big boxes of candy an' takes her to the theayters all the time; an' he is jes' nachelly dizzled her offen her feet an' they is danger that I is gwine lose out. Tha's how come I to git the idea of you bein' a prince."

Napolium looked up. "Says which?"

"I is gotten a li'l' money an' I is gwine inves' it in you, Napolium. I is gwine buy you a book 'bout Africy an' you is gwine read all 'bout African princes an' all what they does. Then I is gwine back to Bummin'ham by myse'f an' let on that I is met up with a ginuwine prince an' what good buddies we was. They ain't ary pusson gwine b'lieve me, an' then I is gwine gitten me a letter fum you sayin' that you is gwine come to Bummin'ham to visit me. An' —— "

Florian looped fingers in the armholes of his vest. "When the Prince Napolium gits to Bummin'ham an' buddies roun' with me, they's a heap of folks in that town, an' specially Miss Marshmallow Jeepers, which is gwine be glad they knows Florian Slappey which knows a prince. Ain't it the truth?"

Napolium admitted that it was the truth. But he denied ambition to royal blood. Florian then turned loose the floodgates of his persuasive logic. And finally Napolium capitulated to the influence of one hundred dollars in currency as forced into his hands by Florian.

That night Florian Slappey boarded the Southern for Birmingham, leaving a frightened and bewildered Napolium Beezly in the colored waiting room clutching in his right hand a frayed volume entitled Tribal Customs in Darkest Africa.

Napolium glanced miserably at the book. "It soun's fine when he tells it," soliloquized the unhappy scion of royalty, "but if'n I ever gits unprinced — oh Lawsy!"

No matter what Florian Slappey may have lacked to make him a valuable member of Birmingham's colored community, he was there seven ways from the ace as a publicity expert. His postulations of the disbelief which would greet his boastings regarding a friendship with a genuine prince were borne out. His friends laughed good-naturedly and kidded him along; his enemies called him harsh names. Maximillion Anslum sneered openly at the obvious effort to impress the wealthy Marshmallow; and as for the lady in the case — she said little and thought less. Marshmallow was not given to too great thought. It caused headaches.

But Florian was persistent, and finally in the minds of Birmingham's dusky society there became well implanted the idea that there was actually a genuine Prince Napolium who did live in New Orleans. They did not believe that Florian knew him, but within a week they raised no question of the press-agented gentleman's genuineness.

Florian stuck gamely to his story and eventually convinced even the most skeptical of the following facts: First, that there was in New Orleans a royal gentleman of leisure, by name Prince Napolium, of Kazombo, Africa. Second, that though Prince Napolium was by birth and breeding a head-hunter, the soothing effect of Occidental culture had modified his inherited murderous tendencies until he had become quite mild. Third, that Prince Napolium was a modest man who lived in a modest way and made friends in truly democratic fashion. Fourth, that he had hinted he might some day come to Birmingham to visit his very good friend, Florian Slappey.

So frequently and so passionately did Florian discourse upon his royal friend that all came to believe in the facts as told by Florian with the exception of the friendship. And long before the day of Napolium's advent to Birmingham the public mind had been lulled to blissful quiescence. It was a certainty that there would be none to doubt the honesty of Napolium's royal pretensions.

And then came the letter to Florian from the prince in New Orleans announcing that, if it suited Florian, the son of an African king would visit for a few weeks in Birmingham. Florian exhibited the letter to his friends, commencing with Marshmallow.

Birmingham colored folk gasped. A prince to walk in their midst! A real, honest-to-goodness prince to be the guest of Florian Slappey! In a trice Florian became a lion. Ambitious matrons clamored for his favors, marriageable daughters made eyes at him and flattered him with the ultimate idea of being presented to Prince Napolium when he should arrive. Maximillion Anslum swore fearfully and knew that he was matrimonially out of it. And as for Marshmallow Jeepers, she beamed beatifically upon Florian and gave him to understand that he was a very nice man indeed.

Florian swelled with importance, bought a new suit and got busy. He was distant and aloof with those who now sought his favors and threw their scoffing back in their teeth. Prince Napolium was not one who wished to be besieged with social attentions, he informed them scornfully. Democratic as he was, he cared nothing about associating with the proletariat. He was coming to Birmingham.

And then Florian negotiated a master stroke. He engaged a suite of two rooms for the prince at the home of Marshmallow. His reasoning was simple: With the prince a resident at the home of Marshmallow, Florian would have an excuse to be there constantly, with every intention of returning a good crop of hay while the royal sun was shining.

Marshmallow almost wept with gratitude when Florian consented to allow the prince to board at her home. In an instant the social eminence which she had long craved was hers. Matrons who had persistently snubbed Marshmallow despite her wealth now hung sycophantically about her parlor.

She was elected to a minor office in The Sons and Daughters of I Will Arise and chosen a member of the Junior Beautifying Society.

Florian looked upon his preliminary work and knew that it was good. Then he progressed a step further. He visited an antique shop and made a few purchases. These were carted to the home of Miss Marshmallow Jeepers and placed in the royal suite the day before the arrival of the prince.

The prince was due in at the L. & N. depot from New Orleans at noon. Birmingham — white and black — quivered under the impact of his advent. Colored folk all found themselves with business which carried them in the general proximity of the depot at train time and the majority of homes in the fashionable South Highlands residential section mourned the absence of cooks, nursemaids and gardeners.

Florian strolled downtown early in the morning, a sartorial epic. He chartered Clarence Carter's seven-passenger taxi for the morning and took in Miss Marshmallow Jeepers as an honored passenger. He whiled away two hours driving in slow magnificence through the principal streets of the colored residential section, basking radiantly in the limelight and spurning overtures of friendship from folk who had been inclined to look down upon him in days immediately past.

At eleven-thirty Florian climbed to the zenith of beatitude when Maximillion Anslum bowed from the sidewalk. The angular Marshmallow snuggled coyly against Florian.

"You don't like Maximillion, does you, Florian?"

"No."

"How come?"

"They's reasons."

"Which reasons?"

"Jes some — tha's all."

"Di'n't you an' him have a fight once?"

Florian fidgeted uncomfortably. His battle with the large and redoubtable Maximillion had added no glories to his own escutcheon.

"Yeh — we fit. He's bigger'n me, an' — well, he hit me in the right eye an' bunged it up, an' then he hit me in the lef' eye an' closed that one. Then he punched me in the stummick an' knocked all the bref outen me. Then he knocked me down 'an jumped on me an' stomped all over me. After that he kicked me in the shins. Hones', Marshmallow, I never gotten so sick of a nigger in all my life."

Marshmallow slipped a bony hand into Florian's eager palm. "You po' feller. He sho done you wrong, di'n't he?"

As train time approached, Florian became silent, apprehension rising to haunt him. His scheme was perfect, he was quite convinced of that, but somehow he could not rid his mind of a picture of Napolium as that gentleman had appeared in New Orleans — little, black, wistful, meek, apologetic, friendless. Florian commenced to fear that perhaps his choice for elevation to royalty was a trifle too negative. Of course if Napolium was able to get by with it Florian knew that he had chosen well, as he was quite confident of his ability to keep Napolium under his thumb and force that gentleman to do his bidding to the letter.

But there was danger that even a ready and believing public might come to doubt.

On time to the minute, the long train rolled under the shed. At the forefront of the crowd ganged before the colored exit stood Florian and Marshmallow. And finally Florian emitted a nervous ejaculation.

"Yonder he is."

The crowd surged forward eagerly. There was no mistaking Napolium.

He was clad in a black-and-white-checked suit which would have been a criminal offense for any below royal station. His enormous shoes were a yellow shriek and his flowing four-in-hand matched. His socks were silky lavender, his hat a white straw with a lavender band. In one gnarled muscular hand he clutched a shiny new straw suitcase and as he stepped gingerly across the tracks toward the exit his large frightened eyes rolled beseechingly in quest of Florian Slappey.

Florian experienced a sudden sinking sensation and only returned to consciousness when he felt Marshmallow's fingers digging relentlessly into his arm. "My Lawd! Ain't he elegant!"

Frankly Florian did not agree with her verdict. He had instructed his protégé to purchase royal raiment, but even his imaginings had not run riot to this extent. He strained his ears for the critical comment of the crowd and breathed easier as it floated to him:

"There's the prince!"

"Ain't he the swelles' thing you ever did see?"

"Sho'ly is. An' them clothes — ain't they wonderful?"

"You is tootin'. I wonder will he notice us."

"Wisht I was Marshmallow Jeepers."

"Ain't it —— "

"Always did think Florian Slappey was the nicest feller in Bummin'ham."

Things were temporarily safe. If only the obviously nervous prince did n't cause the beans to slip from the platter. Finally Napolium spotted his benefactor. He accelerated noticeably and fell upon Florian with an exclamation of infinite relief.

"Brother Slappey!"

"Prince Napolium!" Florian turned grandiloquently to Marshmallow. "Yo' Royal Highness, lemme perduce you to my lady frien', Miss Marshmallow Jeepers."

Their hands met. Said Marshmallow: "Pleased to meet Yo' Honor."

" Yas'm," mumbled the embarrassed Napolium. " Ain't you?"

The crowd fell back respectfully as Florian magnificently led the way toward the waiting automobile. Their eyes were wide and mouths agape. The prince progressed crabwise, hunted eyes darting hither and thither fearfully. They reached the taxi in safety, but just before they drove off a dapper little negro stepped up to the car.

" Prince Napolium?"

" Huh?" gasped the prince.

" Ise a repohter fo' the *Weekly Epoch* an' I wishes to maintain an interview with you."

" I ain't done nothin' —— " started the terrified prince, when Florian interrupted:

" My ve'y good frien', the prince, ain't grantin' no interviews yet. He's all ti'ed out an' also fatigued fum offen his trip. If'n you wishes to see him he will be excruciated to receive you in his rooms at Miss Jeeper's house this afternoon at th'ee o'clock. Ain't it so, prince?"

Napolium nodded dumbly. " Y-y-y-you knows, Mistuh Slappey."

Company awaited them at the Jeepers home. Mrs. Lustisha Atcherson had stolen a march on her rivals and chosen that hour to call upon Marshmallow — an honor which rivaled the visit of the prince in Marshmallow's eyes and established beyond shadow of a doubt that Florian's plan was destined to work beyond expectations, barring accidents.

Mrs. Atcherson gushed. " Prince Napolium — I sho'ly is much obliged to meet up with you. I is read about you so frequint an' my frien', Mistuh Slappey heah, is tol' me so many li'l' exquisite antidotes bouten you that I feel 'sif I'd of knowed you fo' ever so long."

The prince rolled terrified eyes. " Yeh — ain't it?"

" It is, prince; really an' ginuwinely, it is. You don' know how excited I am at meetin' up with a real prince. How long is you been away fum Africa?"

" Huh?"

"How long is you been in this country?"

Napolium hedged. "Long time; soht of *fin-de-siècle*, as it were."

Florian danced a mental jig of elation. Napolium, despite his terror, was more than rising to the occasion.

"I is heah," pursued Mrs. Atcherson, "as president of the Bummin'ham Uplift an' Educationel Sassiety to ast would you address our meetin' Thursday afternoon."

"Says which?"

"Address our sassiety ——"

Florian saw that Napolium was growing panicky. Enough was too much, and Florian stepped into the breach. He blandly informed Mrs. Atcherson that the prince would be delighted to accept, excused himself to the ladies and escorted Napolium to his rooms.

Safe in the antiseptic sanctuary, Napolium dropped limply onto the bed. "My Lawd, Brother Slappey, you sho is gotten me into sumthin'!"

Florian clapped him resoundingly on the back. "You is immense, Napolium! They is eatin' outen yo' han's a'ready."

"Yeh," mumbled the prince fearfully, "but Ise soht of skeered they is gwine bite."

"You ain't got ary worry. They ain't nothin' c'n go wrong. Now lis'en." Florian plunged under the bed and extracted therefrom a paleolithic-looking club. "See this?"

"Yeh."

"Tha's a war club what you useter kill yo' enemies with."

"Huh?"

"You useter kill yo' enemies with that club an' ——"

Napolium rolled startled eyes. "Now lis'en heah, Brother Slappey, they ain't nobody got nothin' like'n to that on me."

"Don' talk foolishments, Napolium. Folks thinks you is a Africa prince which useter fight in wars with war clubs, an' that there is yo'n. Now this heah"—and Florian presented to the frightened gaze of the other a butcher knife of Gargantuan dimensions—"is yo' assegee."

Napolium ducked discreetly. "My who?"

"Yo' assegee; same bein' the knife what you cut the gizzards outen folks with."

Napolium rose and paced the floor. "You is sho'ly gitten me into sumthin', Brother Slappey. S'posin' anyone was to heah 'bout me killin' folks an' cuttin' they gizzards out an' all sech as that? What you reckon they'd do to me, huh? Nossah, what I tell these folks was that when I princed, I princed good an' kin' an' never kilt nobody — never even busted 'em in the nose when they was so' at me on account I is got a kin' heaht. You keep yo' ol' war club an' yo' assegee, Mistuh Slappey, on account I ain't that kin' of a prince."

At length, however, Florian persuaded Napolium to festoon the villainous instruments on the walls of his room. Between them Mr. Slappey hung a group photograph of several frankly immodest hula-hula dancers, which he explained to Napolium once constituted the royal ménage at Kazombo. Napolium gazed upon the ladies of the picture with watery eyes of approval, but openly questioned the propriety of such mural decoration.

The final trophy of darkest Africa presented by Florian to Napolium as a family heirloom was a tom-tom which had for years done yeoman service in a trap-drummer's outfit. The prince tried it out tentatively, approved its reverberating tone, and accepted with pleasure. Then he smoked two of Florian's cigars while preparing to receive the representative of the colored press.

The reporter showed up three minutes ahead of scheduled time. Florian seated himself in a corner where he could signal to the frightened prince without attracting the journalist's attention.

Fortunately the reporter had ideas of his own regarding the flora and fauna of Central Africa which he imparted to the prince, asking verification, which was eagerly given. The result was twofold: The reporter left with what he considered a marvelous interview, and Napolium had learned considerable of value regarding his native land.

The *Weekly Epoch* rolled damply from the press the following morning with a picture of Prince Napolium and the signed interview spread magnificently over the first page, and the triumph of royalty was complete and utter.

Darktown fairly squirmed with glee at the presence of the prince. Folks buzzed round planning receptions and dances and ice-cream festivals in his honor. There was a descent in force upon Birmingham's ladies' ready-to-wear stores and gorgeous raiment was purchased by members of the fair sex on the dollar-down-and-a-dollar-a-week-forever plan. News of the prince spread even unto Cincinnati, whereupon certain colored gentlemen went into executive session, and the following evening one of their number purchased a ticket for Birmingham, climbed aboard the day coach and commenced a twenty-hour journey southward.

As for Florian Slappey, that arch plotter perched comfortably upon the uttermost pinnacle of the Mont d'Extase. The scheme was panning out beyond his wildest anticipations and he was finding Napolium dazed, docile and inexpressibly grateful.

Napolium was in a new and fairy world. For the first time in his life he was being sought after and made much of. He gazed upon life with eyes of wondering doubt and suspicion—intermingled with a growing hint of superb ecstasy. Like all his mental kind, Napolium had always craved public adulation and now he was expanding slowly and commencing to suspect that he had long done himself several injustices. He was slowly but very surely becoming convinced that he was more or less a man of parts. Certainly, he reasoned painstakingly, it required brain, poise and a hitherto unsuspected *élan* to convince folks that he was a genuine prince.

Thursday morning dawned gray and soggy. Napolium waked feeling a lump of gloom sitting damply on his chest. He turned over in bed, grunted and remembered. This was the day on which he was to deliver his African address to the open meeting of the Birmingham Uplift and Educational Society.

Public oratory is the *bête noire* of the uninitiated. As for the prince, he had never even heard a public speech. The gloom of the day was prophetically oppressive. Low-hanging blackish clouds scudded across the heavens and exuded wetness. Automobiles skidded dangerously on rain-glistening streets. Napolium buried his head under the sheets and groaned audibly.

"Ain't gwine make 'em no speech," he moaned. "Ain't got nothin' to say."

There came a knock at the door and, in response to Napolium's invitation, Miss Marshmallow Jeepers entered. Napolium sniffed and sat up straight in bed. Marshmallow bore in her hands a tray of glittering silver plate and spotless napery upon which reposed a cup of steaming, tantalizingly odorous coffee, three toothsome rolls, a pair of soft-boiled eggs and four slices of breakfast bacon broiled to a state of maddening crispness.

"Mawnin', Yo' Honor."

"Mawnin', Miss Jeepers."

"I brung you a li'l' breakfus', prince."

Napolium arranged it on his lap and set to with a will.

"M'm! You make these rolls, Miss Jeepers?"

"Yassuh. Does you like 'em?"

"They's the bes' I ever et. An' this bacon — does you know, Miss Mushmeller, bacon is jes about the fondes' thing I'm of."

"Is it now? Does you have bacon in Kazombo, prince?"

Napolium made a wry face. Mention of Africa awakened thoughts of the impending address and Napolium preferred to forget oppressively unpleasant matters.

"I ain't intrus' in Africa, Miss Mushmeller; Ise intrus' in Bummin'ham right now. This is sho'ly one swell town!"

"Ain't you tootin', Yo' Royal Highness? Co'se it don' look good to no prince."

"Huh! Heap you know 'bouten it. *Honi swat qui mal y pants.* Tha's what I think."

Marshmallow stared in speechless amaze. "You is sho' a wonderful feller, prince."

"You think so?"

"I knows it."

"We-e-ell"—and Napolium sighed with self-satisfaction—"I soht of think I ain't so wuss myse'f."

Silence fell between them while Napolium went to the mat with the eggs. During the *mêlée* Miss Marshmallow Jeepers watched His Royal Highness with eyes which told their own startling story. Had the prince been cursed with more ego he might have understood — have understood that not only had Mr. Maximillion Anslum been put forever out of the running for the hand of Marshmallow but he would have understood also that Mr. Florian Slappey stood no more chance than a nickel in a two-bit crap game.

In brief, Miss Marshmallow Jeepers, proprietrix of rental demesne, had fallen madly, completely, wildly and passionately in love with the representative of the Kazombo emirate. Her infatuation for Mr. Napolium Beezly was no weak and wan passion, but an overpowering, consuming attachment which was flaming hotly in the hitherto rather icy innards of Miss Jeepers and consuming her by its own heat.

Napolium on his part suspected nothing. True, Napolium had gazed upon Marshmallow and found her very desirable. Her noticeable lack of pulchritude affected him rather pleasantly than otherwise, for he himself was by no means overblessed with beauty and he therefore expected less in members of the opposite sex. In fact, Napolium was always more or less embarrassed in the presence of a really beautiful woman. He felt hopelessly out of place, eugenically impossible. Homely as he was, he felt none of this awkwardness with Marshmallow.

He was, however, loyal to Florian Slappey. Toward that debonair and polished gentleman he maintained a steadfast and devoted allegiance. It never occurred to him to consider himself a possibility in Marshmallow's matrimonial lists, for even yet Napolium could not quite grasp the idea that so far as Birmingham was concerned he was a prince. He rather fancied himself a bubble with Florian holding a menacing pin to prick on the instant any too great assumption of authority.

And so Napolium did not allow himself to dwell upon the beatific possibilities of a marital alliance with the wealthy and competent Marshmallow. With gameness and gratitude he bent himself to the task of giving Florian Slappey full benefit of reflected glory — capitalizing for Florian the social prestige that gentleman was able to bestow upon Marshmallow by reason of his intimacy with a real prince.

Meanwhile both Florian and Napolium looked forward with dire dread to the lecture of that afternoon. By one o'clock Napolium was a nervous wreck. At one-thirty Florian assisted in bedecking the princely figure in royal garb from a mail-order house while he imparted last information on how a speaker should conduct himself. Then Florian motored with the prince and Marshmallow to the lodge rooms of The Sons and Daughters of I Will Arise, where the session was to be held.

The hall was a choppy sea of glittering, aggressive color; of floppy hats and saddened, if highly colored, plumes. Reds, yellows, greens, blues and lavenders jazzed in a glorious ensemble which would have put a self-respecting rainbow to the blush.

Mrs. Lustisha Atcherson met the dignitary at the front and fought her way through the crowd to the stage, where she seated herself in the center, with the prince at her right, Florian Slappey at her left and Marshmallow Jeepers slightly to the rear. Marshmallow, gaudy in a too-flimsy Georgette waist and a satin skirt, was agleam with the greatest triumph of her meteoric social career. She gazed with honest approval and overt affection upon the glistening dome of the royal head. Her gratitude seemed misapplied, for instead of vouchsafing her thanks to Florian she lavished it on the supine prince.

The meeting was called to order and Mrs. Atcherson delivered a mellifluous address of welcome. She spoke in glowing malapropisms of the celebrity who had come into Birmingham's midst and announced that it was only after earnest persuasion on her part that he had consented to honor The Birmingham Uplift and Educational Society with his presence. She then introduced the speaker of the afternoon.

Beads of perspiration glistened on the forehead of Napolium as she mentioned his name and the hall rocked with applause from the fair sex packed within. He sat motionless, heart thumping madly against his ribs, his Lilliputian brain refusing to function.

It was only when he heard Florian's hoarse commanding voice, "Git up! Git up, there, cullud man!" that he took a chance on the strength of his skinny knees and staggered to his feet.

Napolium lurched to the front of the stage. It was like the first tentative walkings of a one-year-old. A surge of nausea came over him and the hundreds in the room swam before his gaze as millions. His lips were dry, his tongue parched. And then came silence!

The tumultuous applause had been bad enough, but this hushed, expectant silence was nothing less than fiendish. Napolium's tongue caressed his dry lips.

From the rear came Florian's harsh voice: "Git busy! Tell 'em about it!"

The audience sat forward. Napolium's head wabbled from side to side. He opened his lips and a harsh croak was the result. Dazed, stricken, he tried again.

"Ladies an' gen'lemen — n-n-no! Jes ladies —— "

A wild yell of laughter greeted him. The audience had made the discovery that the speaker was a humorist. Napolium looked over the audience in pained surprise, striving to discover whether they were laughing at or with him.

Instinct counseled the latter. He plunged desperately ahead.

"Me — I comes from Africa. Ise a prince — a real, ginuwine prince ——"

Wild applause, and Napolium took a breathing spell. He commenced to feel a trifle less terrified.

"Yassuh! Ise a ginuwine prince, an' where I comes from in Africa is name' Kazombo." Applause. Napolium gulped.

"Where I comes from is name' Kazombo, an' we is got a large cullud popilation."

Shrieks of laughter. From the center of the house came the approving yell of an almost hysterical woman: "You is the funnin'est man, prince."

The prince gazed in the general direction of the voice with pleased surprise. He saw that all eyes were bent approvingly upon him. He experienced a faint warmish glow of satisfaction. He had never before suspected that he possessed oratorical powers, yet undeniably he had already won over his audience. Knowing as little as he did about public speaking, he was yet responsive to the welcoming mass psychology.

"We is got a large cullud popilation an' I is they prince. I is a quiet feller now, but I useter be wil' — terrible wil'! When we useter have wars we useter beat our inimies over the head with a club an' stew 'em fo' supper."

Again the lecture was stopped by the applause of the wildly enthusiastic ladies of the audience. To the rear of the stage sat Marshmallow, gazing upon the dumpy form of Napolium with eyes of ineffable adoration. As for Florian, he was fairly wriggling with glee. This oratorical prodigy was of his manufacture, it was in his brain that the project had been formulated. He gazed upon the sea of fascinated faces and knew that his work had been good.

Napolium continued talking. Each time he paused there was a tidal wave of applause. The early nervousness departed and in its stead there came a wonderful glow of self-satisfaction. Napolium was coming to understand that he had for twenty-seven years been doing the world an injustice by hiding his light under a bushel. He fell in love with his work. He commenced to take himself seriously. He removed the bushel and let his light shine before all of the spectators.

In brief, Napolium discovered that he was enjoying himself. He had made the discovery that no matter what he said it was greeted with enthusiasm, respect and proper laughter. He commenced to make gestures, to shout as he had seen dusky preachers do. He orated!

In twenty minutes he had exhausted all his fund of information regarding Africa in general and Kazombo in particular. That fazed him not at all. He shifted the scene of his discourse from Kazombo to heaven and from there to hell. He continued his travelogue to include New Orleans and Birmingham. He discussed the Mississippi River, the L. & N. Railroad and Marshmallow's waffles. He shamelessly related stories he had heard other men tell and arrogated their glories unto himself.

A half hour passed, three-quarters, an hour. Florian became fidgety. Once started, there seemed no stopping the verbose prince. Desperately Florian edged his chair across the stage and plucked at the hem of Napolium's coat.

"Hesitate!" he commanded hoarsely. "Quit!"

Napolium looked round, surprised that there was one present who was not valuing his oratory to the full.

"Says which?"

"Cut it out!" grated Florian *sotto voce.* "You is talkin' too much with yo' mouth!"

Napolium was offended. He edged close to Florian and told him as much. "Ain't you want to learn sumthin' 'bout Africa?" he asked.

Florian's jaw dropped. Before his eyes Napolium had changed — had blossomed beyond all reason. For the first time Florian grew a wee mite apprehensive.

At the conclusion of the lecture the Prince Napolium was

driven home in the flivver sedan which made stable Mrs. Atcherson's social leadership. As he bade the ladies adieu and moved up toward the front porch a dignified colored gentleman rose to greet him.

He was a large person, gloriously garbed. He came forward respectfully. "Is this heah the Prince Napolium?"

Napolium nodded grandly. "I are him."

"Dumfee is my name — Zekiah Dumfee, fum Cincinnati. I has come all the way down heah to make talk with you."

Napolium inspected the other with a hint of apprehension. "Fum Cincinnati?"

"Yeah."

"To make talk with me?"

"I is."

"'Bout which?" Napolium was reassured by the respectfulness in the other's manner.

"Business, prince. Jes business. I don' know if'n princes ever talks business, an' of cou'se they ain't so awful much money in this heah fo' you, but —— "

"Come in!" The prince opened the door and ushered the visitor into the royal suite. "Seat yo'se'f down, Brother Dumfee. Yassuh, I smokes seegars. Now, what c'n I do you fo'?"

Brother Dumfee was a sound business man and a good talker. He explained his mission in a few pointed words. It appeared that Brother Dumfee was of the directorate of an Afro-American insurance-fraternal order known as The Kings and Queens of Heavenly Glory, which order had been desperately but ineffectually striving for some time to establish a firm foothold among the better class of negroes in the South.

Thus far they had been unable to secure the moral backing of local dignitaries in the larger colored communities and several efforts had died a-bornin'. In the person of Prince Napolium, however, opportunity was seen. Brother Dumfee impressed upon Napolium that his princely patronage, in view of the fact that he was at present — and promised to continue — a roaring social lion, would establish the order soundly in Birmingham, then in Alabama and thence on through the South.

Prince Napolium was therefore tendered a written and gold-sealed contract for the term of five years with a cash advance of $500 and an annual salary of $1200 in exchange for permission to advertise him as sponsor and chief Alabama officer of The Kings and Queens of Heavenly Glory. He was not required to work and was forced merely to pledge himself not to become associated with any other fraternal order during the contract period.

Napolium hesitated not upon the order of his acceptance, but grabbed immediately at the job. One hundred dollars a month for five years for doing nothing was his idea of heaven. However, in the manner of his acceptance he was nothing if not regal. He gave Brother Zekiah Dumfee distinctly to understand that he was accepting the position with its attendant honorarium only because he was a booster for fraternal work in general and quite convinced that The Kings and Queens of Heavenly Glory was entitled to representation in Birmingham.

News that Prince Napolium had condescended to head the new order in the state of Alabama spread like wildfire through Darktown and by eleven o'clock the following morning the temporary offices opened by Brother Dumfee in the Penny Prudential Bank Building were swarming with gentlemen and ladies eager to file their applications and pay the initial fees. Brother Dumfee perspired at his desk, but at the same time a broad grin of satisfaction decorated his colorado-maduro face. Thought of enlisting the aid of a genuine prince to further his interests had been little less than genius.

As for Napolium, he lounged round the lodge offices, appearing unutterably bored and quite out of tune with his labor. He was the center of an eager throng and the recipient of every imaginable sort of invitation. He accepted the fulsome attention languidly, supremely confident now in the power which had come to him.

Two weeks slipped by, two weeks during which The Kings and Queens of Heavenly Glory became organized and established on a solid financial footing and the Prince Napolium was unanimously elected Grand Noble and Exalted Supreme King of Birmingham Lodge Number 17. The two weeks passed, and in those two weeks Napolium circulated imperiously from reception to dance, from dance to dinner, from dinner to more dinner and from there to reception again. He delivered lectures to his lodge, to the Over the River Burying Society and to the Junior Beautifying Society. He discussed affairs with various matrons, legal matters with Lawyer Evans Chew and Africa with all who would listen. Strange French phrases rolled with frequent phonographic accuracy — and understanding — from his tongue. He accepted calmly and quietly his rôle of lion and decided unanimously that Birmingham was the best little old city in the world, better even than his figmented Kazombo.

At the end of that fortnight Florian Slappey paid a formal and abrupt call upon his protégé. Napolium fidgeted uncomfortably at sight of his caller; worldly and urbane as he had become, he had not yet rid himself of his pristine awe of the man whose magic touch had made it all possible.

Florian delivered his ultimatum tersely and commandingly.

"Napolium," he declared, "I brung you to Bummin'ham fo' a purpose an' same ain't be'n did. I is seein' a good deal of Marshmallow but it ain't gittin' me nowheres. Now what I says to you is — s'posin' you quit this princin' fo' a li'l' while an' see cain't you make Marshmallow ma'y me."

Napolium looked up docilely. "Yassuh, Flo'ian. I sho'ly will do my durndest with Mushmeller — yassuh."

"Yo'd better," returned Florian darkly. "'Cause'n this heah prince business ain't wukkin' out jes like I espected.

Befo' you come heah I was somebody. Now I ain't nothin' on'y somebody's frien'."

That evening the Prince Napolium of Kazombo paid royal call upon Miss Marshmallow Jeepers. He was dressed in his checkered best and wore largely upon the lapel of his coat the glittering emblem of The Kings and Queens of Heavenly Glory.

Napolium was very serious. More, consumed as he was with love for the homely but sterling Marshmallow, there was no hint of disloyalty in his mind. He understood clearly that Florian had brought him to Birmingham in order to assure success in his courtship of Marshmallow. Napolium felt that he had succeeded; certainly Maximillion Anslum, Florian's hated and theretofore successful rival, had faded into a pale oblivion.

Marshmallow was dressed bewitchingly, fluffs and flounces concealing the harshness of Nature in depriving her of all the curves with which the average woman is blessed. Her mahogany complexion had been embellished with Nemonia Collins' Lavender-Brown Complexion Powder and her hair was redolent of Nada Thompson's Hair-Apparent Lotion. Pearl beads nestled uncomfortably against a skinny neck and many rings sparkled valiantly from long bony fingers.

Withal, Napolium found Marshmallow good to look upon. Napolium had been educated in the school of practicalities and understood that beauty was but skin deep. Personally he preferred to overlook her alarming lack of pulchritude in favor of her wealth and culinary ability. Napolium frankly envied Florian and entered into his task with a lack of relish which bespoke much for his devotion.

They seated themselves beside each other on the sofa and for half an hour were content with generalities — the latest serial picture on view at the Champion Theater, the six-cent street-car fare — and gradually the conversation veered to personal channels. Napolium broke the ice.

"That Flo'ian Slappey, he sho is a fine feller."

Marshmallow shrugged uninterestedly. "Reckon so, prince."

"He is!" repeated Napolium with vast enthusiasm. "I thinks a heap of him."

"Then I reckon he mus' be some good anyways."

"He's pow'ful fine lookin'."

"Looks never gotten nobody no eatments."

"He dresses good."

"So does corpses."

"He's lucky down to the lott'ry — sometimes."

"Wuss luck fo' him. He never does no wuk."

Napolium paused. He began to suspect that whatever passion Marshmallow might possess was not lavished upon Florian. Then he continued desperately to extol the virtues of his friend.

"He's gwine make a fine husban' fo' some woman."

"Reckon they's some wimmin would think any husban' was a fine husban'."

"He stan's good."

"Stan's good ain't is good. In my 'pinion, prince, Mistuh Flo'ian Slappey jes nachelly ain't!"

"Ain't which?"

"Ain't nothin'."

"How come you to think that?"

Marshmallow answered deliberately. "Heah's the how of it, prince: W'en a man is, it's plumb easy to say what he is, but when he ain't, nothin' c'n be said bouten him 'ceptin' that he ain't."

"Y-y-you means you don' love Flo'ian?"

"Love Flo'ian Slappey?" Marshmallow turned startled eyes upon Napolium. "Love that no-'count, dressin' up, none-wukkin', lady-lovin', cullud bunch of wuthlessness? Me love him? My Lawd! Prince, does I look that foolish?"

"We-e-ll, no," agreed Napolium readily, "you does n't."

"An' I don't. I woul'n't ma'y that feller if'n they wa'n't no other man in the world 'ceptin' on'y him."

"H'm!" cogitated Napolium. "Tha's funny."

"What's funny?"

"You feelin' that way 'bout Flo'ian."

"How come?"

"Reckon you ain't in love with nobody, is you, Mushmeller?"

Marshmallow's eyes dropped modestly and a purplish blush stained her lavendered cheeks. "I is too."

"Maximillion Anslum?"

"Him? He's wuss'n Flo'ian. He's all what Flo'ian ain't an' nothin' what Flo'ian is. Nossuh, 'tain't Maximillion."

"Then who 't is?"

"I — I — I ain't gwine tell."

"Not even me?"

"Not even specially you."

"Why not specially me?"

"'Cause!"

"'Cause which?"

"'Cause you is a prince!"

Napolium Beezly maintained an absolute silence for perhaps half a minute. And during that half minute a thought percolated slowly through his mind. Suddenly he looked up.

"My Lawd, Mushmeller! Does you mean me?"

"Says who?"

"I says, does you mean me?"

She averted her eyes with old-maidenly modesty. Her voice was low-pitched, but vibrant with feeling. "Brother Cupid's arrers hits in funny places sometimes."

"M'm!" Napolium's head started whirling. It wabbled uncertainly on his neck and his fingers groped. They closed about the warm and responsive palm of Marshmallow Jeepers.

"Mushmeller!"

"Yo' honor!"

"Does you love me, Mushmeller?"

"Yeah. Does you love me, prince?"

"Does I love you? Sufferin' tripe! Mushmeller, I loves you so much I c'd — c'd — bite!"

His arm was about her waist, her lips upturned to his. Napolium forgot Florian Slappey, forgot his regal pretensions, forgot that the woman he held was no dusky Venus. He remembered only that he was gripped by divine passion.

Five minutes later he released her — released her reluctantly. And he asked a question.

"Mushmeller?"

"Yeh — sweethea't?"

"Does you know what a prince is, honey bunch?"

"What he is, Napolium?"

"A prince is somebody," quoted Napolium, "which when he ma'ies a gal she gits to be a princess!"

The exhilarating midnight air fanned the hot cheeks of Napolium Beezly. That gentleman, hat in hand, head held pridefully high, strode masterfully up Eighteenth Street.

Napolium was happy with the superlative happiness which comes to a man but once in a lifetime. In the face of his present beatitude the brummagem enjoyment of the past month faded into a drab nothingness.

Napolium felt that he had much to be grateful for. He was blessed with the adoration of the woman he worshiped, he knew that she was more than ordinarily well fixed in this world's goods and was a capable housewife. He held in his pocket a five-year contract, at a stupendous yearly figure, with The Kings and Queens of Heavenly Glory. Altogether there was no single thing to mar the divine placidity of the moment. Except Florian Slappey.

Florian Slappey! Napolium exhaled suddenly and audibly. He slackened pace perceptibly. He envisioned Florian awaiting his coming with tidings of Marshmallow, Florian waiting eagerly to be informed that the landed lady was soon to become Mrs. Florian Slappey.

It was pretty tough on Florian. Even Napolium admitted

as much; pretty tough. But — and Napolium accelerated again — what was, was, an' they wa'n't no use tryin' to change things.

It was with an attitude of ninety-nine per cent cocksureness and a single percentum of apprehension that Napolium stepped into Florian's room at a half hour beyond midnight. He found that dapper little gentleman, sleepy-eyed and silk-pyjamaed, reclining on the bed, engaged in the absorbing game of shooting a small smoke ring through a large one. Florian sat upright.

"What luck?" he asked pointedly.

Napolium ducked. "I is been thinkin'," he stalled.

"Thinkin'? You?"

"Yeh — I. Is you plumb sho', Flo'ian, that it woul'n't be a mistake fo' you to ma'y Mushmeller?"

Florian glared at Napolium. Napolium refused to meet the eyes of his friend. He wanted to break the news gently.

"No, 'tain't no mistake!" snapped Florian peevishly. "I is gwine ma'y Marshmallow."

"No you ain't," corrected Napolium.

"Says which?"

"I says you ain't."

Florian's feet came to the floor. "What kin' of talk is you doin' with yo' mouth, cullud man?"

"I says you ain't gwine ma'y Mushmeller." Napolium was surprised at the nuance of strength in his own tones.

"How come you to know that?"

"'Cause," repeated Napolium firmly, "Ise gwine ma'y her myownse'f!"

"Wh-wh-what?"

Florian rose and trembled. Napolium put out a restraining hand. He was sorry for his friend and something of princely dignity sat upon his shoulders as he tried to explain away the harshness of the blow.

"'Twa'n't my fault, Flo'ian; hones' it wa'n't. Gives you my word. If'n you is got to blame somebody —

blame yo'ownse'f on account the reasons she woul'n't make ma'iage with you was 'cause'n you is wuthless an' no 'count an' don' wuk an' you gambles an' you is too stuck on yo'se'f an'———"

"You—you—you———" Florian was trembling with violent passion. "You says———"

"'Tain't me," explained Napolium mildly; "tha's what Mushmeller says!"

And then Florian exploded. Vituperation flowed from his lips in a steady, unbroken stream for perhaps ten minutes. He started with the ancestry of Napolium ten generations removed and stigmatized them even unto the fifteenth or twentieth generation of Napolium's descendants. He dwelt with particular and colorful venom upon Napolium himself.

Only once did Napolium interrupt: "Better be careful, Flo'ian—you is li'ble to make me mad!"

But Florian did not cease. He established new records for forceful profanity and insoluble invective. And Napolium listened—listened attentively, but with a growing rancor. Enough was very much too much and too much was aplenty. Napolium's dignity was being twisted and tortured. Napolium was not used to this. It smacked too strongly of lese majesty.

"An' as fo' what Ise gwine do fo' you, Napolium Beezly," concluded Florian wildly—"it's gwine be aplenty. Ise gwine tell folks—Ise gwine tell 'em a few things. In jes 'bout one day they is gwine know you ain't nothin' on'y Napolium Beezly—plain cullud pusson an' not no prince. Wait 'll I tells 'em all I knows 'bout you. An' Ise gwine do it—I sho'ly is. I is———"

A great quiet calm settled itself over Napolium. He gazed with imperial disdain upon the raving Florian. He felt genuinely sorry for the man and somewhat embarrassed by the bourgeois display of temper.

"Says you is gwine espose me?" queried Napolium quietly.

"Says I is! I is, tha's what. Ise gwine tell folks."

"You done it!" reminded Napolium in a suave tone. He was above arguing with such as Florian.

"Yeh! An' Ise gwine undone it. I is gwine——"

"Lis'en heah, Flo'ian Slappey." Napolium seated himself calmly in the one easy-chair, tore the gilt band from a ten-cent cigar, lighted it and inhaled a delicious lungful. "All what you says intrus's me, but also I is got sumthin' to say.

"What happen' to-night I cain't he'p. 'Tain't my fault if'n Mushmeller is gotten enough jedgment to love me mo'n you. I done my durndest to make her see that you ain't so wuss. Now Ise heah to say you is done a heap fo' me. Ise even willin' to admit you is a wonderful feller. You puck me up when I wa'n't nothin' an' you made me sumthin'. Co'se you had good mate'ial to wuk with, but you done yo' job good.

"You brung me an' you teached me what I knows 'bout bein' a prince. You gotten me into sassiety an' you fixed me right. You is a great man, Flo'ian—I says that cheerful. But, Flo'ian, I says also one thing mo', as per this: They's on'y one thing in this heah world, Flo'ian Slappey, which you cain't do! An' that one thing, Flo'ian, is to make the cullud folks of Bummin'ham b'lieve I ain't no prince! You cain't do it, Flo'ian, an' they ain't no use to try!"

The Prince Napolium, of Kazombo, Africa, gazed calmly into the wide and wondering eyes of Florian Slappey. He deliberately blew a cloud of smoke into that gentleman's face.

"In fac'," concluded the royal gentleman confidently, "you cain't even make me b'lieve it!"

RING W. LARDNER

Ring W. Lardner writes in a dialect of his own; he seems to be a mixture of all the arts which our humorists of the cruder type, beginning with "Artemus Ward" and "Josh Billings", have found effective. Still a pervading originality masks an unusually alert and observant eye for contemporary life. Mr. Lardner has had a very wide vogue from the beginning of his "You know me, Al" stories and his reputation is a growing one. Like many other American humorists, he is a graduate from newspaperdom. He was born in Niles, Michigan, March 6, 1885.

RITCHEY [1]

WELL, I was just getting used to the Baldwin and making a few friends round there when Ella suddenly happened to remember that it was Griffin who had recommended it. So one day, wile Kate was down to the chiropodist's, Ella says it was time for us to move and she had made up her mind to find an apartment somewheres.

"We could get along with six rooms," she said. "All as I ask is for it to be a new building and on some good street, some street where the real people lives."

"You mean Fifth Avenue," said I.

"Oh, no," she says. "That's way over our head. But we'd ought to be able to find something, say, on Riverside Drive."

"A six room apartment," I says, "in a new building on Riverside Drive? What was you expecting to pay?"

"Well," she said, "you remember that time I and Kate visited the Kitchells in Chi? They had a dandy apartment

[1] From "The Big Town." Copyright, 1921, by Bobbs-Merrill Company. Reprinted by permission of the author and publishers.

on Sheridan Road, six rooms and brand new. It cost them seventy-five dollars a month. And Sheridan Road is Chicago's Riverside Drive."

"Oh, no," I says. "Chicago's Riverside Drive is Canal Street. But listen: Didn't the Kitchells have their own furniture?"

"Sure they did," said Ella.

"And are you intending to furnish us all over complete?" I asked her.

"Of course not," she says. "I expect to get a furnished apartment. But that don't only make about twenty-five dollars a month difference."

"Listen," I said: "It was six years ago that you visited the Kitchells; beside which, that was Chi and this is the Big Town. If you find a six room furnished apartment for a hundred dollars in New York City to-day, we'll be on Pell Street in Chinatown, and maybe Katie can marry into a laundry or a joss house."

"Well," said the wife, "even if we have to go to $150 a month for a place on the Drive, remember half of it's my money and half of it's Kate's, and none of it's yours."

"You're certainly letter perfect in that speech," I says.

"And further and more," said Ella, "you remember what I told you the other day. Wile one reason we moved to New York was to see Life, the main idear was to give Kate a chance to meet real men. So every nickel we spend making ourself look good is just an investment."

"I'd rather feel good than look good," I says, "and I hate to see us spending so much money on a place to live that they won't be nothing left to live on. For three or four hundred a month you might get a joint on the Drive with a bed and two chairs, but I can't drink furniture."

"This trip wasn't planned as no spree for you," says Ella. "On the other hand, I believe Sis would stand a whole lot better show of landing the right kind of a man if the rumor was to get out that her brother-in-law stayed sober once in a wile."

"Well," I said, "I don't think my liberal attitude on the drink question affected the results of our deal in Wall Street. That investment would of turned out just as good whether I was a teetotaler or a lush."

"Listen," she says: "The next time you mention ancient history like that, I'll make a little investment in a lawyer. But what's the use of arguing? I and Kate has made up our mind to do things our own way with our own money, and to-day we're going up on the Drive with a real estate man. We won't pay no more than we can afford. All as we want is a place that's good enough and big enough for Sis to entertain her gentleman callers in it, and she certainly can't do that in this hotel."

"Well," I says, "all her gentleman callers that's been around here in the last month, she could entertain them in one bunch in a telephone booth."

"The reason she's been let alone so far," says the Mrs., "is because I won't allow her to meet the kind of men that stays at hotels. You never know who they are."

"Why not?" I said. "They've all got to register their name when they come in, which is more than you can say for people that lives in $100 apartments on Riverside Drive."

Well, my arguments went so good that for the next three days the two gals was on a home-seekers' excursion and I had to spend my time learning the eastern intercollegiate kelly pool rules up to Doyle's. I win about seventy-five dollars.

When the ladies come home the first two nights they was all wore out and singing the landlord blues, but on the third afternoon they busted in all smiles.

"We've found one," says Ella. "Six rooms, too."

"Where at?" I asked her.

"Just where we wanted it," she says. "On the Drive. And it fronts right on the Hudson."

"No!" I said. "I thought they built them all facing the other way."

"It almost seems," said Katie, "like you could reach out and touch New Jersey."

"It's what you might call a near beer apartment," I says.

"And it's almost across the street from Grant's Tomb," says Ella.

"How many rooms has he got?" I says.

"We was pretty lucky," said Ella. "The people that had it was forced to go south for the man's health. He's a kind of a cripple. And they decided to sublet it furnished. So we got a bargain."

"Come on," I says. "What price?"

"Well," she says, "they don't talk prices by the month in New York. They give you the price by the year. So it sounds a lot more than it really is. We got it for $4,000."

"Sweet patootie!" I said. "That's only half your income."

"Well, what of it?" says Ella. "It won't only be for about a year and it's in the nicest kind of a neighborhood and we can't meet nothing only the best kind of people. You know what I told you."

And she give me a sly wink.

Well, it seems like they had signed up a year's lease and paid a month's rent in advance, so what was they left for me to say? All I done was make the remark that I didn't see how we was going to come even close to a trial balance.

"Why not?" said Katie. "With our rent paid we can get along easy on $4,000 a year if we economize."

"Yes," I said. "You'll economize just like the rest of the Riverside Drivers, with a couple of servants and a car and four or five new evening dresses a month. By the end of six months the bank'll be figuring our account in marks."

"What do you mean 'our' account?" says Ella.

"But speaking about a car," said Katie, "do you suppose we could get a good one cheap?"

"Certainly," I said. "They're giving away the good ones for four double coupons."

"But I mean an inexpensive one," says Kate.

"You can't live on the River and ride in a flivver," I said. "Besides, the buses limp right by the door."

"Oh, I love the buses!" said Ella.

"Wait till you see the place," says Katie to me. "You'll go simply wild! They's a colored boy in uniform to open the door and they's two elevators."

"How high do we go?" I said.

"We're on the sixth floor," says Katie.

"I should think we could get that far in one elevator," I says.

"What was it the real estate man told us?" said Ella. "Oh, yes, he said the sixth floor was the floor everybody tried to get on."

"It's a wonder he didn't knock it," I said.

Well, we was to have immediate possession, so the next morning we checked out of this joint and swooped up on the Drive. The colored boy, who I nicknamed George, helped us up with the wardrobe. Ella had the key and inside of fifteen minutes she'd found it.

We hadn't no sooner than made our entrée into our new home when I knew what ailed the previous tenant. He'd crippled himself stumbling over the furniture. The living room was big enough to stage the high hurdles, and that's what was in it, only they'd planted them every two feet apart. If a stew with the blind staggers had of walked in there in the dark, the folks on the floor below would of thought he'd knocked the head pin for a goal.

"Come across the room," said Ella, "and look at the view."

"I guess I can get there in four downs," I said, "but you better have a substitute warming up."

"Well," she says, when I'd finally fell acrost the last white chalk mark, "what do you think of it?"

"It's a damn pretty view," I says, "but I've often seen the same view from the top of a bus for a thin dime."

Well, they showed me over the whole joint and it did

look O. K., but not $4,000 worth. The best thing in the place was a half full bottle of rye in the kitchen that the cripple had n't gone south with. I did.

We got there at eleven o'clock in the morning, but at three P. M. the gals was still hanging up their Follies costumes, so I beat it out and over to Broadway and got myself a plate of pea soup. When I come back, Ella and Katie was laying down exhausted. Finally I told Ella that I was going to move back to the hotel unless they served meals in this dump, so her and Kate got up and went marketing. Well, when you move from Indiana to the Big Town, of course you can't be expected to do your own cooking, so what we had that night was from the delicatessen, and for the next four days we lived on dill pickles with dill pickles.

"Listen," I finally says: "The only reason I consented to leave the hotel was in the hopes I could get a real home cook meal once in a wile and if I don't get a real home cook meal once in a wile, I leave this dive."

"Have a little bit of patience," says Ella. "I advertised in the paper for a cook the day before we come here, the day we rented this apartment. And I offered eight dollars a week."

"How many replies did you get?" I asked her.

"Well," she said, "I have n't got none so far, but it's probably too soon to expect any."

"What did you advertise in, the world almanac?" I says.

"No, sir," she says. "I advertised in the two biggest New York papers, the ones the real estate man recommended."

"Listen," I said: "Where do you think you're at, in Niles, Michigan? If you get a cook here for eight dollars a week, it'll be a one-armed leper that has n't yet reached her teens."

"What would you do, then?" she asked me.

"I'd write to an employment agency," I says, "and I'd tell them we'll pay good wages."

So she done that and in three days the phone rung and the agency said they had one prospect on hand and did we want her to come out and see us. So Ella said we did and out come a colleen for an interview. She asked how much we was willing to pay.

"Well," said Ella, "I'd go as high as twelve dollars. Or I'd make it fifteen if you done the washing."

Kathleen Mavourneen turned her native color.

"Well," I said, "how much do you want?"

"I'll work for ninety dollars a month," she said, only I can't get the brogue. "That's for the cookin' only. No washin'. And I would have to have a room with a bath and all day Thursdays and Sunday evenin's off."

"Nothing doing," said Ella, and the colleen started for the door.

"Wait a minute," I says. "Listen: Is that what you gals is getting in New York?"

"We're a spalpeen if we ain't," says the colleen bawn.

Well, I was desperate, so I called the wife to one side and says: "For heaven's sakes, take her on a month's trial. I'll pay the most of it with a little piece of money I picked up last week down to Doyle's. I'd rather do that than get dill pickled for a goal."

"Could you come right away?" Ella asked her.

"Not for a couple days," says Kathleen.

"It's off, then," I said. "You cook our supper to-night or go back to Greece."

"Well," she says, "I guess I could make it if I hurried."

So she went away and come back with her suitcase, and she cooked our supper that night. And Oh, darlint!

Well, Beautiful Katie still had the automobile bug and it wasn't none of my business to steer her off of it and pretty near every day she would go down to the "row" and look them over. But every night she'd come home whistling a dirge.

"I guess I've seen them all," she'd say, "but they're too expensive or else they look like they wasn't."

But one time we was all coming home in a taxi from a show and come up Broadway and all of a sudden she yelled for the driver to stop.

"That's a new one in that window," she says, "and one I never see before."

Well, the dive was closed at the time and we couldn't get in, but she insisted on going down there the first thing in the morning and I and Ella must go along. The car was a brand new model Bam Eight.

"How much?" I asked him.

"Four thousand," he says.

"When could I get one?" says Katie.

"I don't know," said the salesman.

"What do you mean?" I asked him. "Haven't they made none of them?"

"I don't know," says the salesman. "This is the only one we got."

"Has anybody ever rode in one?" I says.

"I don't know," said the guy.

So I asked him what made it worth four thousand.

"Well," he says, "what made this lady want one?"

"I don't know," I said.

"Could I have this one that's on the floor?" says Katie.

"I don't know," said the salesman.

"Well, when do you think I could get one?" says Katie.

"We can't promise no deliveries," says the salesman.

Well, that kind of fretted me, so I asked him if they wasn't a salesman we could talk to.

"You're talking to one," he said.

"Yes, I know," said I. "But I used to be a kind of a salesman myself, and when I was trying to sell things, I didn't try and not sell them."

"Yes," he says, "but you wasn't selling automobiles in New York in 1920. Listen," he says: "I'll be frank with you. We got the New York agency for this car and was glad to get it because it sells for four thousand and anything that sells that high, why the people will eat up, even if it's a pearl-handle ketchup bottle. If we ever do happen to get a consignment of these cars, they'll sell like oil stock. The last word we got from the factory was that they'd send us three cars next September. So that means we'll get two cars a year from next October and if we can spare either of them, you can have one."

So then he begin to yawn and I said, "Come on, girls," and we got a taxi and beat it home. And I wouldn't of said nothing about it, only if Katie had of been able to buy her Bam, what come off might of never came off.

It wasn't only two nights later when Ella come in from shopping all excited. "Well," she said, "talk about experiences! I just had a ride home and it wasn't in a street car and it wasn't in a taxi and it wasn't on the subway and it wasn't on a bus."

"Let's play charades," said I.

"Tell us, Sis," says Katie.

"Well," said the wife, "I was down on Fifth Avenue, waiting for a bus, and all of a sudden a big limousine drew up to the curb with a livery chauffeur, and a man got out of the back seat and took off his hat and asked if he couldn't see me home. And of course I didn't pay no attention to him."

"Of course not," I said.

"But," says Ella, "he says, 'Don't take no offense. I think we're next door neighbors. Don't you live acrost the hall on the sixth floor of the Lucius?' So of course I had to tell him I did."

"Of course," I said.

"And then he said," says Ella, "'Is that your sister living with you?' 'Yes,' I said, 'she lives with my husband and I.' 'Well,' he says, 'if you'll get in and let me take you home, I'll tell you what a beautiful girl I think she is.' So I seen then that he was all right, so I got in and come home with him. And honestly, 'Sis,' he's just wild about you!"

"What is he like?" says Katie.

"He's stunning," says the wife. "Tall and wears dandy clothes and got a cute mustache that turns up."

"How old?" says Kate, and the Mrs. kind of stalled.

"Well," she said, "he's the kind of a man that you can't tell how old they are, but he's not old. I'd say he was, well, maybe he's not even that old."

"What's his name?" asked Kate.

"Trumbull," said the Mrs. "He said he was keeping bachelor quarters, but I don't know if he's really a bachelor or a widower. Anyway, he's a dandy fella and must have lots of money. Just imagine living alone in one of these apartments!"

"Imagine living in one of them whether you're a bachelor or a Mormon," I says.

"Who said he lived alone?" asked Katie.

"He did," says the Mrs. "He told me that him and his servants had the whole apartment to themselves. And that's what makes it so nice, because he's asked the three of us over there to dinner to-morrow night."

"What makes it so nice?" I asked her.

"Because it does," said Ella, and you can't ever beat an argument like that.

So the next night the two girls donned their undress uniforms and made me put on the oysters and horse radish and we went acrost the hall to meet our hero. The door was opened by a rug peddler and he showed us into a twin brother to our own living room, only you could get around it without being Houdini.

"Mr. Trumbull will be right out," said Omar.

The ladies was shaking like an aspirin leaf, but in a few minutes, in come mine host. However old Ella had thought he wasn't, she was wrong. He'd seen baseball when the second bounce was out. If he'd of started his career as a barber in Washington, he'd of tried to wish a face massage on Zachary Taylor. The only thing young about him was his teeth and his clothes. His dinner suit made me feel like I was walking along the station platform at Toledo, looking for hot boxes.

"Ah, here you are!" he says. "It's mighty nice of you to be neighborly. And so this is the young sister. Well," he says to me, "you had your choice, and as far as I can see, it was heads you win and tails you win. You're lucky."

So when he'd spread all the salve, he rung the bell and in come Allah with cocktails. I don't know what was in them, but when Ella and Katie had had two apiece, they both begin to trill.

Finally we was called in to dinner and every other course was hootch. After the solid and liquid diet, he turned on the steam piano and we all danced. I had one with Beautiful Katie and the rest of them was with my wife, or, as I have nicknamed them, quarrels. Well, the steam run out of three of us at the same time, the piano inclusive, and Ella sat down in a chair that was made for Eddie Foy's family and said how comfortable it was.

"Yes," says Methuselah, "that's my favorite chair. And I bet you wouldn't believe me if I told you how much it cost."

"Oh, I'd like to know," says Ella.

"Two hundred dollars," says mine host.

"Do you still feel comfortable?" I asked her.

"Speaking about furniture," said the old bird, "I've got a few bits that I'm proud of. Would you like to take a look at them?"

So the gals said they would and we had to go through the entire apartment, looking at bits. The best bits I seen was tastefully wrapped up in kegs and cases. It seemed like every time he opened a drawer, a cork popped up. He was a hundred per cent. proofer than the governor of New Jersey. But he was giving us a lecture on the furniture itself, not the polish.

"I picked up this dining room suit for eighteen hundred," he says.

"Do you mean the one you've got on?" I asked him, and the gals give me a dirty look.

"And this rug," he says, stomping on an old rag carpet. "How much do you suppose that cost?"

It was my first guess, so I said fifty dollars.

"That's a laugh," he said. "I paid two thousand for that rug."

"The guy that sold it had the laugh," I says.

Finally he steered us into his bedroom.

"Do you see that bed?" he says. "That's Marie Antoinette's bed. Just a cool thousand."

"What time does she usually get in?" I asked him.

"Here's my hobby," he said, opening up a closet, "dressing gowns and bathrobes."

Well, they was at least a dozen of them hanging on hangers. They was all colors of the rainbow including the Scandinavian. He dragged one down that was redder than Ella's and Katie's cheeks.

"This is my favorite bathrobe," he said. "It's Rose D. Barry."

So I asked him if he had all his household goods and garments named after some dame.

"This bathrobe cost me an even two hundred," he says.

"I always take baths bare," I said. "It's a whole lot cheaper."

"Let's go back in the living room," says Katie.

"Come on," said Ella, tugging me by the sleeve.

"Wait a minute," I says to her. "I don't know how much he paid for his toothbrush."

Well, when we got back in the living room, the two gals acted kind of drowsy and snuggled up together on the davenport and I and the old bird was left to ourself.

"Here's another thing I didn't show you," he says, and pulls a pair of African golf balls out of a drawer in his desk. "These dice is real ivory and they cost me twelve and a half berries."

"You mean up to now," I said.

"All right," he said. "We'll make it a twenty-five dollar limit."

Well, I didn't have no business in a game with him, but you know how a guy gets sometimes. So he took them first and rolled a four.

"Listen," I says: "Do you know how many times Willard set down in the first round?"

And sure enough he sevened.

"Now solid ivory dice," I said, "how many days in the week?"

So out come a natural. And as sure as I'm setting here, I made four straight passes with the whole roll riding each time and with all that wad parked on the two thousand dollar rug, I shot a five and a three. "Ivory," I said, "we was invited here to-night, so don't make me pay for the entertainment. Show me eighter from Decatur."

And the lady from Decatur showed.

Just then they was a stir on the davenport, and Ella woke up long enough to make the remark that we ought to go home. It was the first time she ever said it in the right place.

"Oh," I says, "I've got to give Mr. Trumbull a chance to get even."

But I wasn't in earnest.

"Don't bother about that," said Old Noah. "You can accommodate me some other time."

"You're certainly a sport," I says.

"And thanks for a wonderful time," said Ella. "I hope we'll see you again soon."

"Soon is to-morrow night," said mine host. "I'm going to take you all up the river to a place I know."

"Well," I says to Katie, when we was acrost the hall and the door shut, "how do you like him?"

"Oh, shut up!" says Katie.

So the next night he come over and rung our bell and said Ritchey was waiting with the car and would we come down when we was ready. Well, the gals had only had all day to prepare for the trip, so in another half hour they had their wraps on and we went downstairs. They wasn't nothing in front but a Rools-Royce with a livery chauffeur that looked like he'd been put there by a rubber stamp.

"What a stunning driver!'' said Katie when we'd parked ourself in the back seat.

"Ritchey?" said mine host. "He is a nice looking boy, but better than that, he's a boy I can trust."

Well, anyway, the boy he could trust took us out to a joint called the Indian Inn where you wouldn't of never knew they was an eighteenth amendment only that the proprietor was asking twenty berries a quart for stuff that used to cost four. But that didn't seem to bother Methuselah and he ordered two of them. Not only that but he got us a table so close to the orchestra that the cornet player thought we was his mute.

"Now, what'll we eat?" he says.

So I looked at the program and the first item I seen was "Guinea Hen, $4.50."

"That's what Katie'll want," I says to myself, and sure enough that's what she got.

Well, we eat and then we danced and we danced and we danced, and finally along about eleven I and Ella was out on the floor pretending like we was enjoying ourself, and we happened to look over to the table and there was Katie and Trumbull setting one out and to look at either you could tell that something was wrong.

"Dance the next one with her," says Ella, "and find out what's the matter."

So I danced the next one with Katie and asked her.

"He squeezed my hand," she says. "I don't like him."

"Well," said I, "if you'd of ordered guinea hen on me I wouldn't of stopped at your hand. I'd of went at your throat."

"I've got a headache," she says. "Take me out to the car."

So they was nothing to it but I had to take her out to the car and come back and tell Ella and Trumbull that she wasn't feeling any too good and wanted to go home.

"She don't like me," says the old guy. "That's the whole trouble."

"Give her time," says Ella. "Remember she's just a kid."

"Yes, but what a kid!" he says.

So then he paid the check without no competition and we went out and clumb in the big limmie. Katie was pretending like she was asleep and neither Ella or Trumbull acted like they wanted to talk, so the conversation on the way home was mostly one-sided, with me in the title rôle. Katie went in the apartment without even thanking mine host for the guinea hen, but he kept Ella and I outside long enough to say that Ritchey and the car was at our service any time we wanted them.

So Ella told her that the next noon at breakfast. "And you'd ought to be ashamed of yourself," says Ella, "for treating a man like that like that."

"He's too fresh," says Katie.

"Well," said Ella, "if he was a little younger, you wouldn't mind him being fresh."

"No," said Katie, "if he was fresh, I wouldn't care if he was fresh. But what's the number of the garage?"

And she didn't lose no time taking advantage of the old bird. That same afternoon it seemed she had to go shopping and the bus wasn't good enough no more. She was out in Trumbull's limmie from two o'clock till pretty near seven. The old guy himself come to our place long about five and wanted to know if we knew where she was at. "I haven't no idear," said Ella. "I expected her home long ago. Did you want to use the car?"

"What's the difference," I said, "if he wanted to use the car or not? He's only the owner."

"Well," says Trumbull, "when I make an offer I mean it, and that little girl is welcome to use my machine whenever she feels like it."

So Ella asked him to stay to dinner and he said he would if we'd allow him to bring in some of his hootch, and of course I kicked on that proposition, but he insisted. And when Katie finally did get home, we was all feeling good and so was she and you'd never of thought they'd been any bad feelings the night before.

Trumbull asked her what she'd been buying.

"Nothing," she says. "I was looking at dresses, but they want too much money."

"You don't need no dresses," he says.

"No, of course not," said Katie. "But lots of girls is wearing them."

"Where did you go?" said Ella.

"I forget," says Katie. "What do you say if we play cards?"

So we played rummy till we was all blear-eyed and the old guy left, saying we'd all go somewheres next day. After he'd gone Ella begin to talk serious.

"Sis," she says, "here's the chance of a lifetime. Mr. Trumbull's head over heels in love with you and all as you have to do is encourage him a little. Can't you try and like him?"

"They's nobody I have more respect for," said Katie, "unless it's George Washington."

And then she gave a funny laugh and run off to bed.

"I can't understand Sis no more," said Ella, when we was alone.

"Why not?" I asked her.

"Why, look at this opportunity staring her in the face," says the Mrs.

"Listen," I said: "The first time I stared you in the face, was you thinking about opportunity?"

Well, to make a short story out of it, I was the only one up in the house the next morning when Kathleen said we had a caller. It was the old boy.

"I'm sorry to be so early," he says, "but I just got a telegram and it means I got to run down to Washington for a few days. And I wanted to tell you that wile I'm gone Ritchey and the car is at your service."

So I thanked him and he said good-by and give his regards to the Mrs. and especially Katie, so when they got up I told them about it and I never seen a piece of bad news received so calm as Katie took it.

"But now he's gone," I said at the breakfast table, "why not the three of us run out to Bridgeport and call on the Wilmots?"

They're cousins of mine.

"Oh, fine!" said Ella.

"Wait a minute," says Katie. "I made a kind of an engagement with a dressmaker for to-day."

Well, as I say, to make a short story out of it, it seems like she'd made engagements with the dressmaker every day, but they wasn't no dresses ever come home.

In about a week Trumbull come back from Washington and the first thing he done was look us up and we had him in to dinner and I don't remember how the conversation started, but all of a sudden we was on the subject of his driver, Ritchey.

"A great boy," says Trumbull, "and a boy you can trust. If I didn't like him for nothing else, I'd like him for how he treats his family."

"What family?" says Kate.

"Why," says Trumbull, "his own family: his wife and two kids."

"My heavens!" says Katie, and kind of fell in a swoon.

So it seems like we didn't want to live there no more and we moved back to the Baldwin, having sublet the place on the Drive for three thousand a year.

So from then on, we was paying a thousand per annum for an apartment we didn't live in two weeks. But as I told the gals, we was getting pretty near as much for our money as the people that rented New York apartments and lived in them, too.

OLIVER HERFORD

Some one remarked of Oliver Herford — it was in print some few years ago — that he was "an American institution." Certainly a finer and more versatile genius than his — poet, artist, wit, humorist — does not exist among us, although he is chiefly accepted, owing to his irrepressible gift of fun-making, as the latter. Born in England, in 1863, he has been in this country so long that everybody has quite forgotten his true nationality. For more than a quarter of a century he has poured out a steady stream of the finest and most original fancies in verse and prose and line. His book titles as listed in "Who's Who in America" number thirty-one and that represents but a portion of his work. He is at present on the editorial staff of *Life*.

ARE CATS PEOPLE?[1]

IF a fool be sometimes an angel unawares, may not a foolish query be a momentous question in disguise? For example, the old riddle: "Why is a hen?" which is thought by many people to be the silliest question ever asked, is in reality the most profound. It is the riddle of existence. It has an answer, to be sure, but though all the wisest men and women in the world *and* Mr. H. G. Wells have tried to guess it, the riddle "Why is a hen?" has never been answered and never will be. So, too, the question: "Are Cats People?" seemingly so trivial, may be, under certain conditions, a question of vital importance.

Suppose, now, a rich man dies, leaving all his money to his eldest son, with the proviso that a certain portion of it shall be spent in the maintenance of his household as it then existed, all its members to remain under his roof, and receive the same comfort, attention, or remuneration they had received in his (the testator's) lifetime. Then suppose the son, on coming into his money, and being a hater of cats, made haste to rid himself of a feline pet that had lived in the family from early kittenhood, and had been an especial favorite of his father's.

Thereupon, the second son, being a lover of cats and no hater of money, sues for possession of the estate on the ground that his brother has failed to carry out the provisions of his father's will, in refusing to maintain the household cat.

The decision of the case depends entirely on the social status of the cat.

Shall the cat be considered as a member of the household? What constitutes a household anyway?

The definition of " Household " in the Standard Dictionary is as follows: "*A number of persons living under the same roof.*"

If cats are people, then the cat in question is a person and a member of the household, and for failing to maintain her and provide her with the comfort and attention to which she has been used, the eldest son loses his inheritance. Having demonstrated that the question " Are Cats People?" is anything but a trivial one, I now propose a court of inquiry, to settle once for all and forever, the social status of *felis domesticus*.

And I propose for the office of judge of that court — myself!

In seconding the proposal and appointing myself judge of the court, I have been careful to follow political precedent by taking no account whatever of any qualifications I may or may not have for the office.

For witnesses, I summon (from wherever they may be) two great shades, to wit: King Solomon, the wisest man of his day, and Noah Webster, the wordiest.

And I say to Mr. Webster, " Mr. Webster, what are the common terms used to designate a domestic feline whose

Christian name chances to be unknown to the speaker?"
and Mr. Webster answers without a moment's hesitation:

"Cat, puss, pussy and pussy-cat."

"And what is the grammatical definition of the above terms?"

"They are called nouns."

"And what, Mr. Webster, is the accepted definition of a noun?"

"A noun is the name of a person, place or thing."

"Kindly define the word 'place'."

"A particular locality."

"And 'thing'."

"An inanimate object."

"That will do, Mr. Webster."

So, according to Mr. Noah Webster, the entity for which the noun cat stands, must, if not a person, be a locality or an inanimate object!

A cat is surely not a locality, and as for being an inanimate object, her chance of avoiding such a condition is nine times better even than a king's.

Then a cat *must* be a person.

Suppose we consult King Solomon.

In the Book of Proverbs, Chapter XXX, verse 26, Solomon says: " The coneys are but a feeble folk, yet they make their houses in the rocks."

A coney is a kind of rabbit; folk, according to Mr. Webster, only another word for people.

That settles it! If the rabbits are people, cats are people. Long lives to the cat!

OUR LEISURE CLASS [1]

Once — and not so terribly long ago at that — we used to be very fond of telling ourselves (and our visitors from Europe) that in America we have no Leisure Class.

[1] From "Neither Here Nor There." Copyright, 1922, by George H. Doran and Company. Reprinted by permission of the author.

That there were people of leisure in our midst, we could not deny, though we preferred to call them idle rich, but as for a special class whose whole business in life was to abstain from all useful activity — oh, no!

Even our idle rich, unblest as they are with the hereditary gift for idling, and untaught save by a brief generation or two of acquired experience, find the profession of Leisure a strenuous not to say noisy task, for while those to the leisure born know by the very feel of it that the habit of idleness is a perfect fit, the newly-idle must look for confirmation in the mirror of public admiration; hence Publicity, the blare of the Sunday Supplement.

But taken as a class our idle rich (though it is being rapidly licked or lick-spittled into shape) is at best an amateur aristocracy of leisure. For the real thing, for the genuine hunting, sporting, leisure-loving American aristocracy, we must go back to the aboriginal Red Man.

And how the busybody Puritan hated the Indian! With his air of well-bred taciturnity, his love of sport, of rest, of nature, and his belief in a happy Hereafter, the noble Red Man was in every respect his hateful opposite, yet if any Pilgrim brother had dared even to hint that the Indian might have points of superiority it would have been the flaming woodpile for his, or something equally disagreeable in the purifying way.

How different it might have been!

If only the Puritan had been less stuck up and self-righteous, the Red Man less reserved! If they could but have understood that Nature intended them for each other, these opposites, these complements of each other.

Why else had Nature brought them together from the ends of the earth?

But alas, Eugenics had not yet been invented and the Puritan and the Indian just naturally hated each other at first sight and so (like many another match-maker) Mother Nature slipped up in her calculations, and a wonderful flower of racial possibility was forever nipped in the bud.

If the Puritan, with his piety and thrift and domesticity and his doctrine of election and the Noble Red Man, with his love of paint and syncopated music and dancing and belief in a happy Hereafter, had overcome their mutual prejudices and instead of warring with flintlocks and tomahawks, had pursued each other with engagement rings and marriage licenses, what a grand and glorious race we might be today!

What a land of freedom might be ours!

ROBERT C. BENCHLEY

Robert C. Benchley, one of the very newest recruits to the ranks of our professional fun-makers, was born in Worcester, Massachusetts, September 15, 1889. Since graduating from Harvard in 1912, he has been engaged in newspaper and periodical work, principally in New York. He is dramatic editor of *Life*. His first book "Of All Things", published in 1921, was most favorably received and his second, "Love Conquers All", fully realized anticipations. He is a genuine accession.

THE TORTURES OF WEEK–END VISITING [1]

THE present labor situation shows to what a pretty pass things may come because of a lack of understanding between the parties involved. I bring in the present labor situation just to give a touch of timeliness to this thing. Had I been writing for the Christmas number, I should have begun as follows: "The indiscriminate giving of Christmas presents shows to what a pretty pass things may come because of a lack of understanding between the parties involved."

The idea to be driven home is that things may come to a pretty pass by the parties involved in an affair of any kind if they do not come to an understanding before commencing operations.

I hope I have made my point clear. Especially is this true (watch out carefully now, as the whole nub of the article will be coming along in just a minute), especially is this true in the relations between host and guest on week-end visits. (There, you have it! In fact, the title to this whole thing might very well be, "The Need for a Clearer

---

[1] From "Of All Things!" Copyright, 1923, by Henry Holt and Company. Reprinted by permission of the author.

Definition of Relations between Host and Guest on Week-end Visits," and not be at all overstating it, at that.)

The logic of this will be apparent to any one who has ever been a host or a guest at a week-end party, a classification embracing practically all Caucasians over eleven years of age who can put powder on the nose or tie a bow-tie. Who has not wished that his host would come out frankly at the beginning of the visit and state, in no uncertain terms, the rules and preferences of the household in such matters as the breakfast hour? And who has not sounded his guest to find out what he likes in the regulation of his diet and *modus vivendi* (mode of living)? Collective bargaining on the part of labor unions and capital makes it possible for employers to know just what the workers think on matters of common interest. Is collective bargaining between host and guest so impossible, then?

Take, for example, the matter of arising in the morning. Of course, where there is a large house-party the problem is a simple one, for you can always hear the others pattering about and brushing their teeth. You can regulate your own arising by the number of people who seem to be astir. But if you are the only guest there is apt to be a frightful misunderstanding.

"At what time is breakfast?" you ask.

"Oh, any old time on Sundays," replies the hostess with a generous gesture. "Sleep as late as you like. This is 'Liberty Hall.'"

The sentiment in this attitude is perfectly bully, but there is nothing that you can really take hold of in it. It satisfies at the time, but in the morning there is a vagueness about it that is simply terrifying.

Let us say that you awake at eight. You listen and hear no one stirring. Then, over on the cool pillow again until eight-twenty. Again up on the elbow, with head cocked on one side. There is a creak in the direction of the stairs. They may all be up and going down to breakfast! It is but the work of a moment, to bound out of bed and listen at the door. Perhaps open it modestly and peer out. Death-like silence, broken only, as the phrase goes, by the ticking of the hall clock, and not a soul in sight. Probably they are late sleepers. Maybe eleven o'clock is their Sunday rising hour. Some people *are* like that.

Shut the door and sit on the edge of the bed. More sleep is out of the question. Let's take a look at the pictures in the guest-room, just to pass the time. Here's one of Lorna Doone. How d'e do, Lorna? Here's a group — taken in 1902 — showing your host in evening clothes, holding a mandolin. Probably a member of his college musical-club. Rather unkempt looking bunch, you *must* say. Well, how about this one? An etching, showing suspicious-looking barges on what is probably the Thames. Fair enough, at that.

Back to the door and listen again. Tick-tock-tick-tock. Probably, if you started your tub, you'd wake the whole house. Let's sit down on the edge of the bed again.

Hello, here are some books on the table. "Fifty Famous Sonnets," illustrated by Maxfield Parrish. Never touch a sonnet before breakfast. "My Experiences in the Alps," by a woman mountain-climber who has written on the fly-leaf, "To my good friends the Elbridges, in memory of many happy days together at Chamounix. October, 1907." That settles *that*. "Essay on Compensation" in limp leather, by R. W. Emerson, published by Houghton, Mifflin & Co. Oh, very well! You suppose they thought that would be over your head, did they? Well, we'll just show them! We'll read it just for spite. Opening, to the red ribbon:

"Of the like nature is that expectation of change which instantly follows the suspension of our voluntary activity. The terror of cloudless noon —"

By the way, it must be nearly noon now! Ten minutes past nine, only! Well, the only thing to do is get dressed and go out and walk about the grounds. Eliminate the tub as too noisy. And so, very cautiously, almost clandestinely, you proceed to dress.

And now, just to reverse the process. Suppose you are the host. You have arisen at eight and listened at the guest's door. No sound. Tip-toe back and get dressed, talking in whispers to your wife (the hostess) and cramming flannel bears into the infant's mouth to keep him from disturbing the sleeper.

"Bill looked tired last night. Better let him sleep a little longer," you suggest. And so, downstairs on your hands and knees, and look over the Sunday papers. Then a bracing walk on the porch, resulting in a terrific appetite.

A glance at the watch shows nine o'clock. Sunday breakfast is usually at eight-thirty. The warm aroma of coffee creeps in from the kitchen and, somewhere, *some one* is baking muffins. This is awful! You suppose it feels something like this to be caught on an ice-floe without any food and so starve to death. Only there you can't smell coffee and muffins. You sneak into the dining-room and steal one of the property oranges from the sideboard, but little Edgar sees you and sets up such a howl that you have to give it to him. The hostess suggests that your friend may have the sleeping-sickness. Weakened by hunger, you hotly resent this, and one word leads to another.

"Oh, very well, I'll go up and rout him out," you snarl.

Upstairs again, and poise, in listening attitude, just in front of the guest's door. Slowly the door opens, inch by inch, and, finally his head is edged cautiously out toward yours.

"Hello, Bill," you say flatly, "what are you getting up this time of the morning for? Thought I told you to sleep late."

"Morning, Ed," he says, equally flatly, "hope I haven't kept you all waiting." Then you both lie and eat breakfast.

Such a misunderstanding is apt to go to almost any length. I once knew of a man on a week-end visit who spent an entire Sunday in his room, listening at his door to see if the family were astir, while, in the meantime, the family were, one by one, tip-toeing to his door to see if they could detect any signs of life in him.

Each thought the other needed rest.

Along about three in the afternoon the family threw all hospitality aside and ate breakfast, deadening the sound of the cutlery as much as possible, little dreaming that their guest was looking through the " A Prayer for Each Day " calendar for the ninth time and seriously considering letting himself down from the window on a sheet and making for the next train. Shortly after dark persistent rumors got abroad that he had done away with himself, and every one went up and sniffed for gas. It was only when the maid, who was not in on the secret, bolted into the room to turn down his bed for the night, that she found him tip-toeing about, packing and unpacking his bag and listening eagerly at the wall. (Now don't ask how it happened that the maid didn't know that his bed hadn't been made that morning. What difference does it make, anyway? It is such questions as *that,* that blight any attempt at individual writing in this country.)

Don't think, just because I have taken all this space to deal with the rising-hour problem that there are no other points to be made. Oh, not at all. There is, for instance, the question of exercise. After dinner the host says to himself: " Something must be done. I wonder if he likes to walk." Aloud, he says: " Well, Bill, how about a little hike in the country?"

A hike in the country being the last thing in the world that Bill wants, he says, " Right-o! Anything you say." And so, although walking is a tremendous trial to the host, who has weak ankles, he bundles up with a great show of heartiness and grabs his stick as if this were the one thing he lived for.

After about a mile of hobbling along the country-road the host says, hopefully: " Don't let me tire you out, old man. Any time you want to turn back, just say the word."

The guest, thinking longingly of the fireside, scoffs at the idea of turning back, insisting that if there is one thing in all the world that he likes better than walking it is running. So on they jog, hippity-hop, hippity-hop, each wishing that it would rain so that they could turn about and go home.

Here again the thing may go to almost tragic lengths. Suppose neither has the courage to suggest the return move. They might walk on into Canada, or they might become exhausted and have to be taken into a roadhouse and eat a "$2 old-fashioned Southern dinner of fried chicken and waffles." The imagination revolts at a further contemplation of the possibilities of this lack of coöperation between guest and host.

I once visited a man who had an outdoor swimming-pool on his estate. (Consider that as very casually said.) It was in April, long before Spring had really understood what was expected of her. My first night there my host said:

"Are you a morning plunger?"

Thinking that he referred to a tub plunge in a warm bathroom, I glowed and said: "You bet."

"I'll call for you at seven in the morning, then," he said, "and we'll go out to the pool."

It was evidently his morning custom and I wasn't going to have it said of me that a middle-aged man could outdo me in virility. So, at seven in the morning, in a dense fog (with now and then a slash of cold rain), we picked our way out to the pool and staged a vivid Siberian moving picture scene, showing naked peasants bathing in the Nevsky. My visit lasted five days, and I afterward learned, from one to whom my host had confided, that it was the worst five days he had ever gone through, and that he has chronic joint-trouble as a result of those plunges. "But I couldn't be outdone by a mere stripling," he said, "and the boy certainly enjoyed it."

All of this might have been avoided by the posting of

a sign in a conspicuous place in my bedroom, reading as follows: "Personally, I dislike swimming in the pool at this time of the year. Guests wishing to do so may obtain towels at the desk." How very simple and practical!

The sign system is the only solution I can offer. It is crude and brutal, but it admits of no misunderstanding. A sign in each guest-room, giving the hours of meals, political and religious preferences of the family, general views on exercise, etc., etc., with a blank for the guest to fill out, stating his own views on these subjects, would make it possible to visit (or entertain) with a sense of security thus far unknown upon our planet.

CALL FOR MR. KENWORTHY![1]

A great many people have wondered to themselves, in print, just where the little black laundry-studs go after they have been yanked from the shirt. Others pass this by as inconsequential, but are concerned over the ultimate disposition of all the pencil stubs that are thrown away. Such futile rumination is all well enough for those who like it. As for me, give me a big, throbbing question like this: "Who are the people that one hears being paged in hotels? Are they real people or are they decoys? And if they are real people, what are they being paged for?"

Now, there's something vital to figure out. And the best of it is that it *can* be figured out by the simple process of following the page to see whether he ever finds any one.

In order that no expense should be spared, I picked out a hotel with poor service, which means that it was an expensive hotel. It was so expensive that all you could hear was the page's voice as he walked by you; his footfalls made no noise in the extra-heavy Bokhara. It was just a mingling of floating voices, calling for "Mr. Bla-bla, Mr. Schwer-a-a, Mr. Twa-a-a."

[1] From "Of All Things!" Copyright, 1923, by Henry Holt and Company. Reprinted by permission of the author.

Out of this wealth of experimental material I picked a boy with a discouraged voice like Wallace Eddinger's, who seemed to be saying, " I 'm calling these names — because that 's my job — if I was n't calling these — I 'd be calling out cash totals in an honor system lunchery — but if any one should ever answer to one of these names — I 'd have a poor spell."

Allowing about fifteen feet distance between us for appearance's sake, I followed him through the lobby. He had a bunch of slips in his hand and from these he read the names of the pagees.

" Call for Mr. Kenworthy — Mr. Shriner — Mr. Bodkin — Mr. Blevitch — Mr. Kenworthy — Mr. Bodkin — Mr. Kenworthy — Mr. Shriner — call for Mr. Kenworthy — Mr. Blevitch — Mr. Kenworthy."

Mr. Kenworthy seemed to be standing about a 20 per cent better chance of being located than any of the other contestants. Probably the boy was of a romantic temperament and liked the name. Sometimes that was the only name he would call for mile upon mile. It occurred to me that perhaps Mr. Kenworthy was the only one wanted, and that the other names were just put in to make it harder, or to give body to the thing.

But when we entered the bar the youth shifted his attack. The name of Kenworthy evidently had begun to cloy. He was fed up on romance and wanted something substantial, homely, perhaps, but substantial.

So he dropped Kenworthy and called: " Mr. Blevitch. Call for Mr. Blevitch — Mr. Shriner — Mr. Bodkin — Mr. Blevitch — "

But even this subtle change of tactics failed to net him a customer. We had gone through the main lobby, along the narrow passage lined with young men waiting on sofas for young women who would be forty minutes late, through the grill, and now had crossed the bar, and no one had raised even an eyebrow. No wonder the boy's voice sounded discouraged.

As we went through one of the lesser dining-rooms, the dining-room that seats a lot of heavy men in business suits holding cigarettes, who lean over their plates the more confidentially to converse with their blond partners, in this dining-room the plaintive call drew fire. One of the men in business suits, who was at a table with another man and two women, lifted his head when he heard the sound of names being called.

"Boy!" he said, and waved like a traffic officer signaling, "Come!"

Eagerly the page darted forward. Perhaps this was Mr. Kenworthy! Or better yet, Mr. Blevitch.

"Anything here for Studz?" said the man in the business suit, when he was sure that enough people were listening.

"No, sir," sighed the boy. "Mr. Blevitch, Mr. Kenworthy, Mr. Shriner, Mr. Bodkin?" he suggested, hopefully.

"Naw," replied the man, and turned to his associates with an air of saying: "Rotten service here — just think of it, no call for me!"

On we went again. The boy was plainly skeptical. He read his lines without feeling. The management had led him into this; all he could do was to take it with as good grace as possible.

He slid past the coat-room girl at the exit (no small accomplishment in itself) and down a corridor, disappearing through a swinging door at the end. I was in no mood to lose out on the finish after following so far, and I dashed after him.

The door led into a little alcove and another palpitating door at the opposite end showed me where he had gone. Setting my jaw for no particular reason, I pushed my way through.

At first, like the poor olive merchant in the Arabian Nights I was blinded by the glare of lights and the glitter of glass and silver. Oh, yes, and by the snowy whiteness

of the napery, too. " By the napery of the neck " would n't
be a bad line to get off a little later in the story. I 'll
try it.

At any rate, it was but the work of a minute for me to
realize that I had entered by a service entrance into the
grand dining-room of the establishment, where, if you are
not in evening dress, you are left to munch bread and butter
until you starve to death and are carried out with your
heels dragging, like the uncouth lout that you are. It was,
if I may be allowed to phrase, a galaxy of beauty, with
every one dressed up like the pictures. And I had entered
'way up front, by the orchestra.

Now, mind you, I am not ashamed of my gray suit. I
like it, and my wife says that I have n't had anything so becoming for a long time. But in it I did n't check up very
strong against the rest of the boys in the dining-room. As a
gray suit it is above reproach. As a garment in which to appear single-handed through a trapdoor before a dining-room
of well dressed Middle Westerners it was a fizzle from start
to finish. Add to this the items that I had to snatch a
brown soft hat from my head when I found out where I
was, which caused me to drop the three evening papers I
had tucked under my arm, and you will see why my up-
stage entrance was the signal for the impressive raising of
several dozen eyebrows, and why the captain approached me
just exactly as one man approaches another when he is
going to throw him out.

(Blank space for insertion of "napery of neck" line, if
desired. Choice optional with reader.)

I saw that anything that I might say would be used
against me, and left him to read the papers I had dropped.
One only lowers one's self by having words with a servitor.

Gradually I worked my way back through the swinging
doors to the main corridor and rushed down to the regular
entrance of the grand dining-salon, to wait there until my
quarry should emerge. Suppose he should find all of his
consignees in this dining-room! I could not be in at the

death then, and would have to falsify my story to make any kind of ending at all. And that would never do.

Once in a while I would catch the scent, when, from the humming depths of the dining-room, I could hear a faint "Call for Mr. Kenworthy" rising above the click of the oyster shells and the soft crackling of the "potatoes Julienne" one against another. So I knew that he had not failed me, and that if I had faith and waited long enough he would come back.

And, sure enough, come back he did, and without a name lost from his list. I felt like cheering when I saw his head bobbing through the mêlée of waiters and 'bus-boys who were busy putting clean plates on the tables and then taking them off again in eight seconds to make room for more clean plates. Of all discouraging existences I can imagine none worse than that of an eternally clean plate. There can be no sense of accomplishment, no glow of duty done, in simply being placed before a man and then taken away again. It must be almost as bad as paging a man who you are sure is not in the hotel.

The futility of the thing had already got on the page's nerves, and in a savage attempt to wring a little pleasure out of the task he took to welding the names, grafting a syllable of one to a syllable of another, such as "Call for Mr. Kenbodkin — Mr. Shrineworthy — Mr. Blevitcher."

This gave us both amusement for a little while, but your combinations are limited in a thing like that, and by the time the grill was reached he was saying the names correctly and with a little more assurance.

It was in the grill that the happy event took place. Mr. Shriner, the one of whom we expected least, suddenly turned up at a table alone. He was a quiet man and not at all worked up over his unexpected honor. He signaled the boy with one hand and went on taking soup with the other, and learned, without emotion, that he was wanted on the telephone. He even made no move to leave his meal to answer the call, and when last seen he was adding pepper with one hand and taking soup with the other. I suspect that he was a "plant," or a plain-clothes house detective, placed there on purpose to deceive me.

We had been to every nook of the hotel by this time, except the writing-room, and, of course, no one would ever look there for patrons of the hotel. Seeing that the boy was about to totter, I went up and spoke to him. He continued to totter, thinking, perhaps, that I was Mr. Kenworthy, his long-lost beau-ideal. But I spoke kindly to him and offered him a piece of chocolate almond-bar, and soon, in true reporter fashion, had wormed his secret from him before he knew what I was really after.

The thing I wanted to find out was, of course, just what the average is of replies to one paging trip. So I got around it in this manner: offering him another piece of chocolate almond-bar, I said, slyly: "Just what is the average number of replies to one paging trip?"

I think that he had suspected something at first, but this question completely disarmed him, and, leaning against an elderly lady patron, he told me everything.

"Well," he said, "it's this way: sometimes I find a man, and sometimes I can go the rounds without a bite. Tonight, for instance, here I've got four names and one came across. That's about the average — perhaps one in six."

I asked him why he had given Mr. Kenworthy such a handicap at the start.

A faint smile flickered across his face and then flickered back again.

"I call the names I think will be apt to hang round in the part of the hotel I'm in. Mr. Kenworthy would have to be in the dressy dining-room or in the lobby where they wait for ladies. You'd never find him in the bar or the Turkish baths. On the other hand, you'll never find a man by the name of Blevitch anywhere except in the bar. Of course. I take a chance and call every name once in so often, no matter where I am, but, on the whole, I uses my own discretion."

I gave him another piece of chocolate and the address of a good bootmaker and left him. What I had heard had sobered me, and the lights and music suddenly seemed garish. It is no weak emotion to feel that you have been face to face with a mere boy whose chances of success in his work are one to six.

And I found that he had not painted the lily in too glowing terms. I followed other pages that night — some calling for "Mr. Strudel," some for "Mr. Carmickle," and one was broad-minded enough to page a "Mrs. Bemis." But they all came back with that wan look in their eyes and a break in their voices.

And each one of them was stopped by the man in the business suit in the downstairs dining-room and each time he considered it a personal affront that there wasn't a call for "Studz."

Some time I'm going to have him paged, and when he comes out I shall untie his necktie for him.

CHRISTOPHER WARD

Christopher Ward, a newcomer in the ranks of humorists, was born in Wilmington, Delaware, October 6, 1868, educated at Rugby Academy and Friends School, Wilmington; Williams College (A.B. 1890); Harvard (LL.B. 1893). He has practised law in Wilmington since 1893, so that amusing the reading public is his avocation. He has published articles in the *Atlantic Monthly* and *Yale Review* and parodies on current novels in the *Literary Review* of the *New York Evening Post*. His first book was "The Triumph of the Nut and Other Parodies" from which the accompanying selection was taken. This year he is represented with two books, "Gentleman Into Goose" and "Twisted Tales." As one authority has said, Mr. Ward "has recovered the lost art of parody."

THE BLUNDERER OF THE WASTELAND [1]

By JANE GREY

I

"*B*UENAS *dias, señor!*"
The girl's liquid accents exactly fitted the dark, piquant, little face whence they had emerged. The slender grace of her slight form, the delicate arch of her instep, the shapely grace of her dainty ankle, all marked her as the child of a Mexican laborer, Margarita the Maid of Muchacho.

"*Muchus gracious, seenora!*"

Adam Larey's Spanish was not that of the lower class of Mexicans, but it was the best he had. Adam Larey's face flushed beneath its coat of tan and his breath came in short pants, for he was clothed in the innocence of eighteen summers. Though his lofty stature betokened budding

[1] From "The Triumph of the Nut." Copyright, 1923, by Henry Holt and Company. Reprinted by permission of the author and publishers.

manhood, Adam Larey had never before spoken to a woman other than his mother or an occasional sister.

Then, suddenly, Margarita launched herself upon him. Her slender twining form enveloped him like a wind of flame, like a lissom spectre. A strong shuddering shook his heart. His blood leaped, beat, burnt in his veins. He was gathered in her close embrace.

"Don't! don't!" he gasped. "You mustn't! Someone will see ——"

His words were stifled by those eager searching lips and —*she kissed him.*

It was over in a single, scorching, flaming moment. Exerting his enormous strength to the utmost, he tore himself from her twining arms, half ran, half stumbled up the rocky path to his cabin, flung himself upon his bed and burst into a blinding flood of tears.

II

Adam Larey's aching eyelids opened on the cold gray dawn of the morning after. Simultaneously, the dread realization of his loss overwhelmed him, devastated him, made him feel very bad. He had been through the fires of passion, through the flames of dishonor. He could never, never be the same pure man again as previously he had been before. She must atone. She must marry him, make an honest man of him.

He found her in converse with his brother Guerd Larey — tall, superbly built, handsome, bold, keen, reckless, gay Guerd Larey — whose face was perfect of feature, not a single one missing — Guerd Larey, a creature of G — dlike beauty, with a heart as false as h—l!!

"Margarita! Maggie! Mag!" he faltered. "Will you —won't you — ain't you going to — marry me? After what happened — last night — you won't, will you? — I mean, you will, won't you? You ain't chucked me, are you? I'm on, ain't I? You can't can me, can you? Aw! You know what I mean!"

" *Nachitoches, señor!* " she answered lightly.

" Meaning? " he inquired.

" Nay — no — not — nix — never — not at all — nothing doing — and several other expressions of like import," said she.

" Ha! ha! " commented Guerd Larey.

His mocking tones roused all the d—vil in the breast of Adam Larey.

" Take care, Guerd Larey! " he said omnivorously.

" Say not so, Adam! say not so! " taunted Guerd Larey, and at the same time seized a huge rock of several hundred-weight and hurled it at his brother. It struck Adam Larey full in the face and dazed him for a moment.

Then a rushing gush of rage overwhelmed him. He snatched his gun from its holster.

" You have snore your last sneer, Guerd Larey! " he cried, closed both eyes and pulled the trigger — or whatever you call that little thing that makes it shoot — turned and fled to the desert — the registered trade-mark of Cain upon him.

III

Adam Larey's dull eyelids opened on the grim, dim dawn of the zanegrey desert. Before him a wide, barren, endless, bleak, lifeless, silent, desolate plateau — illimitable space and silence and solitude and desolation stretched illimitably to an illimitable horizon — wild and black and sharp — colossal buttresses, chocolate mountain ranges, bare and jagged peaks, silhouetted against the hazel dawn.

Here and there were sparse, vague tufts of sage-brush, greasewood, sneezewood, *cacti, neckti, octopi, ocatilla, ocarina* and similar hardy perennials — the strange verbiage of the desert.

On the left, lofty Pistachio lifted its pale green peak. On the right Eskimopi, in lofty grandeur, heaved its chocolate height.

IV

Two weeks had elapsed since Adam Larey had flown the coop. Two weeks without food, without water, had left him both hungry and thirsty. Punctured by cactus-spines, his boots had suffered several important blow-outs and now he was traveling practically on his rims.

More than fifty miles a day he had fled over the desert floor, composed chiefly of sand, gravel, lime, cement and other building materials, yet every one of the last ten nights he had slept in the same place.

Morning after morning, he had set out. Day after day, he had followed his own trail, now a broad, well-beaten track. Night after night, he had reached the same starting point. *The doom of the desert had fallen on the wanderer.* HE WAS TRAVELING IN A CIRCLE.

V

The blazing disc of the sun mounted the coppery sky — the lord of day ascending the throne of this, his empire. The desert seemed aflame, when Adam Larey set out on his daily round. The rocks were hot as red-hot plates of iron or steel. The sand was very warm, also.

And now a low, seeping, silken rustle filled the air, sometimes rising to a soft roar—the dread simoom of the desert! It whipped up the sand in clouds, sheets, blankets, quilts, mattresses, till all the air was pale yellow, thick and opaque and moaning. It was hot with the heat of a blast-furnace, heavy with the weight of leaden fire.

It burned Adam Larey's brow, charred his cheeks and baked his brains — seared, scorched the rest of him. His blood was boiling in his head. His motometer burst, steam issued from his ears and there was no water to replenish his radiator. Still doggedly Adam Larey strove forward.

Fiercer and hotter blew the wind. His hair was ignited. His celluloid collar button exploded. His shirt was charred to tinder. His suspender buttons melted. His trousers fell from him. Still doggedly Adam Larey strove forward.

Fiercer and hotter blew the wind. His skin dried, shriveled, was calcined, blew away in dust. His flesh followed. As deep inroads were thus made in his muscular substance, unarticulated bones, having no means of support, were detached and fell from him. Still doggedly Adam Larey strove forward.

But when both knee-caps dropped and his knee-joints worked with equal ease forward or backward, even he could no more. The skeleton of Adam Larey fell rattling to the ground.

VI

There Dismukes, the old prospector, found him. It was a heart-breaking job to re-build Adam Larey — to find the missing parts. But the pertinacity of the old prospector was rewarded. Adam Larey's chassis was re-assembled. A few cups of soup were administered, carefully at first because the gas-tank leaked, and at last Adam Larey, re-built, re-finished throughout, stood erect once more.

Dismukes gave him a new outfit, including a burro, showed him how to pack the burro neatly, so the drawers would close, and Adam Larey set out again on his travels.

VII

Eight years Adam Larey dwelt in the desert, growing daily stronger, finer, purer in its illimitable wilds — the abode of purity, silence and tarantulas. Climbing inaccessible heights, striding over impassable plains, stalking the savage antelope, the impatient grizzly, the querulous bob-cat, he acquired the eye of a mountain-sheep, the ear of a deer, the nose of a wolf and many other trophies of the chase.

He loved the lure of the desert. He learned its lore. The secrets of nature were disclosed to him. He knew whether the antelope chews her cud with a full set of teeth, upper and lower, or has to gum it in part — why grizzly-bears always walk in single file and why they never do — why the bark of a coyote or of a tree, whichever it is, is always rougher on the north or the south side, as the case may be — wherein the joyous cry of the great blue condor, weeping for its children, differs from the melancholy note of the lounge lizard courting its mate — whether the gray desert wolf is indigenous, like the horned toad, or monogamous, like the rattlesnake — whether the jack-rabbit's tail curls in the direction of the movement of hands of a watch, like the trailing arbutus, or counter-clockwise, like the lesser celandine — whether the giraffe lies down to sleep or merely appears to do so — whether the mesquite-bush attracts lightning or whether it is the lightning's own fault — whether sound travels faster in the direction in which it is going or in the opposite direction — whether the vulture finds carrion by the odor emanating from its prey or by its own sense of smell — whether the bob-cat can see in the dark as well or not as well or better or worse or at all or not at all or at night or partially or impartially or which, if any — Adam Larey at last knew the answers to all these questions as well as Stewart Edward White or any Boy Scout in America.

He had adopted the name of Woncefell — in memory of his single lapse from virtue, his momentary liaison with Margarita, the Maid of Muchacho. As Woncefell, the Wanderer, he was known and feared throughout that desert land.

VIII

Death Valley! Surrounded by ragged, jagged peaks, floored with ashes, borax, sand-soap, dutch-cleanser, watered by arsenic springs, swept by furnace blasts, it was, indeed, an unpleasant place. "The lid of h—ll," a profane prospector had called it.

Yet there, in a rude shack on the sloping mountain side, overhung by an impending mass of loose rock, from which ever and anon gigantic fragments detached themselves to roll with a booming crash into the valley below, missing the cabin only by inches, dwelt Magdalene Virey and Elliott, her husband.

She was a woman of noble proportions, though frail — at least she had been on one occasion. She suffered from insomnia because Elliott spent his nights in the mass of rocks above the cabin, detaching great boulders and rolling them down with a booming crash into the valley below, trying to frighten his wife to death.

Elliott did not love his wife and he was a very disagreeable man. He was, perhaps, a little mad, but his wife never got that way. She had a very sweet forgiving nature. The great boulders always narrowly missed the tiny cabin. They bounded over, knocking the top off the chimney, and she had to rebuild it every morning. But the sad-eyed saint never complained.

IX

Thither came Woncefell, the Wanderer.

"Magdalene Virey, why do you dwell in this horrible place?" he asked.

"Woncefell, the Wanderer," she answered, "I love the silence, the loneliness, the mystery of the great open spaces and, besides, dear Elliott finds his rock-golf so amusing. He is so ambitious to make the chimney in one.

"I can endure it only because I am sustained by my faith in G—d and by the hope that some night he'll break his dod-gasted neck or pinch his fingers or something."

"Magdalene Virey," he said, "why does he do it?"

"Woncefell, the Wanderer," she said, "because my daughter Ruth is not Elliott Virey's daughter."

"Magdalene Virey, who *is* Elliott Virey's daughter, then?" he asked.

"Woncefell, the Wanderer, I do not know," she answered.

"Magdalene Virey, my G—d!" he exclaimed.

Who *was* Elliott Virey's daughter? The mystery was insoluble. It was plain to him now that he must kill Elliott Virey with his bare hands, like he had killed Baldy McKue, breaking his arms, one at a time, then his legs, then his ribs *seriatim*, then his neck — and that was about all.

X

That night Elliott Virey engaged as usual in his favorite outdoor sport. Rock after rock, boulder and yet more bould, crashed, streaked, hurtled down the mountain. Singly, in pairs, in column of fours, in mass formation, by dozens and hundreds, they crashed and boomed as the madman hurled them at the humble dwelling of his lawful wife.

The time had come! Adam Larey started up the slope.

"*Virey,*" he roared above the thunder of the rocks, "*I'm going to break your bones like I done Baldy McKue's.*"

The madman heard him.

"*Fore!*" he yelled and with one last supreme effort tore loose the whole mountain side. Down it came with a thunderous roar, a cataclysmic rush, and with it came Virey. It swept the cabin from its underpinning.

As the mass of rocks bearing the little shack crashed past Adam Larey, the saintly woman leaned far out o'er the window sill and handed him a small photograph.

"Woncefell, the Wanderer," she said in a low, clear voice, "take it. It is my daughter, my child, not Elliott's. With the clairvoyant truth given to a dying woman, I tell you that you and she will meet. Go find her. And now, I do not know where we're going but we're certainly on our way. You'll excuse my leaving you, won't you? Her name is Ruth. *Au revoir!*"

"What a pretty name," said Adam Larey, musingly, as the avalanche and Mr. and Mrs. Virey spilled over into the declivity below, lifting to heaven a thick, crashing, rolling roar of thunder. When the last rumble died away, silence and solitude reigned over all. Adam Larey was alone at last.

XI

He did meet Ruth on page 392. Her mother had evidently been reading ahead.

"Oh, you Sheik," she said. "Desert man, I am lonesome. Stay — stay, desert man, and make me a woman."

Gosh! was n't she awful? Adam Larey fled. The younger generation was too much for him. Besides, he had yet to atone for his brother's death — to surrender to the sheriff, be hanged for murder — then, only then, would his conscience cease its seventeen years' bickering — then, only then, could he return and claim her for his bride.

XII

Muchacho again — the scene of his boyhood — and his old friend, Merrywell.

"Old friend," said Adam Larey, "lead me to my brother's grave."

"His grave?" said Merrywell. "Gosh! he ain't got none, as I knows on."

"What?" cried Adam Larey. "Why did n't they bury him?"

"'Cause he ain't dead yit."

"Did n't I kill him?"

"Gosh, no! Your pistol missed fire. Guerd Larey's 'live as you be."

"Do you mean to say," cried Adam Larey, "that I 've been expiating Guerd Larey's death in the desert for seventeen years with sand-storms and tarantulas and everything, and he ain't dead? This is an outrage! Somebody 'll pay for this!"

"Go easy, young man," said Merrywell. "Ain't you been workin' fer Mr. Zane Grey? Well, don't you know as Mr. Grey don't never let his heroes do nothin' 'at 's really bad?"

SAM HELLMAN

Sam Hellman, the latest addition to contemporary writers of humor who have attained book publication, specializes in slang and modern malapropisms. Born in San Francisco, July 4, 1885, he is a graduate of the University of California and was a newspaper writer for twenty years before he devoted himself to fiction. He is a regular contributor to the *Saturday Evening Post*, in which his best story, "Low Bridge", originally appeared, prior to book publication, in 1924, in a volume entitled "Low Bridge and Punk Pungs."

LOW BRIDGE [1]

I

WHEN me and my egg-scrambler teams up in the better-or-worser monologue back in them days when the marriage ceremonies was considered, anyways, serious enough to call for a clean shave and your other shirt, the light of my life pulls this one on me after we is alone at last.

"Honey," says she, "like other couples maybe we will have some tiffs and spats in our wedding careers. Let's you and me make a agreement that no matter how sore we is, if ever, we won't never fail to kiss each other good night."

"Me get sore at you!" I comes back. "They ain't no more chances of me and you having spats than they is of me wearing 'em."

"Maybe no," says the bride of a hour, "but Lizzie Magruder done it, and it works wonderful. She and Jim gets

[1] From "*Low Bridge and Punk Pungs.*" Copyright, 1923, 1924, by Sam Hellman. Published by Little, Brown, and Company.

along lovely, because you can't keep up no fight after you has been kissed, can you?"

"You don't compare me with that planked shad, does you?" I wants to know, indignant. "I don't need no agreements to tell me how to treat no wives, and I won't make none." I finishes up kinda strong, figuring this time was no worser than any other for showing who is the mister of the house.

The agreement turns out to be the ace in the domestical deck. We ain't hardly back from having our pictures took in raincoats at Niagara Falls when we gets into a fuss about some triffle and in about five minutes I get wised up to what a lotta bums my family is. I curve a pretty fair insult myself, and in a little while her folks is down in the gutter with mine, hiding out from the coppers. The next act in the row is a dumb show, and from supper to hay time they ain't enough words passed between me and the wife to take up half a line in the lexington.

When she starts for her own room I looks kinda curious, but she's a sport. She holds 'em up, and I obliges, and the humors of kissing after what we been pulling makes us both bust out laughing. After that they ain't nothing to do but pass the buck about who begun the trouble, me insisting it's my fault and she taking the versa-visor. I finally wins by calling myself a brute and a caddy, and the missis letting it go at that, without no more objections.

In the next ten years we has plenty of run-ins about this and those and them, and me and my family is kept hopping in and outta the frying pan, but the kiss racket still hits on all four lips and they ain't never no morning hangovers to the insult souses of the day before. Me and the old lady is getting along as well as could be suspected when some cuckoo that ain't had no luck filling bob-tailed flushes springs a new game to get even with the guys that's been trimming him, by busting up their families. It's like waving a red flag, so he calls it auction.

I hears lots about this bridge and the wife takes a flyer at it, but personally I think it's the bunk, being a kinda combination of five hundred, a four-cornered debate and a coroner's inquest. Anyways I ain't got no use for no game where you got to have the papers to win and where you can't do no scientific bluffing; besides, how could it be worth a whoop if the frails could play it good?

"Listen here," says my lady friend one night. "Know why we ain't invited out no more?"

"I ain't noticed no smallpox signs on myself," I answers, "but I'll give an imitation of a fish for you. Why?"

"Because you don't play bridge," she snaps.

"That's only fifty per cent of it Katie dear," I comes back. "No game that a half-witted maroon is a champ at is gonna get a fall outta your favorite husband."

"You talking about me?" busts out the frau.

"Who said you played good?" I asks. "Didn't you tell me the other day that that Magruder hen was a curly she-wolf at the pastimes?"

"She's a wonderful player," admits the missis, "and so is Jim."

"That'll be all," says I. "Lizzie ain't got enough sense to pour water outta pitcher that ain't got no bottom. Anything she's strong on, I'm off of."

"She's strong on food," shoots back Katie, "so I guess you'll go on a hungry strike, huh? How much brains do you have to use up to lose all the times at poker, anyways?"

"I ain't had such good breaks lately," I replies, "but watch my smoke."

"I been inhaling it for ten years," sneers the wife, "but I ain't seen no fire yet, unless you count that job they pulled out from under you last year."

That's a mean jab and calls for a snappy come-back. I pulls it and I can see Katie getting ready to drag my family in by the ears and pelt them with mud balls when the bell blings and in waltzes Jim Magruder and the thin

Lizzie he is willing to admit is his wife. My ideas is that the city owes him a refund for the dollar and a half they hooked him for the license tag, but at that she didn't snatch nothing worth writing home about, except maybe on paper with black edges.

I got about as much use for Magruder as a skinned eel has for a haircut and a shoeshine. They ain't hardly nothing this baby don't know at the leastest a hundred per cent's worth, and he don't figure nobody in his classes as a snappy cracker excepting his wife's husband and his old man's son, Jim. "I tells him where to head in" is his pet line, which gives you a full-length picture of this bozo without me going in for no more details.

Liz is the trained seal, pa excellency. Nearly everything she squeaks begins "Jim says." If she and him was to walk into the house ringing wet and with a umbrella in each hand the chances is she would start off the evening's entertainments with the walloping news that "Jim says it's raining something awful." The only reason us and the Magruders is on socialist terms is because Kate and Lizzie was side kicks in the days when they was both man-trapping among the illegible lads.

I'm kinda glad to see 'em on account of their busting in just in time to save my family from being sent back to the workhouse and the nut factory, so I greets the set of flat-tires jovial.

"Cold out?" asks the wife.

Lizzie throws a natural. "Jim says he thinks it's gonna snow before morning."

"The weather man don't guess so," I cuts in. "He's playing Fair and Warmer right on the nose."

"You don't mean to say," sneers Magruder, "that you is still falling for that bull? I'll bet you that——"

"Don't you do it," giggles Lizzie. "Jim is wonderful when it comes to figuring the weather. You remember what a swell day Monday was? Well, I was going downtown and Jim says to me to take a umbrella. It seemed kinda silly, but sure enough I wasn't back home more 'an a hour when it began coming down, cats and dogs, as Jim calls a heavy rain."

I starts to say something, but Katie flashes me the shut-up, and I switches what I has on my mind to something that turns out to be worser.

"How's tricks?" I asks Magruder, and the evening is spoiled.

"That reminds me," says Katie. "Me and Tillie Olson had a argument about a hand this afternoon. You see, I had five hearts to the ace and bid —— "

"I think you was right," says Liz at the end of the crime wave.

"No," opines Jim. "You shoulda let Tillie play the hand with four diamonds. How much was you set?"

"I wasn't," says the wife. "I made a grand slam."

Even then I knows enough about bridge to be wise to the fact that a grand slam is the snake's shins, but the wife's come-back don't jar Magruder none.

"Just the same, you was wrong," he pulls. "If you'd 'a' played the hand proper you'd 'a' been set one trick." And Lizzie nods yes.

"What woulda happened," I asks, "if the four diamonds had been played?"

"Tillie woulda made 'em," he answers.

"A grand slam?" I wants to know.

"No," he says. "Just four."

"Well," says I, "either you're cuckoo or the game is."

"You wouldn't understand," comes back Jim, slipping me a charity look. "They is certain forms and conventions that —— "

"I gets you," I interrupts. "It would be like a runner, holding his hands over his head, making the hundred in nine flat, while another baby, keeping his arms by his side, like it says in the book, doing it in eleven. You'd slip the tin medal to the bozo with the form that went to them conventions. What the hell difference does it make how you play 'em if you cop the white meat?"

"Please cut out them gutter gags," snaps the wife, "and please don't compare them barroom athaletics with a gentile and dignified game like bridge. They is lotta difference between people that don't use nothing excepting their arms and legs and them that depends on their brains for pleasures and profits."

"Jim says," horns in Lizzie, "that it takes a wonderful mind to play proper."

"That lets me and Katie out then," says I. "She ain't got enough sense to keep outta the way of making a grand slam, and I ain't got enough to know why she should."

"Don't call me she," comes back the wife. "Maybe I was wrong about them hearts. I wish you wouldn't be so stubborn, and try to learn how to play. Then we four could get together more."

"I don't think he's cut out for a bridge player," says Magruder.

"You don't eh?" I shoots back. "How long did it take you to learn the game good?"

"About a year," he answers.

"That means," says I, "it will take me about four days at the mostest."

"Want me to teach you?" grins Magruder.

"What with?" I asks. "You don't mean to tell me you got brains enough to play bridge and besides enough left over to waste on me?"

About that time the wife cuts in and throws the switch on this line of conversation. In a few minutes the Magruders give themselves the night air, leaving me and my family at the mercies of the wife.

After we kisses good night, though, Katie says to me, "Is you really gonna to learn to play bridge like you told Jim?"

"You bet I am!" I comes back. "I'll show that cuckoo where he heads in."

II

The next day I hunts up High Spade Kennedy, a bozo that is a champ at every kinda card game from old maid to that French game that sounds something like shimmy the fare. Him and me is good pals, me having staked him lotta times when he gets trimmed by sitting in sessions with decks that is perfect strangers to him.

"What do you know about bridge?" I asks him.

"What is they to know that I don't?" he comes back.

"Is it easy to get hep to?" I continues.

"Yeh," says he, "even for you. Know the old whist-game, don't you?"

I tells him I remember something about it and that I has watched maybe a half a dozen games of bridge.

"The big stuff is the bidding," explains High Spade. "Any flathead can play 'em after they're down."

"How long," I asks, "at the rate of two hours per day, will it take you to teach this flathead to play the game good?"

"You oughtta be pretty fair in a week," says Kennedy; "but why the rush to the auction block?"

I tells him how Magruder's got my gander up with all his bull about the kinda high-spiced brains it takes to collect a lotta points for a flock of honors you ain't even had to reach for, and the grand education you got to have to make a ace of trumps stand up for a trick, and right away High Spade agrees to sit in. He knows Jim.

"I'd swim the river," says he, "to help you pry that leather-vest edition of Tightwads I Has Met loose from a few smackers. That cuckoo thinks more of a dime than he does of his wife."

"In them respects," I comes back, "he ain't got nothing on me excepting maybe nine cents. One of the reasons why I wants to learn how to throw a mean card in this here auction is so I can show that Lizzie of his that even that automat she married muffs 'em oncet in a while."

"All right," says Kennedy; "but don't get no ideas in your head that you don't have to use your dome none in this game. Of course, getting the papers dealt to you is the big thing, and the guy that thought up bridge could lose even his schoolgirl complexion to the worst ham in the world if he don't get no pretty pictures to look at, but what you does with the cards when you gets 'em is got some bearings on whether you cashes or carries. You gotta understand, too, that this ain't no lone-hand proposition, neither. Can your wife play good?"

"I don't know," I answers truthful, "but from hints that she drops around the house careless like she could spot James Q. Whist all the aces and kings in the deck and knock him for a row of grand slams. She's been keeping company with the game about a year three or four times a week, and if she ain't friendly with it now, it ain't because he ain't a sweet kid and sociable and not what you would call snobbish —— "

"Can the comedy," says High Spade. "You'll work yourself up into a crying spell pretty soon over the way you been neglecting that ball and chain of yours. I don't care nothing about her disposition or her looks. Can she play bridge? Answer me those."

"I guess she's as good as the poultry she battles with," I replies, "and, anyway, that Magruder hen ain't got nothing on her. That don't leave you nothing to do but to shape me up to take a fall outta that goof of a husband of hers."

"That oughtn't to be so hard," says Kennedy. "From what I've seen of that baby's play he ain't so much of a much, and you got pretty good card sense, if any. The cards, maybe, will run wrong for you, but I can fix it so you'll win every fourth hand at the leastest."

"How?" I asks.

"You deal every fourth hand, don't you?" comes back High Spade.

"Outta my life!" says I. "Nix on the iced deck! If I

can't beat Magruder on the up and up and by the powers of my brain, I ain't gonna try. Taking dough from him don't interest me none. I just want to show that goof what a cinch a childish game like bridge is to a mastiff mentalities like I got——"

"To get," cuts in Kennedy. "All right, bo, drop over this afternoon. I'll round up a couple of the boys and— don't forget to bring along some decks of cards."

"Don't I always when I play with you?" I comes back.

That bob-tailed compliment don't annoy him none, and before he beats it he tips me off on a book that I should get about bridge which he says won't help me none at playing the game, but which maybe would keep me from acting like I is cheating, bridge being one of them sports where you can be disgraced for life if you is caught doing some innocent thing like talking about shovels when you would like to see a spade led to you.

I buys the book and for the next hour or so I plugs through the rules in back of it. I finds that they is more different ways of pulling bulls in the game than they is of a second-hand lizzie of getting outta order. From what I can see in a quick look a cuckoo could sit in the pastimes all night and without holding no card bigger 'an a six spot grab off all the dough just by watching close and collecting on foul tips and infield errors.

In the afternoon I drifts over to Kennedy's joint and rides the goat. Me knowing something about whist and having picked up a little of this and them about bridge by watching the wife perform, I don't have much troubles getting wise, and by the time the session's run a coupla hours I'm good enough to get into a argument with my partner about a rotten lead he makes and almost win it.

"This is a soft spot," says I to Kennedy when we quits.

"Any game is, the first time you try it," comes back High Spade. "It'll take you six months anyways to find out how much you don't know about it."

Every afternoon for a week I take on Kennedy and his

gang, and even he admits they is worse players than me, which is that bozo's limit in compliments. I don't tell Katie nothing about what I'm doing, and when she asks me when I'm going to take some bridge lessons I stall her off with tired looks and yarns about how busy I is.

About ten days after I starts learning the game and when I'm so good that I ain't afraid to hook up with nobody I brings home the bridge book I been reading.

"I got a coupla minutes to myself today," I tells the wife, "and I scummed through some of this hop. What is they about this game that is supposed to make your brains turn handsprings? It looks like the mush to me."

"Maybe yes," comes back Katie, "but you is so smart I guess you could read a time-tables in the morning and build a locomotive all by yourself in the afternoon."

It ain't in my schemes to get into a row with the wife, so I laughs merrily and changes the subject to one of the mere handfuls outta which even Katie can't get no disagreements with me. After supper I gets back to bridge and tells the wife what I been reading in the book, not really, but what I wants her to think is my styles of play when I does play.

She starts telling me how she does it, and in about a hour I'm hep to what to expect from her.

"How about asking the Nelsons to come in and play a little while tonight?" I asks.

The Nelsons lives across the hall from us and ain't such a bad pair of deuce spots. The wife is tickled, and in a coupla minutes she comes back with 'em.

"You will have to have lots of patience with him," says the frau, meaning me, "because he don't know nothing about the game excepting what he read in a book today."

"I ain't no roaring hell-cat at it myself," comes back Nelson. "What'll we play for?"

"Make it easy," says I. "Ten cents a point is enough for me."

"How much?" gasps Mrs. Nelson.

I gets her the wrong way on purpose, and looks embarrassed by my cheapness.

"Well," says I, "make it twenty cents or thirty or whatever you is used to playing for. I'm willing to pay for my lessons."

"Don't mind him," cuts in the wife. "He's got rubbles in his mind. We'll play for a twentieth a couple. You got any ideas," she asks me, "how much you could lose at a cent a point, even?"

"Three for four dollars?" I guesses.

"A minute," she comes back. "If you was to play for that much and lose two or three rubbers you wouldn't be able to pay no rent until 1956, and I wouldn't never have no chances of getting that machine you is talking about, even if I got any now."

After which we gets busy and while I plays pretty fair I takes care to make enough boob bids to slip the lull to any suspicions the wife might have. The Nelsons ain't much and I coulda butchered them and copped enough outta penalties alone to get a vermin-lined overcoat, but I holds my brains down. A coupla times I forgets myself and puts over some real slick acts, but when Katie looks kinda surprised and pats me on the back I quick turn around and slaps the last trump in the game on her ace of clubs, and a sure rubber goes down on the books for a set of two hundred. I ain't ready yet for her to know how good I is at the game, she and that Magruder frail being too thick for my purposes.

"For a beginner," says Mrs. Nelson, when we quits about even, "you play very good."

"Well," I comes back, "they is two chapters in the book that I ain't had no chances to read yet. When I get them done they won't be nothing left for me to learn. I kinda like the game because it don't take no more than a hour to get to the head of the class in it, providing you has even as many brains as a humming bird with paresis."

When the Nelsons beat it back to their dump the missis turns the hot steam on me.

"That was a sweet crack you made," says she, "about you learning bridge so easy and comparing the Nelsons to cuckoo humming birds."

"Me," I gasps, "compare ——"

"Yeh, you!" cuts in the wife. "Here these people has been trying for a year to learn how to play without even knowing yet whether a finesse is a kinda salad or a part of the game, and you breezes in and practically tells 'em to their faces that they is total losses without no insurance. Where do you get the ideas that you is good, anyways?"

"Ain't I?" I asks.

"I can't even laugh," says she. "If it wasn't for the facts that the Nelsons is no good and you had me for a partner you wouldn't have won one hand, even if you didn't have nothing but pianolas dealt to you. Wait till you try some of them fast brains of yours against the Magruders."

"Lead 'em to me," I comes back.

"They is coming over tomorrow night," says the wife, "and please try to give a imitation of a gentleman. You can learn a lots by watching Jim."

"About the game or being a gentleman?" I wants to know.

"Both," says she.

III

"Well," says I to Katie the next evening, "I finished them other two chapters in the book today."

"Got your diploma with you?" she asks.

"I figure on getting that tonight," I answers, "providing you don't gum the works."

"Me?" she inquires, and I explains.

"When we was playing with the Nelsons you kinda got the idea every time I bid that I was kidding and it was up to you to take it away to save the family honors or something. When I bid I means it. Besides, every time

I was doubled you got into a panic and ran around like a chicken with its feet off. Don't take me outta no doubles. Don't try to get me outta no jams. You don't in nothing else, so why do it in bridge?"

The wife's dragging up the heavy guns for the comeback my stuff calls for when the Magruders arrives. Me and my family owes a lots to them folks. They always pops in at the cricketal moment, just in time to save our coats of arms from being ripped up the back and thrown over the fence to the dogs.

"Halloo," I greets Lizzie. "What's new at the Rialto?"

"Katie tells me you is learning to play bridge," says this baby.

"What do you mean, learning?" I comes back. "I knows all they is to know about it. I read the book through and I took a postal-graduate course with the Nelsons last night."

"Whose book was that?" asks Magruder.

"McGullible on Auction," I tells him.

"McGullible," sneers Jim. "Why, that bozo's stuff was passy ten years before the game was invented. Why didn't you ask me? I'd 'a' tipped you off on a live one."

"Anyways," cuts in Lizzie, "Jim says you can't learn to play no bridge outta no books."

"Maybe he can't," I comes back, "but I can read good and I don't figure the hour I put in with McGullible was wasted. I wasn't so bad last night, was I, Katie?"

"They is a bare chancet," says the frau, "that somebody could be worser; but, serious, though, he done pretty good considering that he didn't never play the game before."

"Against the Nelsons," scoffs Magruder.

"I'm ready for all comers," I announces.

"After reading a has-been book for a hour and playing one game?" asks Jim. "You'd have a swell chancet with a regular player. Do you know even the rules of the game?"

"You bet I do," I answers. "I suppose you folks don't overlook none of them in your sessions?"

"Jim says," breaks in Lizzie, "that bridge ain't bridge unless you live up to all them rules, the way they does in the New York Whist Club, which is like the Four Hundred when it comes to what is right in this picture."

"Let's play a little while," says Katie, "just to teach Mr. Gullible's friend that a book a day won't keep the losings away. How about it, Jim?"

"All right," says he. "We'll just fool around for nothing."

"Not with me, you won't," I replies. "I can play as good as you cuckoos right now, and I'm ready to put my jack on the witness stand to prove it. Give that a sneer."

"Don't be silly," suggests Katie.

"We'll play for a cent a point or we don't play," I comes back. "I ain't gonna waste a whole day learning bridge without no chance of cashing in. It's a kid game, anyways, and I got to be paid for putting my time to it."

"All right," says Jim with a grin, but I sees him tip the wink to the wife, meaning that he'll slip back to her all the dough he cops.

This don't worry me none, me not figuring on losing to that cuckoo, even if I has to do something to the back of the deck. Besides, I don't care nothing about the money, my whole ideas being to make the Magruders mark down their brains from one dollar to one mark after seeing what a cinch the game is for a lad that's got bottled-in-bond gray matter and not stuff that was bought from a boot-legger.

So we all sits down and the riot opens up. I catch the deal on a deuce spot and if I'd spread 'em out face up I couldn't 'a' done better for myself. I ain't got nothing worth talking about excepting three aces, four kings, a mess of typewriters and a jack here and there.

"Four no trumps," says I.

"How many?" asks the wife.

"Four, f-o-u-r," I repeats. "Let's keep out the grocery clerks."

"You understand," cuts in Magruder, "that you got to make ten tricks to get away with that, don't you?"

"That's what McGullible says," I comes back. "You folks got anything to say or is you just talking."

Nobody peeps, and Lizzie flips outta card. I grabs it off, and before me and the dummy — which don't describe my wife a-tall — quits operating back and forth I ain't done nobody no harm except to slap 'em in the face with a small slam. Magruder cashes in with the ace I ain't got.

"That's sixty below the line and eighty above," says Lizzie.

"And some," I adds. "Turn over your cards, kid, and I'll show you where you revoked back yonder."

"Me," she yelps. "I ain't never revoked in my life."

"You mean," says I, "you ain't never played with anybody with brains enough to catch you at it. No wonder you folks win so often. Turn 'em over."

Which Magruder does, and sure enough Lizzie ain't acted right with her clubs.

"We won't count it," says the wife. "It wouldn't have made no difference in the score, anyways."

"It's all right with me to pass it up," I comes in, sarcastic, "but Jim says that bridge ain't bridge unless you live up to all them rules. Hey, Jim?"

Magruder looks kinda funny, but mumbles that I is right, so I takes what is coming to me.

"How you like my stuff?" I asks Jim. "Not bad for a beginner, huh?"

"Even you couldn't ball the hand," he shoots back.

"Me and Mr. McGullible thanks you," I grins. "Deal 'em out, Lizzie."

Which she done, but towards the end she flips an eight spot face up.

"Deal 'em over," says I. "Card exposed."

"Come on, play," growls Magruder. "A eight ain't no honor."

"What of it?" I wants to know. "I guess you ain't read Section 27 A of the rule book lately."

"Don't be so smart," chimes in the wife. "You ain't in no gambling house now. This is a friendly game and ———"

"Listen here," I cuts in. "I ain't so particular, but I wouldn't want Jim here to get in bad with the New York Whist Club by busting any of the rules."

This time I ain't got such a wolf of a mitt, but I finally gets the play for three hearts doubled.

"Try and make it," says Magruder.

"Cinch," I comes back, giving the dummy the O. O., "now that I know where the eight spot is."

I gets by with a coupla tricky finesses, works a stunt which High Spade told me about to make Lizzie discard what she oughtn't of and cops with four odd. To capper the climax Magruder pulls a boner that's so crude that even Lizzie forgets whose wife she is and hands him the razz.

"So this is the game it took you a year to learn which calls for such a wonderful mind," I jeers. "What's there to it?"

"The evening's young," says Magruder, "and you ain't gonna have all the luck. I'll show you where to head in before the night's out. You and McGullible!"

In a other hour we is carrying about twenty-five hundred points and I ain't playing the cards no more. Magruder's so mad by this time he's making bids that is cuckoo and he's got his wife jumping sideways with the bawling-outs he hands her. I just play him like a fish and he falls for any kinda bait.

Then the luck changes. I handles the cards all right,

but when you ain't got the papers everything you do looks blah; anyways it does to Katie, and I comes in for my end of the razzing. I think the wife's sore, anyways, at how good I been playing, me only having one lesson, so she thinks, and her and them side kicks having been messing around with auction for a year, anyways.

When we is nearly even and Jim is feeling better I says to him, "How's my stuff?"

"I got to admit you is there for a beginner," he answers. "What's the name of that book you been reading?"

"McGullible," I tells him. "But he was a has-been twenty years ago, I hear."

"I got the names mixed," says he. "I remembers now, McGullible is the latest authorities. You sure you only played once before this?"

"Ask the wife," I comes back.

For the next hour we sticks around even, but I put over some trick stuff that makes Magruder and the janes look goggle-eyed. When we is playing the last rubber and we each is got a game, I get the kinda hand I been hoping for all night so as to put over a snappy act that High Spade says is the best ever if you gets away with it. They is eight spades with the four top honors, a coupla side tricks and a blank in hearts. I'm the dealer.

"Four hearts," I says.

I see the wife look funny, I figures because I jumps in so high. Lizzie passes and I don't feel so good, but Magruder grins and saves the day, for a minute, anyways.

"Double," says he. "I might as well grab off a coupla hundred points before taking the rubber."

I looks at the cards a long time without saying nothing, scratching my head and going through all the motions of a guy that's got one foot in a beaver trap and the other on a hole in the ice.

"Four spades," I finally says in a kinda weak voice.

"Double," jumps in Lizzie quick, without doing no more thinking than is usual with that frail.

The wife looks kinda dopey and is giving me the open mouth. She acts like she's gonna say something but don't.

"Pass," says Magruder, and I'm sitting on top of the world.

"Redouble," I yelps, and starts figuring up the score and the laughs I'll hand Jim and his hen.

Lizzie passes, and then blam, down I slide on my neck.

"Five hearts," says the wife, defiant like.

I loses all commands to myself and flops the cards face up on the table.

"Of all the total losses in the world!" I yelps. "Ain't I told you a million times not to take me outta no doubles? I'm through! This ain't no game for a guy with brains if his wife ain't got none."

"Who ain't got none?" snaps Katie. "Don't you talk to me like that! What do you want me to do with this hand?" And she lays down a mitt with all the hearts in the world. She's just as strong in them as I was in spades.

"What do I care what you got?" I howls. "Why the hell didn't you let me alone? I'd 'a' sure taken these babies to the cleaners."

"Don't you hell me!" yipps the wife. "How do I know anything about them barroom tricks you got from that McGullible book? Don't you open your mouth or I'll throw the cards in your face."

"We're all about even, anyways," says Magruder. "Let's go, Lizzie."

Me and the wife don't say a word while we is cleaning up the room, but we could easily get a divorce apiece for what we is thinking.

After we is done I asks, "Ain't you gonna kiss me good night?"

"You should live so long," she comes back.

"Busting the agreement, huh?" I sneers. "Gone to bed without kissing me."

"I ain't busting no agreement," says Katie. "I ain't gone to bed. I'm gonna sit up all night, you cheap gambler! You and your whole rotten family——"

So this is bridge!